C000072039

A Stanley Gibbons Catalogue

Collect
Autographs

An illustrated guide to collecting autographs

2nd Edition

Stanley Gibbons Ltd
London and Ringwood

Published by Stanley Gibbons Ltd
Editorial, Publications Sales Offices
and Distribution Centre:
Parkside, Christchurch Road, Ringwood,
Hants BH24 3SH

1st Edition December 2007
2nd Edition December 2008

© Stanley Gibbons Ltd 2009

ISBN 13: 978-0-85259-714-9

ISBN 10: 0-85259-714-2

Item No. R2993-09

Printed by Latimer Trend & Company Ltd
Plymouth

Stanley Gibbons Holdings Plc.
HEAD OFFICE, 399 STRAND, LONDON WC2R 0LX
Telephone 020 7836 8444 and
Fax 020 7836 7342
Website: *www.stanleygibbons.com* for all
departments.

**Stanley Gibbons Ltd, Stanley Gibbons
Auctions.**
Auction Room and Specialist Stamp Departments:
Open Monday-Friday,
9.30 a.m. to 5 p.m.
Shop: Open Monday-Friday 9 a.m. to 5.30 p.m.
and Saturday 9.30 a.m. to 5.30 p.m.
E-mail: *enquiries@stanleygibbons.co.uk*

Fraser's Autographs
Open Monday-Friday 9 a.m. to 5.30 p.m.
and Saturday 10 a.m. to 4 p.m.
Website: *www.frasersautographs.com*
E-mail: *info@frasersautographs.co.uk*

RINGWOOD OFFICE,
PARKSIDE, CHRISTCHURCH ROAD, RINGWOOD,
HANTS BH24 3SH
Telephone 01425 472363
(24 hour answer phone service),
Fax 01425 470247.
Website: *www.stanleygibbons.com*
E-mail: *info@stanleygibbons.co.uk*

Stanley Gibbons Publications.
Publications Mail Order: FREEPHONE 0800 611622
Monday-Friday 8.30 a.m. to 5 p.m.
Stanley Gibbons Publications has overseas licensees
and distributors for Australia, Belgium, Canada,
Denmark, Finland, France, Hong Kong, Israel, Italy,
Japan, Luxembourg, Netherlands, New Zealand,
Norway, Singapore, Sweden and Switzerland.
Please contact the Ringwood address for details.

Contents

Collecting Autographs

by Paul Fraser, founder of Fraser's Autographs
(From the 1st Edition)

Foreword

I have bought literally thousands of autographed items, in fact, well over 100,000 different items over a 30-year period. I have always believed, and still believe today, that most are still undervalued by the general market.

Prices have risen dramatically as the realisation has begun to set in that there are an ever-increasing amount of collectors and new investors chasing a decreasing amount of the very top quality items.

It is estimated that there are probably over two million collectors worldwide, with 20-30,000 being added each year. This hobby of philography is still in its infancy on a global basis. This is very exciting, given the fact that collecting autographs is more diverse and easier to start than many collecting fields. I have held documents from all the Kings and Queens of England from Edward IV to Queen Elizabeth II, all the great authors from the dawn of printing, the best sportsmen and women, political figures, film stars, music maestros—in fact, the list is almost endless of those people who have made a difference in their lives, and to the world in which we live.

Autograph collecting has given me the pleasure of speaking to some of these people when asking for their autograph. I have met seven of the 12 men to have walked on the moon (currently, Neil Armstrong's autograph carries the highest price for someone still alive, as he is a difficult signer, and will be collected forever as the 'First Man on the Moon').

Out of context, it is sometimes difficult to recognise even the greatest personalities alive today, which makes the joy of collecting in person all the more interesting.

No other collecting area gives you the opportunity to hold history in your hands in such an important way. Albert Einstein writing about the theory of relativity, Elizabeth I discussing the Armada, handwritten lyrics with corrections that have become the anthems of our time, documents of surrender, resignation and even abdication, letters from artists discussing their work with their benefactors with illustrations of current studies, movements in history captured on paper and the surprise that so many important documents are held by collectors in the private domain.

The aura that surrounds a handwritten Charles Dickens letter is almost palpable, as you imagine the writer and the context of this letter in his life.

The key factor when collecting is, of course, authentication. Once you focus clearly on a particular subject or person, your own passion and interest will start to build and develop your skills in ascertaining the authenticity and value of the piece. You can rely on certain studies by previous collectors and academics and also dealers especially known for particular areas of expertise. You will develop a checklist, which becomes a forensic examination, but in the end a sixth sense comes into play based on all the evidence and the years you have looked at similar examples.

Certain autograph examples are nigh on impossible, or unknown. There are no examples known of the Italian poet, Dante, or the German printer, Gutenberg. There are only six examples known of Shakespeare and if one ever came available to the market, it would probably achieve over £2 million.

Once you have chosen a particular person, it becomes important to know the first thing and the last thing they are known to have written, as well as what could be considered their most important.

An objective valuation should be based on six things - signer, content, rarity, condition, date and medium used. There is clearly a difference between a handwritten document and a signed scrap of paper. Any subjective valuation based on sentimental value does not enhance the true value.

Famous people themselves have collected autographs through the ages from Cicero to J. F. Kennedy to Queen Victoria and we have a number of major current day stars as customers.

Fraser's Autographs started in 1978 at the back of a shop selling collectible records and memorabilia. The first autograph item we sold was a signed Beatles album for £45, which today would realise in excess of £45,000. It was not until 1981 that a major auction house started selling modern autographs and, even then, signed Beatles albums were only £120-£180.

When we first started, a set of Apollo XI autographs was selling for £60 (now £7500) and most of the popular stars of the 20th Century were still under £100.

This price guide will give you an ideal start in the world of autograph collecting. You may have purchased this catalogue out of simple curiosity or you may already be the proud owner of an autograph collection. Either way, this price guide will be a vital source of information for you, giving you the latest market prices for key figures across a range of collecting areas. I am sure that you will find this book both interesting and informative, whatever your reason for purchasing it.

The field of autograph collecting is open to all and most people in the world have an interest in some form of human endeavour or achievements and are often surprised about what is available to collect. It is a combination of patience, money and luck when trying to find the most elusive signers. The more passion you have, the more you will enjoy your collecting and it will give you years of pleasure. I wish you all good luck in finding those pieces that matter to you!

The worlds number one site for authentic autographed memorabilia!

www.bid4sport.com

There's always something worth bidding for.

Introduction

2nd edition

Once again we are pleased to present an updated autograph price guide. We are hoping that everyone interested in either collecting autographs or investing in this alternative area will find the book a useful tool while putting their collections together.

As the autograph market grows and the interest in signatures increases we felt that the millions of collectors worldwide should be provided with up-to-date information about the autograph price performance. Following the first, 2008, edition of Collect Autographs we have prepared a listing of names, prices and images of over 3,000 collectable personalities. We aimed to add the names which were missing in the previous edition and – being fully aware that there are still thousands to include – we hope the expanded list will be a handy guide on the most collectable signatures.

Classification by subject

The personality names have been grouped in major collecting areas starting from Art to Sport. The information provided in the book has been based on items stocked and sold by Fraser's Autographs.

Names are listed in alphabetical order by surname within each category. If a particular person is famous in two fields (e.g. music and film) we have placed them in what we perceive to be the person's primary field of work. There is a comprehensive index to support your search.

Prices

The prices listed in Collect Autographs 2009 have been based on retail prices achieved for those particular autographs.

Many factors influence the value of an autograph, amongst them are:

Authenticity.

This is the most important factor. There are thousands of facsimile, secretarial, autopen, stamped or simply forged signatures on the market. There are a number of reference books written by specialists available to collectors, but with time every collector will build their own experience and knowledge about signatures. It is always useful to keep a reference archive of examples of the same signature. Seeing and comparing autographs helps to develop a 'sixth sense' and skills to detect a fake. Of course, for an autograph collector nothing but the truly genuine signatures will do.

Rarity of the signature.

There are many popular celebrities who sign a lot and whose autographs are easily obtainable. Their signatures usually do not command high prices. Truly desirable for an investor are the exceptionally rare signatures. Collectors also tend to search for those pieces that are most uncommon. Sometimes this refers not to the autograph itself but a particular form of it, i.e. signed photographs of Marylin Monroe are much rarer than cheques signed by her, documents written by Napoleon are easily available but letters written entirely in his hand are uncommon. As in any other area of collecting, the rarer the piece, the higher its value and the demand for it.

Signer and desirability for a particular name.

Quite often, some signatures are not particularly rare but are very popular among collectors. This usually happens with some names from the film and music industries, but the rule does also apply to some other historical names such as Napoleon, Einstein or Montgomery of Alamein. Such pieces are usually subject to sentimental attachment, and although this does not reflect the true value of an item, it is impossible to ignore this factor while pricing an item.

Medium used.

This is a very subjective criterion. Many collectors do favour a particular type of autographed piece. Some prefer photographs for their presentation, others go for documents with unusual content. This might influence the market as particular pieces might appear in higher demand and command higher prices.

Content of the document and its association.

The item will command higher prices if its content has any relation to the body of work or personal life of the signer.

Condition.

The condition of an autograph always influences its value. As a matter of fact, some signatures are easily obtainable in a clipped or damaged form but extremely rare on well preserved documents. Any traces of soiling, foxing, staining as well as folds, creases, holes, tears and even problems to the adhesion of the ink will affect the price. The quality of storage materials or framing has to be considered as incorrect materials – as well as storing autographs in humid conditions - might badly damage the piece.

Date.

Some signers date their autographs and those items are preferred by a majority of collectors. Lack of dating does not necessarily devalue the piece but the date and place of signing does add detail and sometimes provenance to the item. It can also help to authenticate the item, although we have to stress that this is not the most important factor when authenticating an autograph.

Provenance.

When buying an autograph it is good to know the history of the item. In fact some of the items might have already been researched and published in bibliographies or biographies. Such facts would certainly add to the value of the item. Otherwise, any additional proof of the item's authenticity such as letters from previous owners, members of the signer's family, etc. add provenance and make the item more interesting. It is important that the items are obtained from recognised sources and ideally accompanied by a guarantee of authenticity.

Fraser's Autographs has stocked over 70,000 autographs over the last 30 years. The range of stock is wide and includes names from current celebrities to historical figures. The prices used in this guidebook have been based on the retail prices realised by Fraser's over the years, however we have given a particular attention to the most recent values. The prices reflect all the aspects of the particular pieces from Fraser's Autographs taken into consideration.

For the sake of collectors in different parts of the world we have kept price listings in three different currencies based on the exchange rates in October 2008:

£   Pounds Sterling
$ American Dollars
€   Euros

Symbol * in the listing means that the item is either very rare, or the scale of the prices is very wide and difficult to generalise. It might also mean that there are not known examples of the signature in this particular form.

Illustrations

In the 2009 edition of Collect Autographs we have kept the colourful format of the book. We have provided new examples of signatures for most of the autographs. The illustrations used in the guide are examples of genuine autographs supplied by Fraser's Autographs (items currently offered for sale or sold in the past). Colours may differ from the originals and some of the images may illustrate only a part of the document, such as the signature itself.

Classification by type

The listing includes three types of autographed material.
SP stands for 'signed photograph'. This listing covers photographs or images of the signers personally signed by them. Group photographs signed by a group of people i.e. music bands or football teams should be signed by all the members of the group. Original photographs usually command higher prices than reproductions.

DS stands for 'document, signed'. This category covers most other complete items personally signed. This category contains such pieces as letters (handwritten or typed), notes, cheques, official documents (contracts, divorce papers, resignations, claims, complaints, commissions, etc.) and works (books, CD and LP records, DVD and videos, lyrics, music sheets, etc.). Handwritten documents usually command higher values than printed or typed ones. Some of the documents may be written by secretaries and just signed by the famous person in question. The content of the document has a great importance to its value.

AP stands for 'album page, signed'. This category covers signatures alone on a piece of paper. The page can come from a collector's album or can be clipped from a bigger document.

Collecting autographs was a favourite pastime in Victorian times but it actually started a long time before then. J.S. Bach was known for collecting manuscripts of Handel, Beethoven collected manuscripts of Mozart, and Schuman collected works of Beethoven. Collecting autographs gives an opportunity of an intimate meeting with the past, with the masters of art, literature, architecture, music, science and politics - with the people who shaped the history of mankind.

The authors of this price guide sincerely hope that the book will come in handy to those who already collect and perhaps will spark some interest to those who are completely new to autograph collecting. We wish everyone lots of joy in putting their autograph collection together.

November 2008

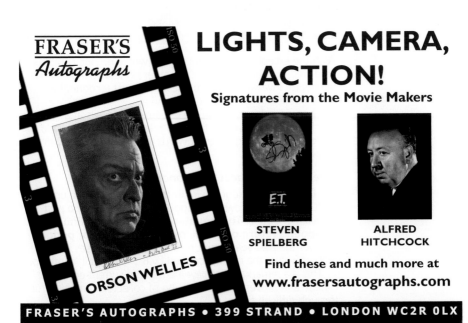

Investment in Autographs

Investment

Autographs provide an alternative investment and an alternative to losing your money in the current economic climate

The past year has been an exciting one in the world of autographs and historical signatures.

I don't know about you, but I am weary from the constant barrage of bad news in the press and on the TV every day... House prices set to crash by 40%, millions to become unemployed, inflation to soar, etc. etc. Whilst in the world of collectibles, autograph prices continue to rise quite nicely thank you despite all this bad news.

An exciting year...To whet your appetite...

The table below gives a flavour of some key price increases in this year's catalogue compared to last year:

Personality	Type	2008	2009	% Growth
Henry VIII	DS	£29,500	£40,000	36%
Elizabeth I	DS	£29,500	£39,000	32%
Apollo 11	SP	£5,950	£7,500	26%
The Beatles	SP	£19,500	£21,000	8%
Winston Churchill	SP	£4,950	£5,500	11%
Albert Einstein	SP	£4,950	£5,500	11%
Heath Ledger	SP	£75	£350	367%

With the exception of Heath Ledger - where no one could have predicted his sudden death – the other signatures are obvious targets for investment. The biggest and most recognisable names generally outperform the market.

The reason for this is simple... Demand prevails at a consistently high level for the "biggest names" in the world of signatures forcing prices upwards as supply inherently must diminish.

Rare autographs beat the economic blues

The Fraser's 100 autograph index listed on Bloomberg updated to 30 April 2008 shows a compound increase over the past 11 years of 280%. **This equates to an average annual compound return of 12.9% over an eleven year period.**

Over the past year, whilst most other asset classes have fallen in value, the index increased by 6.5% or double inflation.

This is a remarkable achievement in the current economic climate and proves that the passion of collectors remains strong through difficult times.

This passion is what underpins the non-correlating qualities of investing in autographs. Yet despite the strong growth in prices of autographs over the past 11 years, I think autographs represent one of the few remaining cheap asset classes available.

When I say "cheap", I don't mean that in the "cheap and nasty" way...

I mean "cheap" in the "under-valued" way... at a discount to real worth.

The Fraser's 100 Autograph Index

You can view the full components of the index at: www. stanleygibbons.com/investments/invest-in-autographs/fraser's-rarities-index.aspx

Fifty-four items within the index increased in value over the past year. Thirty-four of those increased by more than 10%.

Some of our current investors will be pleased to have taken our past recommendations.

The chart below shows the performance of the Fraser's 100 autograph index compared to other popular investment classes over the 10 year period from 1 May 1998 to 30 April 2008:

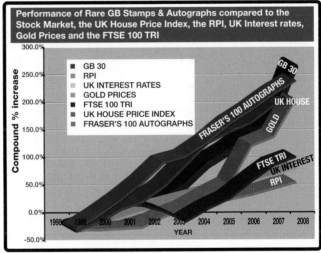

Performance of Rare GB Stamps & Autographs compared to the Stock Market, the UK House Price Index, the RPI, UK Interest rates, Gold Prices and the FTSE 100 TRI

What we are seeing now though are the real benefits of diversification. This is because the long bull market in equities and property appears to have come to an end... This is when the benefits of investing in collectibles becomes more visible as our growth curve relentlessly progresses upwards waving to all the other asset classes on the way down.

Gold on first glance seems to offer similar characteristics but there is an inverse correlation between gold and other asset classes.

Collectibles have no correlation with other asset classes. That is the distinction. Investors buy gold to make a profit then drop it like a stone (but a bit heavier) when other asset classes look to give better opportunities.

Collectors buy items they cherish then won't let go. New collectors come along and can't find what they want because

Investment

Investment

other collectors are holding onto them.

When an item appears on the market, frustrated collectors often chase the same item. The outcome is a fight to secure that item at whatever price it takes, forcing prices up.

One of the few remaining cheap asset classes available

In recent years, markets have become more sophisticated in everything… And more accessible to the masses through online trading… As a result gold, oil, wine, etc. have all soared. Despite significant increases in the prices fetched for rare signatures over the past 10 years, prices remain low compared to similar asset classes.

To illustrate, in 1997 you would only have needed to invest £80,720 to buy the components of the Fraser's 100 Autograph Index. Today, your investment would be worth £306,500…

I believe we are still at the early stages in a growth market in the world of signatures…

The collector market in autographs is still relatively immature. Our business in autographs only started trading in 1978 at which time you could pick up a signed Beatles album cover for as little as £45. Today, that album could fetch as much as £45,000 at auction.

The market for autographs is still quite small particularly in rare signatures. This is now changing… Our autograph division is the highest growth part of our business with sales up 37% over the past year. We are recruiting more and more new customers every week.

The point is… you don't need to be an autograph collector to want to own an autograph. Most people have a passion in life such as sport, music, theatre or art.

So if you are passionate about golf you would probably like a framed signed photo of Tiger Woods hanging up at home…

If you are a Bob Dylan fan, you would probably love to have original lyrics to "Blowin' in the Wind" in your hands…

Or how about a wonderful sketch by Picasso signed and dated… the list is endless.

This wide cross-over of interest creates a much larger potential market for rare signatures.

Compared to the prices paid for fine art and antiques, rare signatures represent an opportunity to own a fascinating piece of history for a fraction of the price of most other rare collectibles.

If you would like a personal consultation on the best way to get into this exciting market, please contact our Investment Director, Adrian Roose today on:

+44 (0) 1481 708 277
email investment@stanleygibbons.co.uk
TOLL FREE from the USA 1 866 644 6146

Mike Hall
Chief Executive
The Stanley Gibbons Group

P.S. It's well worth a visit to our autograph gallery at 399 Strand if you happen to be passing. We have over 60,000 autographs in stock. Very few people leave without finding something of interest, such is the diversity of our stock range.

FRASER'S Autographs

The Fraser's Top 30 Selling Autographs Index

Fraser's Top 30

Let us introduce you to the TOP 30 selling autographs over the past year. These are the autographs that we have sold most of in quantity over a 12-month period.

Each and every month, we update this index to show the trends in the market and changes in demand that we experience, so you can keep track of your favourite celebrities and their popularity rating. Find out if your favourite makes it into the top 30.

Some of these items make great investments by virtue of their perpetual popularity and hence demand forcing prices upwards.

This is a bit like momentum investing whereby simply by following the crowd, you can make money. It is an obvious investment. Demand is high, supply is limited, prices rise.

It is as simple as that...

Not all of the items appearing in the top 30 are an investment but all of them are fascinating individuals in their own right.

So without further ado, please be upstanding for our current top 30 heroes*:

Fraser's Top 30 Selling Autographs

No	Last month	Personality	Category
1	(1)	Madonna	Music
2	(2)	Angelina Jolie	Film, TV & Theatre
3	(3)	Heath Ledger	Film, TV & Theatre
4	(4)	Johnny Depp	Film, TV & Theatre
5	(7)	Winston Churchill	Politics
6	(8)	Al Pacino	Film, TV & Theatre
7	(10)	Norman Wisdom	Film, TV & Theatre
8	(6)	George Lazenby	Film, TV & Theatre
9	(17)	Apollo 11	Space & Aviation
10	(13)	David Bowie	Music
11	(15)	Shirley Eaton	Film, TV & Theatre
12	(16)	George Cohen	Sport
13	(27)	John F Kennedy	Politics
14	(19)	Sean Connery	Film, TV & Theatre
15	(20)	Alexey Leonov	Space & Aviation
16	(14)	Lauren Bacall	Film, TV & Theatre
17	(9)	George Clooney	Film, TV & Theatre
18	(25)	Michael Caine	Film, TV & Theatre
19	(22)	Maureen O'Hara	Film, TV & Theatre
20	(18)	Napoleon Bonaparte	Military
21	(23)	Edmund Hillary	Various/Exploration
22	(12)	Tom Hanks	Film, TV & Theatre

No	Last month	Personality	Category
23	NEW	Brad Pitt	Film, TV & Theatre
24	(5)	Orlando Bloom	Film, TV & Theatre
25	(21)	Lois Maxwell	Film, TV & Theatre
26	+2	Laurel & Hardy	Film, TV & Theatre
27	NEW	Charles Dickens	Literature
28	NEW	Emma Watson	Film, TV & Theatre
29	(24)	Keira Knightley	Film, TV & Theatre
30	(11)	The Beatles	Music

Based on October 2008 sales figures.

As you would expect, film and TV personalities are the most represented group. The world loves fame after all and signatures are a special way of getting closer to the stars you adore. One of our customers summed it up well:

"Just think, Johnny Depp touched this..."

Madonna Tops the Charts Again

Madonna with thirteen Number 1 hits in the UK charts, more than any other female performer, is currently the most collected autograph in the world.

Madonna celebrated her 50th birthday on 16th August 2008 but defied her age with her "Sticky and Sweet" world tour.

Death of a star

A year ago, Heath Ledger would not have even appeared in our top 100 selling autographs... He is now Number three in the chart.

The sudden death of Heath Ledger on 22 January 2008 shocked the world. Nominated for an Oscar and a BAFTA for his role in the film "Brokeback Mountain", he was a star very much in his prime, who was only just beginning to gain the recognition he deserved as an actor. Now he is gone forever.

Sound familiar? James Dean is one of the most collected signatures in the world but his signature is hard to come by. A signed photo of the "rebel without a cause" will set you back over £10,000. Yet you can still buy a Heath Ledger signed photo for a few hundred pounds.

Our Missing Heroes

There are some personalities missing from the list that are in higher demand. The fact is, they are so rare that we simply don't handle enough of them to sell them in any quantity.

Examples of missing personalities, which would make it in the top 30 if we could source enough of them, would include Henry VIII, Paul McCartney and Marilyn Monroe.

Watch out for future updates on the top 30 signatures to keep track of who is hot and who is not at www.frasersautographs.com or be the first to hear about the latest updates and amazing items in stock by signing up to our free newsletter at www.stanleygibbons.com/fn.

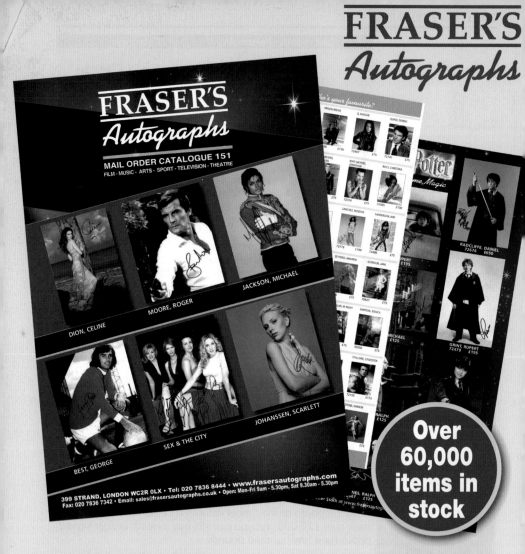

Stanley Gibbons Ltd is delighted to present to you the Opus Collection - A series of epic publications celebrating some of the world's most famous brands and icons

The Opus Collection is no ordinary series of books. Once described by a reviewer "not so much a coffee-table book as the coffee table", these larger-than-life publications honour the greatest iconic names in the world of sport, art, fashion and entertainment.

Typically weighing in at over a staggering 30 kilos, with over 800 pages, each measuring half-a-metre square, an Opus has a wealth of breathtaking content. Words are contributed by the finest specialist writers, accompanied by hundreds of rare and previously unpublished archive images, specially-commissioned photos and exquisite illustrations, all displayed on an unprecedented scale.

worth
the
weight

Beautifully-designed, finished to the highest specification and presented in a luxury format, every Opus is personally signed by a number of legends in their fields and sold worldwide in strictly limited edition print runs, making them collectors' items with excellent investment potential.

The titles within the Opus Collection include:

Super Bowl Opus

The most impressive and exciting tribute to 40 years of the game that stops America. Painstaking research, hundreds of previously unpublished photos, portraits of Super Bowl giants taken by the world's largest Polaroid camera and words by the finest writers in America have truly made this Opus an iconic piece of memorabilia. The Opus also features the most detailed game chart ever, showing every play of every year of the Super Bowl.

A special edition includes the 'MVP Signature Page', which displays the personal signatures of every living MVP – a truly unique piece of sporting history.

Limited Edition

- Strictly limited to 20,000 copies worldwide
- Including the most comprehensive game chart ever produced

MVP Edition

- Strictly limited to 400 copies worldwide

- Each copy personally hand-signed by all living MVP's that have played in the Super Bowl

Arsenal Opus

The *Arsenal Opus* is the exciting tribute to Arsenal FC that covers the club's humble beginnings, also known as the "Highbury years", through to the monumental move to Emirates Stadium.

Exclusive features include the ultimate dream team for Arsenal FC, from "Safe Hands" to "Captain Fantastic", the intense rivalry with Tottenham Hotspur and a unique insight in to the thoughts of the legendary Arsène Wenger.

Classic Edition

- Strictly limited to 1,500 copies worldwide
- Each copy personally hand-signed by legend Arsène Wenger
-

Icons Edition

- Strictly limited to 500 copies worldwide
- Each copy personally hand-signed by Tony Adams, Dennis Bergkamp, Liam Brady, Charlie George, George Graham, Thierry Henry, Frank McLintock, David Seaman, Patrick Vieira, Bob Wilson, Ian Wright and Arsène Wenger

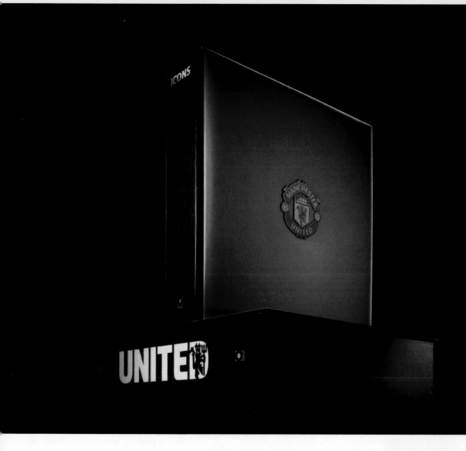

United Opus

The *United Opus* is the most definitive tribute to one of the greatest football clubs in the world. Included inside the Opus are exclusive features untold from the club, including interviews from Sir Bobby Charlton to Wayne Rooney, a selection of the greatest fifty players from the club, unseen and unique details from the tragedy at Munich, and an exciting three-part chapter dedicated to the legendary Sir Alex Ferguson.

Limited Edition

- Strictly limited to 8,950 copies
- Each copy personally hand-signed by legends Sir Bobby Charlton and Sir Alex Ferguson

Icons Edition

- Strictly limited to 500 copies
- Each copy personally hand-signed by Eric Cantona, Denis Law, Bryan Robson, as well as legends Sir Bobby Charlton and Sir Alex Ferguson

Vivienne Westwood Opus

The *Vivienne Westwood Opus* offers a startling insight in to Vivienne Westwood, her manifesto and her stunning designs, which reflect the passion of her collections. A very personal and special project for the Grand Dame of British Fashion, as only a limited number of 900 copies are available to the public in 9 cover designs, all designed and personally signed by Westwood. Featured inside the Opus are 97 Polaroids, all are truly unique that show Westwood's designs as worn by her closest friends and family, including Kate Moss, Naomi Campbell, Bob Geldof and Helena Bonham Carter.

Limited Edition

- ■ Strictly limited to 900 copies worldwide, available in 9 different covers
- ■ Each copy personally hand-signed by Vivienne Westwood

The titles within the Opus Collection are forever growing, with future collaborations with the Saatchi Gallery, Celtic FC, Formula 1, Maradona, Ferrari and many more. To find out more, please call +44 207 213 9587.

www.stanleygibbons.com/opus

Art

For most people, owning a painting by Picasso is way out of reach. As nice as it would be to have a space on your wall which just cries out for a Constable, most of us must face the fact even if you were to win the lottery it would be a pinch to afford one. Paintings by the likes of Warhol, Renoir and Monet command, money more akin to buying hospital wings rather then the average art fan looking for a piece of history. However, there is an alternative and one that does not rely on multiple remortages. That is of course to collect their signatures, after all, for an artist, it is often extremely symbolic and instantly recognisable.

However the collectible potential does not end with art giants of yesteryear. Cartoonists like Matt Groening, creator of the Simpsons, and Chuck Jones of Looney Tunes offer popular and accessible autographs, many of which reflect the humour and fun which made the artist famous in the first place.

There are of course great rarities to look out for. Vincent van Gogh, for example, was a lonely figure in life and one whose art was not to become popular until after his death. There are almost no signed documents available on the open market with most being held by the Van Gogh Museum. As a result a certified Van Gogh document will generally command a six figure sum should one ever come up at auction!

One of the most interesting aspects of collecting art signatures is that many of the artists do not just simply sign the paper but add their own personal artistic content, often with little cartoons or sketches. This makes the collecting of art signatures a hugely varied and exciting genre and something any lover of philography can understand and admire.

BARKS, CARL

SP	£450	$800	€555
DS	£595	$1,055	€735
DS	£295	$525	€365

AYRTON, MICHAEL

SP	£350	$620	€430
DS	£200	$355	€250
DS	£125	$225	€155

ANNIGONI, PIETRO

SP	£295	$525	€365
DS	£200	$355	€250
DS	£100	$180	€125

AWDREY. W

SP	£850	$1,510	€1,045
DS	£500	$890	€615
DS	£275	$490	€340

BACON, FRANCIS

SP	£995	$1,765	€1,225
DS	£700	$1,240	€860
DS	£350	$620	€430

BLAKE, PETER

SP	£100	$180	€125
DS	£75	$135	€95
DS	£30	$55	€40

Illustration by Quentin Blake from The Red Shoes

Taken from The Sixth Sense Treasury of Fairy Tales. Published by Rain'diance, 7th August 1998, £16.95

BLAKE, QUENTIN

SP	**£150**	$270	€185
DS	**£85**	$155	€105
DS	**£50**	$90	€65

BRASSAI

SP	**£2,750**	$4,875	€3,380
DS	**£650**	$1,155	€800
DS	**£500**	$890	€615

CADMUS, PAUL

SP	**£195**	$345	€240
DS	**£125**	$225	€155
DS	**£75**	$135	€95

CEZANNE, PAUL

SP		*	
DS	**£12,500**	$22,145	€15,360
DS	**£7,000**	$12,400	€8,605

CHAGALL, MARC

SP	**£1,250**	$2,215	€1,540
DS	**£895**	$1,585	€1,100
DS	**£650**	$1,155	€800

CONSTABLE, JOHN

SP		*	
DS	**£2,000**	$3,545	€2,460
DS	**£975**	$1,730	€1,200

CRUIKSHANK, GEORGE

SP	**£495**	$880	€610
DS	**£300**	$535	€370
DS	**£200**	$355	€250

DALI, SALVADOR

SP	**£1,250**	$2,215	€1,540
DS	**£1,750**	$3,100	€2,150
DS	**£495**	$880	€610

DAVIS, JIM

SP	**£75**	$135	€95
DS	**£50**	$90	€65
DS	**£30**	$55	€40

DEGAS, EDGAR

SP		*	
DS	**£2,250**	$3,990	€2,765
DS	**£1,750**	$3,100	€2,150

DUCHAMP, MARCEL

SP		*	
DS	**£750**	$1,330	€925
DS	**£495**	$880	€610

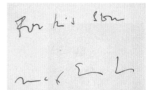

ERNST, MAX

SP	**£650**	$1,155	€800
DS	**£500**	$890	€615
DS	**£250**	$445	€310

ESCHER, M.C

SP	**£1,250**	$2,215	€1,540
DS	**£995**	$1,765	€1,225
DS	**£500**	$890	€615

FIRMIN, PETER

SP	£225	$400	€280
DS	£575	$1,020	€710
DS	£100	$180	€125

GEROME, JEAN LEON

SP	£395	$700	€485
DS	£295	$525	€365
DS	£150	$270	€185

HARGREAVES, ADAM

SP	£75	$135	€95
DS	£250	$445	€310
DS	£50	$90	€65

FRELENG, FRIZ

SP	£195	$345	€240
DS	£275	$490	€340
DS	£160	$285	€200

GILES, CARL

SP	£200	$355	€250
DS	£250	$445	€310
DS	£75	$135	€95

HARING, KEITH

SP	£475	$845	€585
DS	£750	$1,330	€925
DS	£175	$310	€215

GAUGUIN, PAUL

SP		*	
DS	£7,500	$13,290	€9,215
DS	£3,500	$6,200	€4,300

GROENING, MATT

SP	£550	$975	€680
DS	£495	$880	€610
DS	£395	$700	€485

HIRST, DAMIEN

SP	£650	$1,155	€800
DS	£650	$1,155	€800
DS	£395	$700	€485

GEDDES, ANNE

SP	£195	$345	€240
DS	£125	$225	€155
DS	£75	$135	€95

HANNA, BILL

SP	£195	$345	€240
DS	£250	$445	€310
DS	£75	$135	€95

HOCKNEY, DAVID

SP	£350	$620	€430
DS	£275	$490	€340
DS	£195	$345	€240

HOGARTH, WILLIAM

SP	*		
DS	£1,750	$3,100	€2,150
DS	£995	$1,765	€1,225

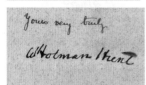

HOLMAN HUNT, WILLIAM

SP	£250	$445	€310
DS	£150	$270	€185
DS	£75	$135	€95

JONES, CHUCK

SP	£120	$215	€150
DS	£80	$145	€100
DS	£50	$90	€65

JUDGE, MIKE

SP	£85	$155	€105
DS	£35	$65	€45
DS	£25	$45	€35

KANE, BOB

SP	£255	$455	€315
DS	£295	$525	€365
DS	£100	$180	€125

KETCHAM, HANK

SP	£150	$270	€185
DS	£195	$345	€240
DS	£75	$135	€95

KOKOSCHKA, OSKAR

SP	£450	$800	€555
DS	£650	$1,155	€800
DS	£250	$445	€310

LANDSEER, SIR EDWIN HENRY

SP	£225	$400	€280
DS	£150	$270	€185
DS	£75	$135	€95

LANTZ, WALTER

SP	£150	$270	€185
DS	£295	$525	€365
DS	£80	$145	€100

LEE, STAN

SP	£95	$170	€120
DS	£75	$135	€95
DS	£50	$90	€65

LEIBOVITZ, ANNIE

SP	£395	$700	€485
DS	£550	$975	€680
DS	£200	$355	€250

LICHTENSTEIN, ROY

SP	£850	$1,510	€1,045
DS	£650	$1,155	€800
DS	£395	$700	€485

MAGRITTE, RENE

SP	£1,250	$2,215	€1,540
DS	£995	$1,765	€1,225
DS	£500	$890	€615

MATISSE, HENRI

SP	*		
DS	£2,950	$5,230	€3,625
DS	£1,750	$3,100	€2,150

MIRO, JOAN

SP	£495	$880	€610
DS	£575	$1,020	€710
DS	£350	$620	€430

MONET, CLAUDE

SP	*		
DS	£5,250	$9,300	€6,450
DS	£4,000	$7,090	€4,915

A. M. MUCHA: MATEŘSKÁ MOUDROST   ELIŠKA PŘEMYSLOVNA

MUCHA, ALPHONSE

SP	£495	$880	€610
DS	£350	$620	€430
DS	£250	$445	€310

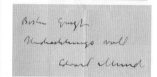

MILLAIS, JOHN EVERETT

SP	£500	$890	€615
DS	£350	$625	€430
DS	£200	$355	€250

MOORE, HENRY

SP	£295	$525	€365
DS	£395	$700	€485
DS	£195	$345	€240

MUNCH, EDVARD

SP	£1,450	$2,570	€1,785
DS	£2,500	$4,430	€3,075
DS	£1,200	$2,130	€1,475

Claude Monet (1840-1926)

Claude Monet was a leading exponent of Impressionism. His 1872 painting *Impression, Sunrise* led to the movement's name (suggested by one distinctly unimpressed critic). Impressionist paintings were initially very controversial, but gained markedly in popularity and continue to command extremely high prices at auction today (a Monet water lily painting sold for over £40 million in June 2008).

Impressionism captures the transient effects of light using distinct juxtaposed brush strokes to vivid effect, and was used by a number of painters such as Renoir, Pissarro and Sisley. Monet's later work is also credited with influencing the rise of Abstract Expressionism and helping to inspire a range of artists such as Pollock, Rothko and De Kooning.

Much of Monet's art was taken from nature, and he often painted and displayed a number of related works together. The series showed movement and variations in light over time, and reflected his response to changing images in landscape. His haystack paintings and his *Creuse Valley* paintings are examples of this. The shimmering Giverny paintings full of light and reflection, depicting his garden with Japanese bridge and water lily pond, remain incredibly popular and the garden itself attracts many visitors each year.

NEIL, MILT

SP	£225	$400	€280
DS	£350	$620	€430
DS	£90	$160	€115

NEWTON, HELMUT

SP	£350	$620	€430
DS	£395	$700	€485
DS	£250	$445	€310

PARK, NICK
SP	**£450**	$800	€555
DS	**£650**	$1,155	€800
DS	**£350**	$620	€430

PICASSO, PABLO
SP	**£3,250**	$5,760	€3,995
DS		*	
DS	**£2,250**	$3,990	€2,765

PIPER, JOHN
SP	**£175**	$310	€215
DS	**£375**	$665	€465
DS	**£125**	$225	€155

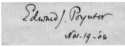

POYNTER, EDWARD
SP	**£100**	$180	€125
DS	**£75**	$135	€95
DS	**£50**	$90	€65

RACKHAM, ARTHUR
SP	**£950**	$1,685	€1,170
DS	**£800**	$1,420	€985
DS	**£475**	$845	€585

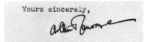

RANSOME, ARTHUR
SP	**£750**	$1,330	€925
DS	**£495**	$880	€610
DS	**£300**	$535	€370

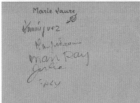

RAY, MAN
SP	**£1,250**	$2,215	€1,540
DS	**£800**	$1,420	€985
DS	**£575**	$1,020	€710

REID, JAMIE
SP	**£100**	$180	€125
DS	**£85**	$155	€105
DS	**£50**	$90	€65

RENOIR, PIERRE AUGUSTE
SP	**£4,750**	$8,415	€5,840
DS	**£4,500**	$7,975	€5,530
DS	**£3,250**	$5,760	€3,995

RHEIMS, BETTINA
SP	**£395**	$700	€485
DS	**£450**	$800	€555
DS	**£250**	$445	€310

RICHMOND, SIR WILLIAM BLAKE
SP	**£60**	$110	€75
DS	**£45**	$80	€55
DS	**£30**	$55	€40

RIZZI, JAMES
SP	**£150**	$270	€185
DS	**£175**	$315	€215
DS	**£90**	$160	€115

ROCKWELL, NORMAN

SP	£550	$975	€680
DS	£450	$800	€555
DS	£375	$665	€465

RODIN, AUGUSTE

SP	£4,500	$7,975	€5,530
DS	£2,500	$4,430	€3,075
DS	£1,500	$2,660	€1,845

ROSSETTI, DANTE GABRIEL

SP	£550	$975	€680
DS	£495	$880	€610
DS	£295	$525	€365

RYAN, JOHN

SP	£150	$270	€185
DS	£180	$320	€225
DS	£100	$180	€125

SARGENT, JOHN SINGER

SP	£750	$1,330	€925
DS	£450	$800	€555
DS	£295	$525	€365

Charles Schulz

Best known for his *Peanuts* characters Charlie Brown, Lucy, Linus and Snoopy, Charles M. Schulz (1922-2000) was the most widely syndicated comic strip artist in history. *Peanuts* was published in over 2,600 newspapers and read by millions in 75 countries. After drawing the *Peanuts* cartoon for over 50 years, he retired for health reasons, but sadly died just hours before his farewell strip appeared.

Charlie Brown embodied Schulz's own insecurities and vulnerabilities. His long-suffering attitude to his misfortunes (which he greeted with a characteristically mild *"Good grief!"*) and his tolerance of the sharp-tongued Lucy's dubious advice made him an endearing and much-loved character.

Snoopy was inspired by the real-life Spike, *"The smartest and most uncontrollable dog"* ever, in Schulz's view. Snoopy often turned his doghouse into an imaginary World War One plane to do battle with the Red Baron, goggles on, silk scarf and ears caught by the wind.

"Why do musicians compose symphonies and poets write poems? They do it because life wouldn't have any meaning for them if they didn't. That's why I draw cartoons. It's my life." – Charles M. Schulz.

SCARFE, GERALD

SP	£50	$90	€65
DS	£35	$65	€45
DS	£25	$45	€35

SCHULZ, CHARLES

SP	£1,950	$3,455	€2,400
DS	£1,750	$3,100	€2,150
DS	£750	$1,330	€925

SEARLE, RONALD

SP	£150	$270	€185
DS	£100	$180	€125
DS	£75	$135	€95

SEGAL, GEORGE

SP	£200	$355	€250
DS	£175	$310	€215
DS	£90	$160	€115

SHEPARD, ERNEST.H

SP	*		
DS	£1,250	$2,215	€1,540
DS	£575	$1,020	€710

Art

Vincent van Gogh (1853-90)   Although most widely recognised as a distinctive post-impressionist painter through his sunflower paintings, and well-known for his struggle with depression and mental illness, Van Gogh was also obsessed with religious and social questions.

He hoped at one time to follow in his father's footsteps to become an evangelical pastor, and developed a deep love for English hymns. Whilst working at a school run by Reverend Thomas Slade Jones in 1876 he wrote out four verses of *"Tell Me the Old, Old Story"* all neatly penned in tiny script. In the verso are written (also in Van Gogh's hand) 32 partial lines of Dutch religious verse. This outstanding piece was originally a part of a visitor's book belonging to Annie Slade-Jones, the wife of Reverend Jones. The visitor's book and Van Gogh's handwritten entry have been documented and verified by the Van Gogh Museum in Amsterdam.

The item is in very fine condition. Handwritten material of Vincent Van Gogh is exceedingly rare and desirable. The few letters that have come onto the market in the last ten years have all sold in the six-figure sterling range.*

SIGNAC, PAUL

SP	**£1,250**	$2,215	€1,540
DS	**£750**	$1,330	€925
DS	**£450**	$800	€555

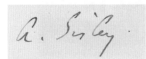

SISLEY, ALFRED

SP	**£3,500**	$6,200	€4,300
DS	**£2,250**	$3,990	€2,765
DS	**£1,500**	$2,660	€1,845

SMYTHE, REG

SP	**£100**	$180	€125
DS	**£195**	$345	€240
DS	**£70**	$125	€90

TENNIEL, JOHN

SP	**£500**	$890	€615
DS	**£350**	$620	€430
DS	**£200**	$355	€250

TOULOUSE-LAUTREC, HENRI DE

SP		*	
DS	**£4,950**	$8,770	€6,085
DS	**£3,000**	$5,315	€3,690

TURNER, J.M.W.

SP	**£2,500**	$4,430	€3,075
DS	**£1,950**	$3,455	€2,400
DS	**£1,500**	$2,660	€1,845

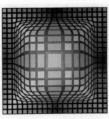

VASARELY, VIKTOR

SP	**£295**	$525	€365
DS	**£275**	$490	€340
DS	**£175**	$310	€215

WARHOL, ANDY

SP	**£1,250**	$2,215	€1,540
DS	**£1,750**	$3,100	€2,150
DS	**£950**	$1,685	€1,170

WHISTLER, JAMES MCNEILL

SP	**£4,250**	$7,530	€5,225
DS	**£2,750**	$4,875	€3,380
DS	**£2,250**	$3,990	€2,765

WRIGHT, FRANK LLOYD

SP	**£1,950**	$3,455	€2,400
DS	**£1,500**	$2,660	€1,845
DS	**£950**	$1,685	€1,170

*Please not that as items have not been highly traded in 2008, there is no full entry for van Gogh.

Aviation / Space

Since the dawn of time space has captivated the philosophical man, the mathematician and the physicist, furthering their desire to explore our seemingly boundless universe. We as humans define ourselves through space and time; we perpetually seek to better understand the matter, energy and momentum that governs our very existence. It is therefore not such a revelation that those individuals that have had the rare, and often envious, task of defining our solar system and skies are subsequently revered for their outstanding achievements.

For those collectors that delve into the realm of space and aviation the rewards are evident. Collecting in space and aviation is exceedingly educational, one that requires the collector to recognise and subsequently appreciate the complex achievements of pilots and astronauts.

In comparison to other fields of collecting, it can be particularly difficult to locate names that are in high demand. Autographed pictorial items, such as photographs or images, are scarce due to the nature of the signer's employment. Naturally photographs of the personality in action, performing their associated role are preferable to posed publicity photographs which tend to be signed in more profusion. A signed posed portrait of Lindbergh, for instance, is preferable to a signed cheque, but an autographed photograph of Lindbergh standing next to his plane exceeds both.

Pioneers within the field tend to be the most collectable and desirable names to collect in the field of space and aviation include the Wright Brothers, renowned for inventing and building the world's first airplane. Likewise, Louis Blériot, Amelia Earhart, Amy Johnson, Yuri Gagarin and the Apollo 11 mission crew – Armstrong, Collins and Aldrin – are all considered pioneers.

The field of space and aviation falls into three main sub-categories of collecting; these are Pilots, Astronauts and Cosmonauts. During the 1960s the popularity of collecting Soviet cosmonauts' names began to rise in conjunction with their achievements, among them was Yuri Gagarin who managed the incredible feat of not only becoming the first man in space but the first to orbit the Earth. The cosmonauts of the '60s, among them Gherman Titov, Valentina Tereshkova and Alexei Leonov have achieved many of the great 'firsts' in space and aviation and as a result they will always remain popular with collectors.

In recent years the popularity of certain names has eclipsed others, the Apollo 11 crew perhaps command the most interest with a 468.6% rise in retail value since 1997 (Fraser's 100 Index). Fully signed single group crew photographs or items of memorabilia directly related to NASA missions are highly sought after as the group photograph and signing can be difficult. To have more than one desirable autograph on the same item is the pièce de résistance. It is worth noting that 2009 will be the 40th Anniversary of the Apollo 11 mission, so you can expect a rise in value for anything related to, or autographed by, the crew.

An exceedingly interesting area of collecting is insurance covers signed by astronauts. Considering that the job of an astronaut is high risk, the covers were produced for crews to sign together in pre-flight quarantine, shortly before their launch. These covers were left behind for the crews' families as a form of insurance: should the crew fail to return, the covers could be sold.

There are hazards though to collecting space and aviation, the market is swamped with autopen signatures of Western astronauts, most of which are produced and sent out by NASA. A good rule is that if the signature appears flat and uniform in colour with a shaky edge to the line across the bottom white margin of a photograph they are more than likely autopen examples. On occasion secretaries are also employed to sign on behalf of the astronauts and these are particularly misleading as they appear to be genuine handwritten examples. It is therefore paramount that when collecting space and aviation that you refer to a certified dealer at all times.

AVIATION

BATTEN, JEAN

SP	£150	$270	€185
DS	£100	$180	€125
AP	£75	$135	€95

BEARNE, GUY

SP	£75	$135	€95
DS	£50	$90	€65
AP	£30	$55	€40

BLERIOT, LOUIS

SP	£950	$1,685	€1,170
DS	£750	$1,330	€925
AP	£650	$1,155	€800

BOLLAND, GUY

SP	£75	$135	€95
DS	£50	$90	€65
AP	£30	$55	€40

BOXER, HENRY

SP	£50	$90	€65
DS	£35	$65	€45
AP	£20	$40	€25

Louis Blériot

Just six years after man's first powered controlled flight, a London newspaper, *The Daily Mail* put up a £1000 prize money competition for the first person who could successfully cross the English Channel, a distance of 26 miles.

Across the channel in France, a 37 year old pilot and aircraft designer, Louis Blériot, who at the time held the European endurance flight record of 36 minutes and 55 seconds, felt that he was the one who could best achieve this unimaginable feat.

On 25th July 1909, he stepped aboard his Blériot XI plane and set out across the English Channel. Just 37 minutes later he had entered the record books and made history for being the first person to cross a large expanse of water in a *"heavier than air"* craft.

Later in life he ran a successful aircraft design company, *Société Pour Aviation et ses Derives* (SPAD), which made combat aircraft during World War I, before creating his own company, *Blériot-Aéronautique, Aéronautique*. Louis died in August 1936, aged 64.

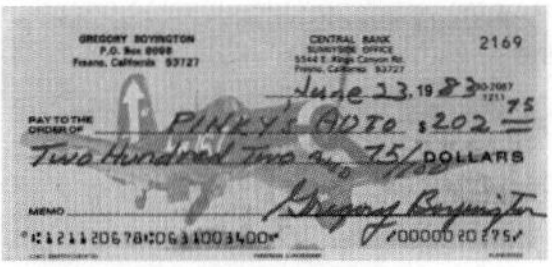

BOYINGTON, GREGORY (PAPPY)

SP	**£175**	$315	€220
DS	**£125**	$225	€155
AP	**£95**	$170	€120

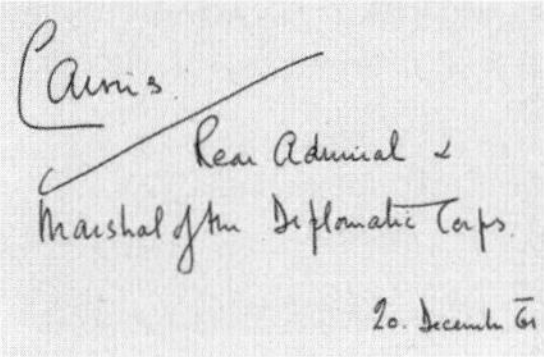

CAIRNS, DAVID 5TH EARL OF

SP	**£75**	$135	€95
DS	**£50**	$90	€65
AP	**£30**	$55	€40

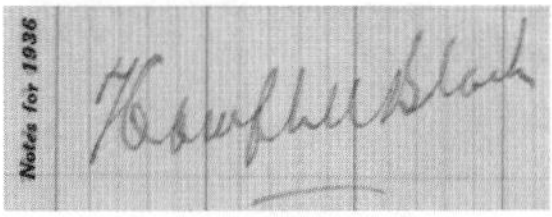

CAMPBELL-BLACK, TOM

SP	**£75**	$135	€95
DS	**£60**	$110	€75
AP	**£40**	$75	€50

CARDENAS, BOB

SP	**£75**	$135	€95
DS	**£60**	$110	€75
AP	**£40**	$75	€50

CHESHIRE, LEONARD

SP	**£125**	$225	€155
DS	**£75**	$135	€95
AP	**£50**	$90	€65

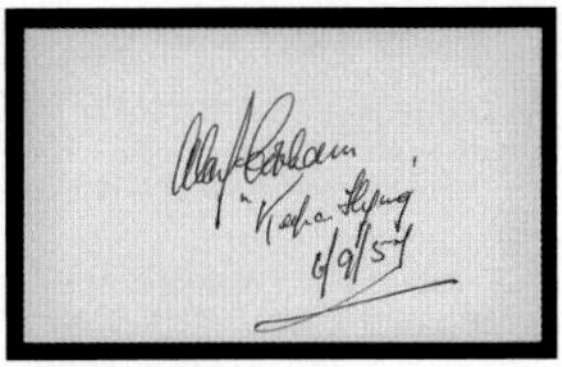

COBHAM, ALAN J

SP	**£200**	$355	€250
DS	**£150**	$270	€185
AP	**£100**	$180	€125

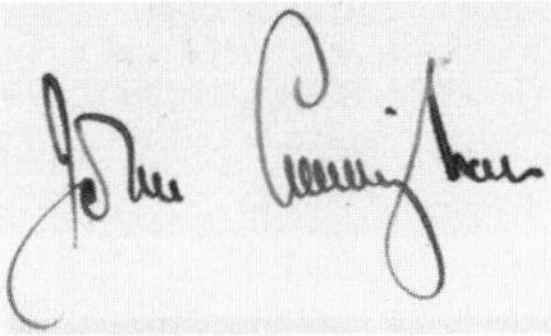

CUNNINGHAM, JOHN

SP	**£95**	$170	€120
DS	**£75**	$135	€95
AP	**£50**	$90	€65

DANNENBERG, KONRAD

SP	**£75**	$135	€95
DS	**£60**	$110	€75
AP	**£40**	$75	€50

EARHART, AMELIA

SP	**£2,500**	$4,430	€3,075
DS	**£2,000**	$3,545	€2,460
AP	**£1,500**	$2,660	€1,845

ENOLA GAY - TIBBETS, VAN KIRK & FEREBEE

SP	**£295**	$525	€365
DS	**£200**	$355	€250
AP	**£150**	$270	€185

HUGHES, HOWARD

SP	**£2,950**	$5,230	€3,625
DS	**£2,000**	$3,545	€2,460
AP	**£1,500**	$2,660	€1,845

JABS, HANS JOACHIM

SP	**£75**	$135	€95
DS	**£60**	$110	€75
AP	**£40**	$75	€50

JOHNSON, AMY

SP	**£650**	$1,155	€800
DS	**£500**	$890	€615
AP	**£375**	$665	€465

KENNEL, KARL

SP	**£75**	$135	€95
DS	**£50**	$90	€65
AP	**£40**	$75	€50

The Wright Brothers

Although not the first to make a successful powered flight, two American brothers in the early 20th century, the Wright brothers, are universally credited with making the first *'controlled'* powered flight.

Although being inventors, the brothers also pursued careers in Publishing and Bicycle manufacturing, before moving on to put their efforts into *'flying machines'*.

On a cold, windy Thursday morning, December 17th 1903, Orville Wright became the first person to undertake a controlled flight, lasting just 12 seconds and covering 165 metres. *"It had"*, he went on later to say, *"made the world smaller"*. During the rest of that day the brothers went on to make a further 3 flights, the last being a distance of 260 metres and lasting 59 seconds.

The town of Kitty Hawk in North Carolina will be forever remembered as the place in which all aviation history first began, and in less than 100 years after the first flight of 165 metres, a man-made space craft had left our solar system, a distance of over 9.4 billion miles from the sun.

KRANZ, EUGENE

SP	£375	$665	€465
DS	£295	$525	€365
AP	£150	$270	€185

LAWRENCE, T.E

SP	£4,500	$7,975	€5,530
DS	£3,750	$6,645	€4,610
AP	£2,800	$4,965	€3,445

LINDBERGH, CHARLES A

SP	£3,950	$7,000	€4,855
DS	£2,750	$4,875	€3,380
AP	£1,750	$3,105	€2,155

MCDIVITT, JIM

SP	£75	$135	€95
DS	£60	$110	€75
AP	£40	$75	€50

PEGG, ARTHUR

SP	£75	$135	€95
DS	£60	$110	€75
AP	£45	$80	€60

SAKAI, SABURO

SP	£350	$625	€435
DS	£250	$445	€310
AP	£175	$315	€220

SCHMETZ, HEINRICH

SP	£60	$110	€75
DS	£50	$90	€65
AP	£40	$75	€50

WALLIS, BARNES

SP	£450	$800	€555
DS	£350	$625	€435
AP	£250	$445	€310

First Free Flight, December 17, 1903
Kitty Hawk, N. C.

WRIGHT, ORVILLE

SP	£3,250	$5,760	€3,995
DS	£2,500	$4,430	€3,075
AP	£1,950	$3,455	€2,400

THE WINTERS NATIONAL BANK   No.

DAYTON, OHIO, March 28, 1910

PAY TO THE ORDER OF Edmund S Lorenz $11,500

Eleven thousand and five Hundred   DOLLARS

Wright Brothers

WRIGHT, WILBUR

SP	*		
DS	£3,950	$7,000	€4,855
AP	£2,500	$4,430	€3,075

ZORNER, PAUL

SP	£45	$80	€60
DS	£40	$75	€50
AP	£35	$65	€45

SPACE

ALDRIN, BUZZ

SP	£950	$1,685	€1,170
DS	£325	$580	€400
AP	£225	$400	€280

APOLLO 11

SP	£7,500	$13,290	€9,215
DS	£5,950	$10,540	€7,315
AP	£4,250	$7,530	€5,225

APOLLO 12

SP	£775	$1,375	€955
DS	£650	$1,155	€800
AP	£4,250	$7,530	€5,225

ARMSTRONG, NEIL

SP	£2,500	$4,430	€3,075
DS	£1,950	$3,455	€2,400
AP	£1,250	$2,215	€1,540

BEAN, ALAN

SP	£225	$400	€280
DS	£175	$310	€215
AP	£125	$225	€155

BELYAEV, PAVEL

SP	£225	$400	€280
DS	£175	$310	€215
AP	£125	$225	€155

BLUFORD, GUION STEWART

SP	£75	$135	€95
DS	£55	$100	€70
AP	£40	$75	€50

BORMAN, FRANK

SP	£395	$700	€485
DS	£300	$535	€370
AP	£250	$445	€310

BYKOVSKY, VALERY

SP	£150	$270	€185
DS	£75	$135	€95
AP	£50	$90	€65

CARPENTER, SCOTT

SP	£295	$525	€365
DS	£200	$355	€250
AP	£150	$270	€185

CERNAN, EUGENE

SP	£275	$490	€340
DS	£200	$355	€250
AP	£150	$270	€185

COLLINS, MICHAEL

SP	£975	$1,730	€1,200
DS	£775	$1,375	€955
AP	£550	$975	€680

CONRAD, CHARLES (PETE)

SP	£450	$800	€555
DS	£250	$445	€310
AP	£150	$270	€185

COOPER, GORDON

SP	£295	$525	€365
DS	£200	$355	€250
AP	£150	$270	€185

CUNNINGHAM, WALTER

SP	£100	$180	€125
DS	£75	$135	€95
AP	£50	$90	€65

DUKE, CHARLES

SP	£295	$525	€365
DS	£250	$445	€310
AP	£100	$180	€125

FEOKISTOV, KONSTANTIN

SP	£225	$400	€280
DS	£175	$310	€215
AP	£100	$180	€125

GAGARIN, YURI

SP	£1,500	$2,660	€1,845
DS	£950	$1,685	€1,170
AP	£650	$1,155	€800

GLENN, JOHN

SP	£495	$880	€610
DS	£375	$665	€465
AP	£275	$490	€340

GORDON, RICHARD

SP	£175	$310	€215
DS	£125	$225	€155
AP	£75	$135	€95

Yuri Gagarin

Throughout the last 45 years, much has been written about space exploration: Neil Armstrong becoming the first man on the moon; Apollo 13 and their crew's race against time to make it home in their damaged space craft and the shuttle Challenger which blew up 70 seconds after lift-off, killing all on board; but what about the one man who really had no idea of what lay before him?

Soon after 09.00 on April 12th 1961, a Russian test pilot named Yuri Gagarin became the first man to go into space. His flight aboard a Vostok One space rocket was a small journey at a little under two hours, but in that brief time he made history. The first human words spoken from space were *"I see Earth, it's so beautiful"*.

He returned to earth and the first beings to great him were an old lady, her grand-daughter and a cow! Tragically, Gagarin was killed just 7 years later doing what he enjoyed, flying, aged just 34.

HAISE, FRED

SP	£350	$620	€430
DS	£250	$445	€310
AP	£150	$270	€185

IRWIN, JAMES

SP	£995	$1,765	€1,225
DS	£650	$1,155	€800
AP	£150	$270	€185

KOMAROV, VLADIMIR

SP	£295	$525	€365
DS	£200	$355	€250
AP	£125	$225	€155

LEONOV, ALEXEY

SP	£275	$490	€340
DS	£200	$355	€250
AP	£125	$225	€155

MITCHELL, EDGAR

SP	£295	$525	€365
DS	£200	$355	€250
AP	£125	$225	€155

MOONWALKERS (SET)

SP	£9,950	$17,630	€12,225
DS	£6,950	$12,315	€8,540
AP	£4,950	$8,770	€6,085

NIKOLAYEV, ANDRIAN

SP	£225	$400	€280
DS	£150	$270	€185
AP	£100	$180	€125

POPOVICH, PAVEL

SP	£225	$400	€280
DS	£150	$270	€185
AP	£80	$145	€100

RIDE, SALLY K.

SP	£75	$135	€95
DS	£60	$110	€75
AP	£40	$75	€50

SCHIRRA, WALTER

SP	£450	$800	€555
DS	£350	$620	€460
AP	£250	$445	€310

SCHMITT, HARRISON

SP	£475	$845	€585
DS	£350	$620	€460
AP	£200	$355	€250

SCOTT, DAVID

SP	£295	$525	€365
DS	£150	$270	€185
AP	£100	$180	€125

SHEPARD, ALAN

SP	£475	$845	€585
DS	£350	$620	€460
AP	£200	$355	€250

SOLOVYEV, ANATOLY

SP	£175	$310	€215
DS	£125	$225	€155
AP	£75	$135	€95

VOLYNOV, BORIS

SP	£175	$310	€215
DS	£125	$225	€155
AP	£75	$135	€95

TERESHKOVA, VALENTINA

SP	£275	$490	€340
DS	£250	$445	€310
AP	£195	$345	€240

WORDEN, AL

SP	£195	$350	€240
DS	£150	$270	€185
AP	£85	$155	€105

TITOV, GHERMAN

SP	£250	$445	€310
DS	£185	$330	€230
AP	£100	$180	€125

NASA

YOUNG, JOHN

SP	£400	$710	€495
DS	£325	$580	€400
AP	£150	$270	€185

Film, TV and Theatre

Collecting autographs of screen and stage stars as well as television personalities is very popular. A lot of collectors like to obtain signatures in person as this gives them the excitement of meeting the celebrity. However, due to its popularity this area of collecting is very volatile: the market is flooded with facsimile, secretarial and printed signatures. Obtaining an autograph from a recognised source is a must.

The most popular from of collecting are individual photographs and cast photographs. Actors are often associated with their key roles, therefore depictions of them in those particular roles often command higher prices. Of course, original photographs, particularly vintage ones, bear premium value and are in very high demand.

Collectors very often tend to obtain other forms of signatures as album pages, cheques, etc. Letters do not seem to be of such a great interest as they are usually sent by fan mail services on request and do not tend to be unique. Another interesting form of collecting in this field are contracts of engagement for particular roles, screen scripts and movie props used by the star.

This market is very dynamic as the popularity of screen and stage stars changes according to their working status. It is possible for a signature to lose value or drastically increase in value due to a particularly popular show or the death of the star. Prices are usually driven by the icons of the screen and those who are popular at the time.

There are, however, screen stars who are immortal and are always in high demand. Some of them are extremely difficult to obtain in certain forms, therefore they are also good investment items. They key names include Marilyn Monroe, Charlie Chaplin, James Dean, Jean Harlow, Bruce Lee, Greta Garbo and a few others. It is essential for an investor to research the market thoroughly or seek professional advice before acquiring expensive film autographs.

ABRAHAM, F. MURRAY

SP	£50	$90	€65
DS	£40	$75	€55
AP	£30	$55	€40

ADAMS, AMY

SP	£75	$135	€100
DS	£60	$110	€80
AP	£40	$75	€55

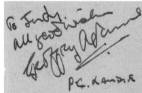

ADAMS, GEOFFREY

SP	£50	$90	€65
DS	£40	$75	€55
AP	£30	$55	€40

ADAMS, JOEY LAUREN

SP	£45	$85	€60
DS	£40	$75	€55
AP	£30	$55	€40

ADAMS, MAUD

SP	£75	$135	€100
DS	£60	$110	€80
AP	£35	$65	€50

ADJANI, ISABELLE

SP	£75	$135	€100
DS	£60	$110	€80
AP	£40	$75	€55

AFFLECK, BEN

SP	£75	$135	€100
DS	£50	$90	€65
AP	£40	$75	€55

AFFLECK, CASEY

SP	£75	$135	€100
DS	£50	$90	€65
AP	£40	$75	€55

AGUTTER, JENNY

SP	£50	$90	€65
DS	£40	$75	€55
AP	£30	$55	€40

AINSWORTH, KACEY

SP	£50	$90	€65
DS	£40	$75	€55
AP	£30	$55	€40

ALBA, JESSICA

SP	£100	$180	€130
DS	£80	$145	€105
AP	£60	$110	€80

ALDA, ALAN

SP	£50	$90	€65
DS	£40	$75	€55
AP	£30	$55	€40

ALDRICH, ROBERT

SP	£100	$180	€130
DS	£80	$145	€105
AP	£50	$90	€65

ALEXANDER, JASON

SP	£50	$90	€65
DS	£40	$75	€55
AP	£30	$55	€40

ALI G

SP	£50	$90	€65
DS	£40	$75	€55
AP	£30	$55	€40

ALLEN, JOAN

SP	£50	$90	€65
DS	£40	$75	€55
AP	£30	$55	€40

ALLEN, KAREN

SP	£50	$90	€65
DS	£40	$75	€55
AP	£30	$55	€40

ALLEN, TIM

SP	£75	$135	€100
DS	£60	$110	€80
AP	£40	$75	€55

ALLEN, WOODY

SP	£75	$135	€100
DS	£60	$110	€80
AP	£40	$75	€55

ALLEY, KIRSTIE

SP	£50	$90	€65
DS	£40	$75	€55
AP	£30	$55	€40

ALTMAN, ROBERT

SP	£50	$90	€65
DS	£40	$75	€55
AP	£30	$55	€40

AMICK, MADCHEN

SP	£50	$90	€65
DS	£40	$75	€55
AP	£30	$55	€40

ANDERSON, GILLIAN

SP	£75	$135	€100
DS	£60	$110	€80
AP	£40	$75	€55

ANDERSON, LONI

SP	£50	$90	€65
DS	£40	$75	€55
AP	£30	$55	€40

ANDERSON, PAMELA

SP	£75	$135	€100
DS	£60	$110	€80
AP	£40	$75	€55

ANDERSON, RICHARD

SP	£50	$90	€65
DS	£40	$75	€55
AP	£30	$55	€40

ANDERSON, SYLVIA

SP	£50	$90	€65
DS	£40	$75	€55
AP	£30	$55	€40

ANDRESS, URSULA

SP	£125	$225	€165
DS	£80	$145	€105
AP	£50	$90	€65

ANDREWS, DANA

SP	£50	$90	€65
DS	£40	$75	€55
AP	£30	$55	€40

ANDREWS, JULIE

SP	£175	$315	€230
DS	£100	$180	€130
AP	£80	$145	€105

ANDREWS, NAVEEN

SP	£75	$135	€100
DS	£60	$110	€80
AP	£40	$75	€55

ANISTON, JENNIFER

SP	£75	$135	€100
DS	£60	$110	€80
AP	£30	$55	€40

ANTHONY, LYSETTE

SP	£50	$90	€65
DS	£40	$75	€55
AP	£30	$55	€40

ANTON, SUSAN

SP	£50	$90	€65
DS	£40	$75	€55
AP	£30	$55	€40

ANWAR, GABRIELLE

SP	£75	$135	€100
DS	£60	$110	€80
AP	£40	$75	€55

APPLEBY, SHIRI

SP	£50	$90	€65
DS	£40	$75	€55
AP	£30	$55	€40

APPLEGATE, CHRISTINA

SP	£50	$90	€65
DS	£40	$75	€55
AP	£30	$55	€40

ARCHER, ANNE

SP	£50	$90	€65
DS	£40	$75	€55
AP	£30	$55	€40

ARGENTO, ASIA

SP	£50	$90	€65
DS	£40	$75	€55
AP	£30	$55	€40

ARNOLD, TOM

SP	£50	$90	€65
DS	£40	$75	€55
AP	£30	$55	€40

ARQUETTE, DAVID

SP	£50	$90	€65
DS	£40	$75	€55
AP	£30	$55	€40

ARQUETTE, ROSANNA

SP	£75	$135	€100
DS	£45	$85	€60
AP	£40	$75	€55

ARQUETTE, PATRICIA

SP	£75	$135	€100
DS	£60	$110	€80
AP	£40	$75	€55

ARTERTON, GEMMA

SP	£75	$135	€100
DS	£60	$110	€80
AP	£40	$75	€55

ASHER, JANE

SP	£50	$90	€65
DS	£40	$75	€55
AP	£30	$55	€40

ASNER, ED

SP	£50	$90	€65
DS	£40	$75	€55
AP	£30	$55	€40

ASQUITH, ANTHONY

SP	£100	$180	€130
DS	£80	$145	€105
AP	£50	$90	€65

ASTAIRE, FRED

SP	£650	$1,160	€845
DS	£500	$890	€650
AP	£275	$490	€360

ATKINS, CHRISTOPHER

SP	£50	$90	€65
DS	£40	$75	€55
AP	£30	$55	€40

ATTENBOROUGH, RICHARD

SP	£50	$90	€65
DS	£40	$75	€55
AP	£30	$55	€40

AUBERJONAIS, RENE

SP	£75	$135	€100
DS	£60	$110	€80
AP	£40	$75	€55

AUMONT, JEAN-PIERRE

SP	£50	$90	€65
DS	£40	$75	€55
AP	£30	$55	€40

ASTIN, SEAN

SP	£50	$90	€65
DS	£40	$75	€55
AP	£30	$55	€40

AUSTIN, STEVE

SP	£75	$135	€100
DS	£60	$110	€80
AP	£40	$75	€55

AUTREY, GENE

SP	£150	$270	€195
DS	£100	$180	€130
AP	£50	$90	€65

AYKROYD, DAN

SP	£50	$90	€65
DS	£40	$75	€55
AP	£30	$55	€40

BACON, KEVIN

SP	£75	$135	€100
DS	£50	$90	€65
AP	£40	$75	€55

BADDELEY, HERMIONE

SP	£45	$85	€60
DS	£35	$65	€50
AP	£25	$45	€35

BAI, LING

SP	£50	$90	€65
DS	£40	$75	€55
AP	£30	$55	€40

BAILEY, PEARL

SP	£50	$90	€65
DS	£40	$75	€55
AP	£30	$55	€40

BAIO, SCOTT

SP	£75	$135	€100
DS	£60	$110	€80
AP	£40	$75	€55

BAKER, COLIN

SP	£75	$135	€100
DS	£60	$110	€80
AP	£40	$75	€55

BAKER, KENNY

SP	£50	$90	€65
DS	£40	$75	€55
AP	£30	$55	€40

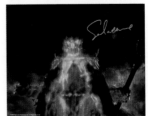

BAKER, SALA

SP	£75	$135	€100
DS	£60	$110	€80
AP	£40	$75	€55

BACALL, LAUREN

SP	£150	$270	€195
DS	£100	$180	€130
AP	£60	$110	€80

BAKER, TOM

SP	£75	$135	€100
DS	£50	$90	€65
AP	£30	$55	€40

BAKULA, SCOTT

SP	£40	$75	€55
DS	£35	$65	€50
AP	£30	$55	€40

BALDWIN, ALEC

SP	£75	$135	€100
DS	£60	$110	€80
AP	£40	$75	€55

BALDWIN, STEPHEN

SP	£50	$90	€65
DS	£40	$75	€55
AP	£30	$55	€40

BALDWIN, WILLIAM

SP	£75	$135	€100
DS	£50	$90	€65
AP	£40	$75	€55

BALE, CHRISTIAN

SP	£100	$180	€130
DS	£80	$145	€105
AP	£50	$90	€65

BALFOUR, ERIC

SP	£50	$90	€65
DS	£40	$75	€55
AP	£30	$55	€40

BALK, FAIRUZA

SP	£50	$90	€65
DS	£45	$85	€60
AP	£40	$75	€55

BALL, LUCILLE

SP	£550	$980	€715
DS	£350	$625	€455
AP	£295	$525	€385

BANA, ERIC

SP	£75	$135	€100
DS	£60	$110	€80
AP	£40	$75	€55

BANCROFT, ANNE

SP	£75	$135	€100
DS	£60	$110	€80
AP	£40	$75	€55

BANDERAS, ANTONIO

SP	£75	$135	€100
DS	£60	$110	€80
AP	£40	$75	€55

BANKHEAD, TALLULAH

SP	£200	$360	€260
DS	£180	$325	€235
AP	£100	$180	€130

BANKS, LESLIE

SP	£50	$90	€65
DS	£40	$75	€55
AP	£30	$55	€40

BANNEN, IAN

SP	£45	$85	€60
DS	£40	$75	€55
AP	£30	$55	€40

BARBEAU, ADRIENNE

SP	£50	$90	€65
DS	£40	$75	€55
AP	£30	$55	€40

BARDOT, BRIGITTE

SP	£125	$225	€165
DS	£90	$165	€120
AP	£60	$110	€80

BARKER, LEX

SP	£50	$90	€65
DS	£40	$75	€55
AP	£30	$55	€40

Sincerely yours,

Christopher Barrie.

BARRIE, CHRIS

SP	£50	$90	€65
DS	£40	$75	€55
AP	£30	$55	€40

BARROWMAN, JOHN

SP	£75	$135	€100
DS	£50	$90	€65
AP	£40	$75	€55

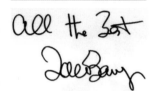

BARRY, JOHN

SP	£200	$360	€260
DS	£175	$315	€230
AP	£100	$180	€130

BARANSKI, CHRISTINE

SP	£45	$85	€60
DS	£40	$75	€55
AP	£30	$55	€40

BARKER, RONNIE

SP	£125	$225	€165
DS	£80	$145	€105
AP	£50	$90	€65

BARRYMORE, DREW

SP	£75	$135	€100
DS	£60	$110	€80
AP	£40	$75	€55

BARRYMORE, JOHN

SP	£1,250	$2,225	€1,625
DS	£1,000	$1,780	€1,300
AP	£750	$1,335	€975

BARTEL, PAUL

SP	£50	$90	€65
DS	£40	$75	€55
AP	£30	$55	€40

BARTHELMESS, RICHARD

SP	£45	$85	€60
DS	£35	$65	€50
AP	£25	$45	€35

BARTHOLOMEW, FREDDIE

SP	£200	$360	€260
DS	£180	$325	€235
AP	£100	$180	€130

BASINGER, KIM

SP	£50	$90	€65
DS	£40	$75	€55
AP	£30	$55	€40

BATEMAN, JASON

SP	£75	$135	€100
DS	£60	$110	€80
AP	£40	$75	€55

BATES, KATHY

SP	£50	$90	€65
DS	£40	$75	€55
AP	£30	$55	€40

BAUMAN, JON

SP	£50	$90	€65
DS	£40	$75	€55
AP	£30	$55	€40

BEACHAM, STEPHANIE

SP	£75	$135	€100
DS	£60	$110	€80
AP	£40	$75	€55

BEAN, SEAN

SP	£75	$135	€100
DS	£60	$110	€80
AP	£40	$75	€55

BEART, EMMANUELLE

SP	£75	$135	€100
DS	£60	$110	€80
AP	£40	$75	€55

BEATTY, WARREN

SP	£100	$180	€130
DS	£80	$145	€105
AP	£60	$110	€80

BECKINSALE, KATE

SP	£75	$135	€100
DS	£60	$110	€80
AP	£40	$75	€55

BEDDOE, DON

SP	£45	$85	€60
DS	£35	$65	€50
AP	£25	$45	€35

BEGLEY, ED JNR

SP	£50	$90	€65
DS	£45	$85	€60
AP	£35	$65	€50

BEL GEDDES, BARBARA

SP	£45	$85	€60
DS	£40	$75	€55
AP	£30	$55	€40

BELL, CATHERINE

SP	£75	$135	€100
DS	£60	$110	€80
AP	£40	$75	€55

BELLO, MARIA

SP	£50	$90	€65
DS	£40	$75	€55
AP	£30	$55	€40

BELLUCCI, MONICA

SP	£75	$135	€100
DS	£60	$110	€80
AP	£40	$75	€55

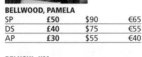

BELLWOOD, PAMELA

SP	£50	$90	€65
DS	£40	$75	€55
AP	£30	$55	€40

BELUSHI, JIM

SP	£50	$90	€65
DS	£40	$75	€55
AP	£30	$55	€40

BENCHLEY, PETER

SP	£75	$135	€100
DS	£80	$145	€105
AP	£50	$90	€65

BENEDICT, DIRK

SP	£75	$135	€100
DS	£60	$110	€80
AP	£40	$75	€55

BENIGNI, ROBERTO

SP	£50	$90	€65
DS	£40	$75	€55
AP	£30	$55	€40

BENNY, JACK

SP	£50	$90	€65
DS	£40	$75	€55
AP	£30	$55	€40

BENSON, JODI

SP	£50	$90	€65
DS	£40	$75	€55
AP	£30	$55	€40

MICHAEL BENTINE

30th July, 1963.

Dear Mr. Parkinson,

Thank you for
your letter. I'm sorry you have not
yet got your script back. I don't
have time to read these myself, but
they are passed on to an associate
script writer at the B.B.C., and I
am sure you will hear from him in
due course.

Thank you for
sending it.

Best wishes,

BENTINE, MICHAEL

SP	£75	$135	€100
DS	£60	$110	€80
AP	£40	$75	€55

BENTLEY, WES

SP	£75	$135	€100
DS	£60	$110	€80
AP	£40	$75	€55

BERFIELD, JUSTIN

SP	£50	$90	€65
DS	£40	$75	€55
AP	£30	$55	€40

BERKLEY, ELIZABETH

SP	£50	$90	€65
DS	£40	$75	€55
AP	£30	$55	€40

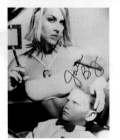

BENZ, JULIE

SP	£75	$135	€100
DS	£60	$110	€80
AP	£40	$75	€55

BERG, PETER

SP	£50	$90	€65
DS	£40	$75	€55
AP	£30	$55	€40

BERNHARD, SANDRA

SP	£50	$90	€65
DS	£40	$75	€55
AP	£30	$55	€40

BERGEN, CANDICE

SP	£50	$90	€65
DS	£40	$75	€55
AP	£30	$55	€40

BERENGER, TOM

SP	£50	$90	€65
DS	£40	$75	€55
AP	£30	$55	€40

BERNHARDT, SARAH

SP	£850	$1,515	€1,105
DS	£650	$1,160	€845
AP	£350	$625	€455

BERESFORD, ELISABETH

SP	£50	$90	€65
DS	£40	$75	€55
AP	£30	$55	€40

BERGMAN, INGRID

SP	£1,250	$2,225	€1,625
DS	£600	$1,070	€780
AP	£350	$625	€455

BERRY, HALLE

SP	£75	$135	€100
DS	£50	$90	€65
AP	£40	$75	€55

BERTINELLI, VALERIE

SP	£50	$90	€65
DS	£40	$75	€55
AP	£30	$55	€40

BETTANY, PAUL

SP	£75	$135	€100
DS	£60	$110	€80
AP	£40	$75	€55

BIEHN, MICHAEL

SP	£75	$135	€100
DS	£60	$110	€80
AP	£50	$90	€65

BIEL, JESSICA

SP	£50	$90	€65
DS	£40	$75	€55
AP	£30	$55	€40

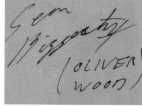

BIGGERSTAFF, SEAN

SP	£50	$90	€65
DS	£40	$75	€55
AP	£30	$55	€40

BIGGS, JASON

SP	£50	$90	€65
DS	£40	$75	€55
AP	£30	$55	€40

BILLINGTON, MICHAEL

SP	£50	$90	€65
DS	£40	$75	€55
AP	£30	$55	€40

BILSON, RACHEL

SP	£75	$135	€100
DS	£60	$110	€80
AP	£40	$75	€55

BINGHAM, TRACI

SP	£50	$90	€65
DS	£40	$75	€55
AP	£30	$55	€40

BINOCHE, JULIETTE

SP	£75	$135	€100
DS	£60	$110	€80
AP	£40	$75	€55

BIRCH, THORA

SP	£75	$135	€100
DS	£60	$110	€80
AP	£35	$65	€50

BIRKIN, JANE

SP	£50	$90	€65
DS	£40	$75	€55
AP	£30	$55	€40

BIRNEY, DAVID

SP	£50	$90	€65
DS	£40	$75	€55
AP	£30	$55	€40

BLACK, KAREN

SP	£50	$90	€65
DS	£40	$75	€55
AP	£30	$55	€40

BLAIR, SELMA

SP	£65	$120	€85
DS	£50	$90	€65
AP	£40	$75	€55

BISSET, JACQUELINE

SP	£75	$135	€100
DS	£60	$110	€80
AP	£30	$55	€40

BLACK, LISA HART

SP	£50	$90	€65
DS	£40	$75	€55
AP	£30	$55	€40

BLAKE, ROBERT

SP	£50	$90	€65
DS	£40	$75	€55
AP	£30	$55	€40

BISSET, JOSIE

SP	£50	$90	€65
DS	£40	$75	€55
AP	£30	$55	€40

BLACKMAN, HONOR

SP	£75	$135	€100
DS	£60	$110	€80
AP	£40	$75	€55

BLAKISTON, CAROLINE

SP	£50	$90	€65
DS	£40	$75	€55
AP	£30	$55	€40

BLACK, JACK

SP	£75	$135	€100
DS	£60	$110	€80
AP	£40	$75	€55

BLAIR, LINDA

SP	£50	$90	€65
DS	£40	$75	€55
AP	£30	$55	€40

"TWEETY"

BLANC, MEL

SP	£50	$90	€65
DS	£40	$75	€55
AP	£30	$55	€40

BLANCHETT, CATE

SP	£100	$180	€130
DS	£80	$145	€105
AP	£60	$110	€80

BLETHYN, BRENDA

SP	£50	$90	€65
DS	£40	$75	€55
AP	£30	$55	€40

BOGARDE, DIRK

SP	£200	$360	€260
DS	£180	$325	€235
AP	£125	$225	€165

BLEASDALE, ALAN

SP	£50	$90	€65
DS	£40	$75	€55
AP	£35	$65	€50

BLOOM, CLAIRE

SP	£45	$85	€60
DS	£35	$65	€50
AP	£25	$45	€35

BOGART, HUMPHREY

SP	£4,950	$8,805	€6,435
DS	£3,950	$7,025	€5,135
AP	£1,750	$3,115	€2,275

BLEETH, YASMIN

SP	£50	$90	€65
DS	£40	$75	€55
AP	£30	$55	€40

BLOOM, ORLANDO

SP	£125	$225	€165
DS	£95	$170	€125
AP	£60	$110	€80

BOLGER, RAY

SP	£395	$705	€515
DS	£250	$445	€325
AP	£195	$350	€255

BLESSED, BRIAN

SP	£50	$90	€65
DS	£40	$75	€55
AP	£30	$55	€40

BLYTH, ANN

SP	£50	$90	€65
DS	£40	$75	€55
AP	£30	$55	€40

BONHAM CARTER, HELENA

SP	£85	$155	€115
DS	£60	$110	€80
AP	£40	$75	€55

BOORMAN, JOHN

SP	£45	$85	€60
DS	£35	$65	€50
AP	£25	$45	€35

BOOTH, SHIRLEY

SP	£45	$85	€60
DS	£35	$65	€50
AP	£25	$45	€35

BOREANAZ, DAVID

SP	£50	$90	€65
DS	£45	$85	€60
AP	£40	$75	€55

BOSWORTH, BRIAN

SP	£50	$90	€65
DS	£40	$75	€55
AP	£30	$55	€40

BOSWORTH, KATE

SP	£75	$135	€100
DS	£60	$110	€80
AP	£40	$75	€55

BOW, CLARA

SP	£995	$1,770	€1,295
DS	£850	$1,515	€1,105
AP	£400	$715	€520

BOXLEITNER, BRUCE

SP	£45	$85	€60
DS	£35	$65	€50
AP	£25	$45	€35

BOYD, BILLY

SP	£75	$135	€100
DS	£60	$110	€80
AP	£40	$75	€55

BOYER, CHARLES

SP	£200	$360	€260
DS	£160	$285	€210
AP	£90	$165	€120

BOYLE, LARA FLYNN

SP	£50	$90	€65
DS	£40	$75	€55
AP	£30	$55	€40

BRADEN, BERNARD

SP	£50	$90	€65
DS	£40	$75	€55
AP	£30	$55	€40

BRADLEY, DOUG

SP	£75	$135	€100
DS	£60	$110	€80
AP	£40	$75	€55

BRAFF, ZACH

SP	£75	$135	€100
DS	£60	$110	€80
AP	£40	$75	€55

BRAGA, SONIA

SP	£45	$85	€60
DS	£40	$75	€55
AP	£30	$55	€40

BRAITHWAITE, LILIAN

SP	£100	$180	€130
DS	£80	$145	€105
AP	£50	$90	€65

BRAMBELL, WILFRID

SP	£850	$1,515	€1,105
DS	£700	$1,245	€910
AP	£575	$1,025	€750

BRANAGH, KENNETH

SP	£75	$135	€100
DS	£60	$110	€80
AP	£40	$75	€55

BRANDAUER, KLAUS MARIA

SP	£100	$180	€130
DS	£80	$145	€105
AP	£50	$90	€65

BRANDO, MARLON

SP	£2,000	$3,560	€2,600
DS	£1,250	$2,225	€1,625
AP	£995	$1,770	€1,295

BRANIGAN, LAURA

SP	£50	$90	€65
DS	£40	$75	€55
AP	£30	$55	€40

BRAY, JIM

SP	£50	$90	€65
DS	£40	$75	€55
AP	£30	$55	€40

BRENT, ROMNEY

SP	£45	$85	€60
DS	£40	$75	€55
AP	£30	$55	€40

BRESSLAW, BERNARD

SP	£65	$120	€85
DS	£50	$90	€65
AP	£25	$45	€35

BRETT, JEREMY

SP	£400	$715	€520
DS	£375	$670	€490
AP	£200	$360	€260

BREWSTER, JORDANA

SP	£50	$90	€65
DS	£40	$75	€55
AP	£30	$55	€40

BRIDGES, ANGELICA

SP	£50	$90	€65
DS	£40	$75	€55
AP	£30	$55	€40

BRIDGES, JEFF

SP	£50	$90	€65
DS	£40	$75	€55
AP	£30	$55	€40

BRIDGES, LLOYD

SP	£50	$90	€65
DS	£40	$75	€55
AP	£30	$55	€40

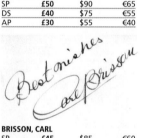

BRISSON, CARL

SP	£45	$85	€60
DS	£35	$65	€50
AP	£25	$45	€35

BROADBENT, JIM

SP	£75	$135	€100
DS	£60	$110	€80
AP	£40	$75	€55

BROCCOLI, ALBERT 'CUBBY'

SP	£300	$535	€390
DS	£275	$490	€360
AP	£150	$270	€195

BRODERICK, MATTHEW

SP	£75	$135	€100
DS	£60	$110	€80
AP	£40	$75	€55

BRODY, ADAM

SP	£75	$135	€100
DS	£60	$110	€80
AP	£40	$75	€55

BRONSON, CHARLES

SP	£100	$180	€130
DS	£60	$110	€80
AP	£40	$75	€55

BROOKS, JAMES L

SP	£50	$90	€65
DS	£40	$75	€55
AP	£30	$55	€40

BROPHY, JED

SP	£45	$85	€60
DS	£40	$75	€55
AP	£30	$55	€40

BROSNAN, PIERCE

SP	£195	$350	€255
DS	£100	$180	€130
AP	£90	$165	€120

BROWN, ERIC

SP	£50	$90	€65
DS	£40	$75	€55
AP	£30	$55	€40

BROWN, JOE. E
SP	£50	$90	€65
DS	£40	$75	€55
AP	£30	$55	€40

BROWN, PHIL
SP	£75	$135	€100
DS	£50	$90	€65
AP	£40	$75	€55

BRUKHEIMER, JERRY
SP	£75	$135	€100
DS	£60	$110	€80
AP	£40	$75	€55

BRYNNER, YUL
SP	£350	$625	€455
DS	£300	$535	€390
AP	£160	$285	€210

BUCHANAN, JACK
SP	£45	$85	€60
DS	£35	$65	€50
AP	£25	$45	€35

BUJOLD, GENEVIEVE
SP	£75	$135	€100
DS	£60	$110	€80
AP	£50	$90	€65

BULLOCH, JEREMY
SP	£45	$85	€60
DS	£40	$75	€55
AP	£30	$55	€40

BULLOCK, SANDRA
SP	£75	$135	€100
DS	£60	$110	€80
AP	£40	$75	€55

BURKE, BILLIE
SP	£50	$90	€65
DS	£40	$75	€55
AP	£30	$55	€40

BURNETT, CAROL
SP	£50	$90	€65
DS	£40	$75	€55
AP	£30	$55	€40

BURNS, GEORGE
SP	£125	$225	€165
DS	£80	$145	€105
AP	£60	$110	€80

BURNSTYN, ELLEN
SP	£50	$90	€65
DS	£40	$75	€55
AP	£30	$55	€40

BURROWS, SAFFRON
SP	£50	$90	€65
DS	£40	$75	€55
AP	£30	$55	€40

Film, TV and Theatre

BURSTYN, ELLEN

SP	£50	$90	€65
DS	£40	$75	€55
AP	£30	$55	€40

Not shown separately

BUSH, SOFIA

SP	£75	$135	€100
DS	£60	$110	€80
AP	£40	$75	€55

BYRNE, PETER

SP	£50	$90	€65
DS	£40	$75	€55
AP	£30	$55	€40

BURTON, RICHARD

SP	£350	$625	€455
DS	£275	$490	€360
AP	£200	$360	€260

BUTLER, YANCY

SP	£75	$135	€100
DS	£60	$110	€80
AP	£40	$75	€55

BYRNES, EDD

SP	£45	$85	€60
DS	£35	$65	€50
AP	£20	$40	€30

CAAN, JAMES

SP	£50	$90	€65
DS	£40	$75	€55
AP	£30	$55	€40

BUSCEMI, STEVE

SP	£100	$180	€130
DS	£90	$165	€120
AP	£40	$75	€55

BYNER, JOHN

SP	£50	$90	€65
DS	£40	$75	€55
AP	£30	$55	€40

CAESAR, SID

SP	£50	$90	€65
DS	£40	$75	€55
AP	£30	$55	€40

BUSFIELD, TIMOTHY

SP	£50	$90	€65
DS	£40	$75	€55
AP	£30	$55	€40

BYNES, AMANDA

SP	£50	$90	€65
DS	£40	$75	€55
AP	£30	$55	€40

CAGE, NICHOLAS

SP	£100	$180	€130
DS	£80	$145	€105
AP	£50	$90	€65

CAGNEY, JAMES

SP	£750	$1,335	€975
DS	£975	$1,735	€1,270
AP	£400	$715	€520

CAIN, DEAN

SP	£50	$90	€65
DS	£40	$75	€55
AP	£30	$55	€40

CAINE, MICHAEL

SP	£75	$135	€100
DS	£60	$110	€80
AP	£40	$75	€55

CALHOUN, RORY

SP	£50	$90	€65
DS	£40	$75	€55
AP	£30	$55	€40

CALLAN, MICHAEL

SP	£50	$90	€65
DS	£40	$75	€55
AP	£30	$55	€40

CALLOW, SIMON

SP	£50	$90	€65
DS	£40	$75	€55
AP	£30	$55	€40

CALVERT, PHYLLIS

SP	£45	$85	€60
DS	£35	$65	€50
AP	£25	$45	€35

CAMPBELL, ALAN

SP	£50	$90	€65
DS	£40	$75	€55
AP	£30	$55	€40

CAMPBELL, BILL

SP	£50	$90	€65
DS	£40	$75	€55
AP	£30	$55	€40

CAMPBELL, BRUCE

SP	£75	$135	€100
DS	£60	$110	€80
AP	£40	$75	€55

CAMPBELL, NEVE

SP	£75	$135	€100
DS	£60	$110	€80
AP	£40	$75	€55

CANNON, DYAN

SP	£45	$85	€60
DS	£40	$75	€55
AP	£30	$55	€40

CAPSHAW, KATE

SP	£50	$90	€65
DS	£40	$75	€55
AP	£30	$55	€40

CARELL, STEVE

SP	£75	$135	€100
DS	£60	$110	€80
AP	£40	$75	€55

CARMICHAEL, IAN

SP	£50	$90	€65
DS	£40	$75	€55
AP	£30	$55	€40

CARMINATI, TULLIO

SP	£50	$90	€65
DS	£40	$75	€55
AP	£30	$55	€40

CARNEY, ART

SP	£50	$90	€65
DS	£40	$75	€55
AP	£30	$55	€40

CARON, LESLIE

SP	£50	$90	€65
DS	£40	$75	€55
AP	£30	$55	€40

CARPENTER, CHARISMA

SP	£50	$90	€65
DS	£40	$75	€55
AP	£30	$55	€40

CARRADINE, DAVID

SP	£50	$90	€65
DS	£40	$75	€55
AP	£30	$55	€40

CARRERA, BARBARA

SP	£75	$135	€100
DS	£60	$110	€80
AP	£40	$75	€55

CARREY, JIM

SP	£75	$135	€100
DS	£60	$110	€80
AP	£40	$75	€55

CARROLL, DIAHANN

SP	£45	$85	€60
DS	£35	$65	€50
AP	£25	$45	€35

CARSON, FRANK

SP	£45	$85	€60
DS	£35	$65	€50
AP	£25	$45	€35

CARTER, LYNDA

SP	£50	$90	€65
DS	£40	$75	€55
AP	£30	$55	€40

CARTWRIGHT, NANCY

SP	£75	$135	€100
DS	£60	$110	€80
AP	£40	$75	€55

CASTELLANETA, DAN

SP	£75	$135	€100
DS	£60	$110	€80
AP	£40	$75	€55

CHABERT, LACEY

SP	£50	$90	€65
DS	£40	$75	€55
AP	£30	$55	€40

CARUSO, DAVID

SP	£75	$135	€100
DS	£60	$110	€80
AP	£40	$75	€55

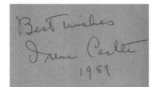

CASTLE, IRENE

SP	£45	$85	€60
DS	£35	$65	€50
AP	£25	$45	€35

CHAMBERLAIN, RICHARD

SP	£50	$90	€65
DS	£40	$75	€55
AP	£30	$55	€40

CASSIDY, DAVID

SP	£50	$90	€65
DS	£40	$75	€55
AP	£30	$55	€40

CATTRALL, KIM

SP	£75	$135	€100
DS	£60	$110	€80
AP	£50	$90	€65

CHAMBERS, JUSTIN

SP	£50	$90	€65
DS	£40	$75	€55
AP	£30	$55	€40

CASSIDY, SHAUN

SP	£50	$90	€65
DS	£40	$75	€55
AP	£30	$55	€40

CAVIEZEL, JAMES

SP	£75	$135	€100
DS	£60	$110	€80
AP	£40	$75	€55

CHAMBERS, MARILYN

SP	£50	$90	€65
DS	£40	$75	€55
AP	£30	$55	€40

CHAN, JACKIE

SP	£75	$135	€100
DS	£60	$110	€80
AP	£30	$55	€40

CHAPLIN, BEN

SP	£75	$135	€100
DS	£60	$110	€80
AP	£40	$75	€55

CHASE, CHEVY

SP	£75	$135	€100
DS	£60	$110	€80
AP	£40	$75	€55

CHANEY, LON (JR)

SP	£2,950	$5,245	€3,835
DS	£2,000	$3,560	€2,600
AP	£1,500	$2,670	€1,950

CHANNING, CAROL

SP	£50	$90	€65
DS	£40	$75	€55
AP	£30	$55	€40

CHAPLIN, CHARLIE

SP	£2,250	$4,005	€2,925
DS	£1,800	$3,205	€2,340
AP	£1,250	$2,225	€1,625

CHEADLE, DON

SP	£50	$90	€65
DS	£40	$75	€55
AP	£30	$55	€40

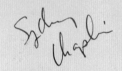

CHAPLIN, SYDNEY

SP	£150	$270	€195
DS	£120	$215	€160
AP	£75	$135	€100

CHAPMAN, BEN

SP	£50	$90	€65
DS	£40	$75	€55
AP	£30	$55	€40

CHEVALIER, MAURICE

SP	£150	$270	€195
DS	£130	$235	€170
AP	£100	$180	€130

CHANNING, STOCKARD

SP	£50	$90	€65
DS	£40	$75	€55
AP	£30	$55	€40

CHARISSE, CYD

SP	£50	$90	€65
DS	£45	$85	€60
AP	£40	$75	€55

CHILES, LOIS

SP	£50	$90	€65
DS	£40	$75	€55
AP	£30	$55	€40

CHRISTENSEN, ERIKA

SP	£50	$90	€65
DS	£40	$75	€55
AP	£30	$55	€40

CHRISTENSEN, HAYDEN

SP	£100	$180	€130
DS	£80	$145	€105
AP	£60	$110	€80

CHRISTIAN, CLAUDIA

SP	£50	$90	€65
DS	£40	$75	€55
AP	£30	$55	€40

CHRISTIE, JULIE

SP	£125	$225	€165
DS	£100	$180	€130
AP	£80	$145	€105

CHURCHILL, SARAH

SP	£50	$90	€65
DS	£40	$75	€55
AP	£30	$55	€40

CLARK, PETULA

SP	£50	$90	€65
DS	£40	$75	€55
AP	£30	$55	€40

CLEESE, JOHN

SP	£75	$135	€100
DS	£60	$110	€80
AP	£40	$75	€55

CLEVELAND, CAROL

SP	£75	$135	€100
DS	£60	$110	€80
AP	£40	$75	€55

CLIFT, MONTGOMERY

SP	£695	$1,240	€905
DS	£400	$715	€520
AP	£295	$525	€385

CLOONEY, GEORGE

SP	£75	$135	€100
DS	£60	$110	€80
AP	£40	$75	€55

CLOSE, GLENN

SP	£75	$135	€100
DS	£60	$110	€80
AP	£40	$75	€55

COBURN, JAMES

SP	£150	$270	€195
DS	£120	$215	€160
AP	£65	$120	€85

COLBERT, CLAUDETTE

SP	£45	$85	€60
DS	£35	$65	€50
AP	£25	$45	€35

COLE, GEORGE

SP	£75	$135	€100
DS	£60	$110	€80
AP	£40	$75	€55

COLEMAN, JACK

SP	£50	$90	€65
DS	£40	$75	€55
AP	£30	$55	€40

COLLETTE, TONI

SP	£50	$90	€65
DS	£40	$75	€55
AP	£30	$55	€40

COLLINS, JOAN

SP	£50	$90	€65
DS	£40	$75	€55
AP	£30	$55	€40

COLTRANE, ROBBIE

SP	£50	$90	€65
DS	£40	$75	€55
AP	£30	$55	€40

CONNELLY, JENNIFER

SP	£75	$135	€100
DS	£50	$90	€65
AP	£40	$75	€55

CONNERY, SEAN

SP	£250	$445	€325
DS	£180	$325	€235
AP	£195	$350	€255

CONNOLLY, BILLY

SP	£75	$135	€100
DS	£60	$110	€80
AP	£40	$75	€55

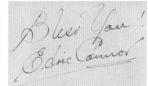

CONNOR, EDRIC

SP	£45	$85	€60
DS	£35	$65	€50
AP	£25	$45	€35

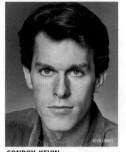

CONNOR, KENNETH

SP	£50	$90	€65
DS	£40	$75	€55
AP	£30	$55	€40

CONROY, KEVIN

SP	£50	$90	€65
DS	£40	$75	€55
AP	£30	$55	€40

COOGAN, JACKIE

SP	£50	$90	€65
DS	£40	$75	€55
AP	£30	$55	€40

COOPER, GARY

SP	£595	$1,060	€775
DS	£450	$805	€585
AP	£200	$360	€260

COOPER, TOMMY

SP	£375	$670	€490
DS	£350	$625	€455
AP	£175	$315	€230

CORBETT, RONNIE

SP	£50	$90	€65
DS	£40	$75	€55
AP	£30	$55	€40

COTTON, JOSEPH

SP	£50	$90	€65
DS	£40	$75	€55
AP	£30	$55	€40

COPE, KENNETH

SP	£50	$90	€65
DS	£40	$75	€55
AP	£30	$55	€40

COSBY, BILL

SP	£50	$90	€65
DS	£40	$75	€55
AP	£30	$55	€40

COURTNEY, NICHOLAS

SP	£50	$90	€65
DS	£45	$85	€60
AP	£40	$75	€55

COPPOLA, FRANCIS FORD

SP	£125	$225	€165
DS	£80	$145	€105
AP	£70	$125	€95

FIELD OF DREAMS

COSTNER, KEVIN

SP	£75	$135	€100
DS	£60	$110	€80
AP	£40	$75	€55

COURTNEY, TOM

SP	£50	$90	€65
DS	£40	$75	€55
AP	£30	$55	€40

COPPOLA, SOPHIA

SP	£75	$135	€100
DS	£60	$110	€80
AP	£40	$75	€55

COTILLARD, MARION

SP	£100	$180	€130
DS	£80	$145	€105
AP	£70	$125	€95

CORBETT, HARRY H

SP	£300	$535	€390
DS	£250	$445	€325
AP	£150	$270	€195

COWARD, NOEL

SP	£275	$490	€360
DS	£250	$445	€325
AP	£130	$235	€170

Film, TV and Theatre

COX, BRIAN

SP	£75	$135	€100
DS	£60	$110	€80
AP	£40	$75	€55

CRAIG, YVONNE

SP	£75	$135	€100
DS	£60	$110	€80
AP	£40	$75	€55

CRAWFORD, MICHAEL

SP	£50	$90	€65
DS	£40	$75	€55
AP	£30	$55	€40

COX, CHARLIE

SP	£65	$120	€85
DS	£50	$90	€65
AP	£40	$75	€55

CRANE, BOB

SP	£750	$1,335	€975
DS	£650	$1,160	€845
AP	£350	$625	€455

CRENNA, RICHARD

SP	£50	$90	€65
DS	£40	$75	€55
AP	£30	$55	€40

COX, COURTENEY

SP	£75	$135	€100
DS	£60	$110	€80
AP	£40	$75	€55

CRANSTON, BRYAN

SP	£50	$90	€65
DS	£40	$75	€55
AP	£30	$55	€40

CRONYN, HUME

SP	£50	$90	€65
DS	£40	$75	€55
AP	£30	$55	€40

CRAIG, DANIEL

SP	£200	$360	€260
DS	£180	$325	€235
AP	£100	$180	€130

CRAWFORD, JOAN

SP	£250	$445	€325
DS	£150	$270	€195
AP	£100	$180	€130

CROOK, MACKENZIE

SP	£75	$135	€100
DS	£60	$110	€80
AP	£40	$75	€55

CROSBY, BILL

SP	£100	$180	€130
DS	£80	$145	€105
AP	£50	$90	€65

CROSBY, BING

SP	£300	$535	€390
DS	£225	$405	€295
AP	£125	$225	€165

CROSBY, DENISE

SP	£50	$90	€65
DS	£40	$75	€55
AP	£30	$55	€40

CROSBY, HARRY

SP	£50	$90	€65
DS	£40	$75	€55
AP	£30	$55	€40

CROWE, RUSSELL

SP	£275	$490	€360
DS	£250	$445	€325
AP	£200	$360	€260

CRUISE, TOM

SP	£75	$135	€100
DS	£60	$110	€80
AP	£50	$90	€65

CRUZ, PENELOPE

SP	£75	$135	€100
DS	£60	$110	€80
AP	£40	$75	€55

CRYSTAL, BILLY

SP	£75	$135	€100
DS	£60	$110	€80
AP	£40	$75	€55

CUCINOTTA, MARIA GRAZIA

SP	£50	$90	€65
DS	£40	$75	€55
AP	£30	$55	€40

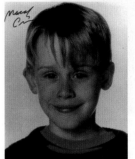

CULKIN, MACAULEY

SP	£75	$135	€100
DS	£60	$110	€80
AP	£40	$75	€55

CUMMING, ALAN

SP	£50	$90	€65
DS	£40	$75	€55
AP	£30	$55	€40

CUMMINGS, CONSTANCE

SP	£45	$85	€60
DS	£35	$65	€50
AP	£25	$45	€35

CUMMINS, PEGGY

SP	£75	$135	€100
DS	£60	$110	€80
AP	£50	$90	€65

CURRY, TIM

SP	£100	$180	€130
DS	£80	$145	€105
AP	£50	$90	€65

CURTIN, JANE

SP	£75	$135	€100
DS	£60	$110	€80
AP	£40	$75	€55

CURTIS, JAMIE LEE

SP	£75	$135	€100
DS	£60	$110	€80
AP	£40	$75	€55

CURTIS, TONY

SP	£75	$135	€100
DS	£60	$110	€80
AP	£40	$75	€55

CUSACK, JOHN

SP	£75	$135	€100
DS	£60	$110	€80
AP	£40	$75	€55

CUSHING, PETER

SP	£250	$445	€325
DS	£125	$225	€165
AP	£80	$145	€105

CUTHBERT, ELISHA

SP	£50	$90	€65
DS	£40	$75	€55
AP	£30	$55	€40

D'ABO, MARYAM

SP	£100	$180	€130
DS	£80	$145	€105
AP	£50	$90	€65

D'ABO, OLIVIA

SP	£100	$180	€130
DS	£80	$145	€105
AP	£50	$90	€65

DAFOE, WILLEM

SP	£75	$135	€100
DS	£50	$90	€65
AP	£40	$75	€55

DALE, ALAN

SP	£75	$135	€100
DS	£60	$110	€80
AP	£40	$75	€55

DALLE, BEATRICE

SP	£100	$180	€130
DS	£80	$145	€105
AP	£50	$90	€65

DALTON, TIMOTHY

SP	£150	$270	€195
DS	£100	$180	€130
AP	£90	$165	€120

DAMON, MATT

SP	£75	$135	€100
DS	£60	$110	€80
AP	£40	$75	€55

DANDRIDGE, DOROTHY

SP	£125	$225	€165
DS	£120	$215	€160
AP	£75	$135	€100

DANES, CLAIRE

SP	£75	$135	€100
DS	£60	$110	€80
AP	£40	$75	€55

DANGERFIELD, RODNEY

SP	£50	$90	€65
DS	£40	$75	€55
AP	£30	$55	€40

DANIELS, JEFF

SP	£75	$135	€100
DS	£40	$75	€55
AP	£30	$55	€40

DANIELS, WILLIAM

SP	£45	$85	€60
DS	£40	$75	€55
AP	£30	$55	€40

DANSON, TED

SP	£50	$90	€65
DS	£40	$75	€55
AP	£30	$55	€40

DAVIDSON, PETER

SP	£60	$110	€80
DS	£50	$90	€65
AP	£40	$75	€55

DAVIS, BETTE

SP	£250	$445	€325
DS	£200	$360	€260
AP	£100	$180	€130

DAVIS, GEENA

SP	£75	$135	€100
DS	£60	$110	€80
AP	£30	$55	€40

DAVIS, JUDY

SP	£50	$90	€65
DS	£40	$75	€55
AP	£30	$55	€40

DAVIS, KRISTIN

SP	£75	$135	€100
DS	£60	$110	€80
AP	£40	$75	€55

DAVIS, WARWICK

SP	£75	$135	€100
DS	£60	$110	€80
AP	£40	$75	€55

DAVISON, PETER

SP	£50	$90	€65
DS	£40	$75	€55
AP	£30	$55	€40

DAWSON, LES

SP	£50	$90	€65
DS	£40	$75	€55
AP	£30	$55	€40

DAY, DORIS

SP	£375	$670	€490
DS	£250	$445	€325
AP	£125	$225	€165

DE CARLO, YVONNE

SP	£50	$90	€65
DS	£40	$75	€55
AP	£30	$55	€40

DE LUISE, DOM

SP	£50	$90	€65
DS	£40	$75	€55
AP	£30	$55	€40

DE MILLE, CECIL B.

SP	£395	$705	€515
DS	£350	$625	€455
AP	£195	$350	€255

DE MORNAY, REBECCA

SP	£50	$90	€65
DS	£40	$75	€55
AP	£30	$55	€40

DE NIRO, ROBERT

SP	£150	$270	€195
DS	£95	$170	€125
AP	£70	$125	€95

DE ROSSI, PORTIA

SP	£50	$90	€65
DS	£40	$75	€55
AP	£30	$55	€40

DEAN, JAMES

SP	£9,500	$16,890	€12,350
DS	£6,500	$11,560	€8,450
AP	£3,950	$7,025	€5,135

DEGENERES, ELLEN

SP	£100	$180	€130
DS	£80	$145	€105
AP	£50	$90	€65

DELANEY, KIM

SP	£50	$90	€65
DS	£40	$75	€55
AP	£30	$55	€40

DENCH, JUDI

SP	£75	$135	€100
DS	£60	$110	€80
AP	£50	$90	€65

DENEUVE, CATHERINE

SP	£150	$270	€195
DS	£100	$180	€130
AP	£80	$145	€105

DEPP, JOHNNY

SP	£195	$350	€255
DS	£125	$225	€165
AP	£80	$145	€105

DEREK, BO

SP	£75	$135	€100
DS	£60	$110	€80
AP	£40	$75	€55

DERN, BRUCE

SP	£50	$90	€65
DS	£40	$75	€55
AP	£30	$55	€40

Walt Disney

Walt Elias Disney was born on December 5th 1901 in Chicago. At 16 Walt was offered a scholarship to Kansas City Art Institute where he met Ub Iwerks. The two men set up their own company and moved to Hollywood in 1923 where they found financial backing from Margaret Winkler and were able to start working on a new animation called *Oswald the Lucky Rabbit*. Before too long, Disney discovered that Winkler and her husband had stolen the animation rights away from him. The same day, on his train ride home, Disney started doodling and drew a picture of a mouse, a mouse now famously known as *Mickey Mouse*. Disney and Iwerks worked together and quickly had *Mickey Mouse* in production. The success of Mickey led to many more cartoons and soon Disney started to venture into the idea of feature animation, starting with *Snow White and the Seven Dwarfs* in 1937.

Following this came *Pinocchio*, *Dumbo*, *Bambi* and many more, all of which were massive hits and loved by children and adults all over the world. He died in 1966 of lung cancer, but Disney's dream to build a theme park was continued. Walt Disney World premiered in 1971. His company is still flourishing today, producing animated and action films. Walt Disney was a man who brought happiness to people's lives and whose memory will live on forever.

Film, TV and Theatre

DERN, LAURA

SP	£50	$90	€65
DS	£40	$75	€55
AP	£30	$55	€40

DEVITO, DANNY

SP	£75	$135	€100
DS	£60	$110	€80
AP	£40	$75	€55

DEY, SUSAN

SP	£50	$90	€65
DS	£40	$75	€55
AP	£30	$55	€40

DIAMOND, PETER

SP	£50	$90	€65
DS	£40	$75	€55
AP	£30	$55	€40

DIAZ, CAMERON

SP	£75	$135	€100
DS	£60	$110	€80
AP	£50	$90	€65

DICAPRIO, LEONARDO

SP	£100	$180	€130
DS	£80	$145	€105
AP	£60	$110	€80

DIETRICH, MARLENE

SP	£250	$445	€325
DS	£225	$405	€295
AP	£100	$180	€130

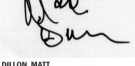

DILLON, MATT

SP	£50	$90	€65
DS	£40	$75	€55
AP	£30	$55	€40

DISNEY, WALT

SP	£5,500	$9,780	€7,150
DS	£3,500	$6,225	€4,550
AP	£2,950	$5,245	€3,835

DOHERTY, SHANNEN

SP	£50	$90	€65
DS	£40	$75	€55
AP	£30	$55	€40

DONAT, ROBERT

SP	£50	$90	€65
DS	£40	$75	€55
AP	£30	$55	€40

DONOHOE, AMANDA

SP	£50	$90	€65
DS	£40	$75	€55
AP	£30	$55	€40

DONOVAN, TATE

SP	£50	$90	€65
DS	£40	$75	€55
AP	£30	$55	€40

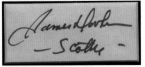

DOOHAN, JAMES

SP	£50	$90	€65
DS	£40	$75	€55
AP	£30	$55	€40

DORFF, STEPHEN

SP	£75	$135	€100
DS	£50	$90	€65
AP	£40	$75	€55

DOUGLAS, KIRK

SP	£350	$625	€455
DS	£200	$360	€260
AP	£125	$225	€165

DOWNEY JR, ROBERT

SP	£100	$180	€130
DS	£60	$110	€80
AP	£40	$75	€55

DORN, MICHAEL

SP	£50	$90	€65
DS	£40	$75	€55
AP	£30	$55	€40

DOUGLAS, MICHAEL

SP	£75	$135	€100
DS	£60	$110	€80
AP	£40	$75	€55

DRESCHER, FRAN

SP	£50	$90	€65
DS	£40	$75	€55
AP	£30	$55	€40

DORS, DIANA

SP	£400	$715	€520
DS	£300	$535	€390
AP	£200	$360	€260

DOURIF, BRAD

SP	£75	$135	€100
DS	£50	$90	€65
AP	£35	$65	€50

DREYFUSS, RICHARD

SP	£75	$135	€100
DS	£60	$110	€80
AP	£30	$55	€40

DOUGLAS, JACK

SP	£60	$110	€80
DS	£50	$90	€65
AP	£40	$75	€55

DOWN, LESLEY-ANNE

SP	£50	$90	€65
DS	£40	$75	€55
AP	£30	$55	€40

DRIVER, MINNIE

SP	£50	$90	€65
DS	£45	$85	€60
AP	£35	$65	€50

DUCHOVNY, DAVID

SP	£75	$135	€100
DS	£60	$110	€80
AP	£40	$75	€55

DUFF, HILARY

SP	£50	$90	€65
DS	£40	$75	€55
AP	£30	$55	€40

DUNAWAY, FAYE

SP	£200	$360	€260
DS	£150	$270	€195
AP	£85	$155	€115

DUNCAN, MICHAEL CLARKE

SP	£75	$135	€100
DS	£60	$110	€80
AP	£40	$75	€55

DUNN, CLIVE

SP	£50	$90	€65
DS	£40	$75	€55
AP	£30	$55	€40

DUNNE, IRENE

SP	£50	$90	€65
DS	£40	$75	€55
AP	£30	$55	€40

DUNST, KIRSTEN

SP	£75	$135	€100
DS	£60	$110	€80
AP	£40	$75	€55

DURBIN, DEANNA

SP	£50	$90	€65
DS	£40	$75	€55
AP	£30	$55	€40

DUSHKU, ELIZA

SP	£75	$135	€100
DS	£45	$85	€60
AP	£35	$65	€50

DUVALL, ROBERT

SP	£50	$90	€65
DS	£40	$75	€55
AP	£30	$55	€40

EARL JONES, JAMES

SP	£50	$90	€65
DS	£40	$75	€55
AP	£30	$55	€40

EASTWOOD, ALISON

SP	£60	$110	€80
DS	£50	$90	€65
AP	£40	$75	€55

EASTWOOD, CLINT

SP	£225	$405	€295
DS	£190	$340	€250
AP	£125	$225	€165

EATON, SHIRLEY

SP	£100	$180	€130
DS	£80	$145	€105
AP	£50	$90	€65

EBSEN, BUDDY

SP	£50	$90	€65
DS	£40	$75	€55
AP	£25	$45	€35

EDEN, BARBARA

SP	£50	$90	€65
DS	£40	$75	€55
AP	£30	$55	€40

EDWARDS, ANTHONY

SP	£50	$90	€65
DS	£40	$75	€55
AP	£30	$55	€40

EKBERG, ANITA

SP	£50	$90	€65
DS	£40	$75	€55
AP	£30	$55	€40

EKLAND, BRITT

SP	£60	$110	€80
DS	£50	$90	€65
AP	£40	$75	€55

ELECTRA, CARMEN

SP	£75	$135	€100
DS	£60	$110	€80
AP	£40	$75	€55

ELIZABETH, SHANNON

SP	£75	$135	€100
DS	£60	$110	€80
AP	£40	$75	€55

ELLIOT, SAM

SP	£75	$135	€100
DS	£60	$110	€80
AP	£40	$75	€55

ELTON, BEN

SP	£60	$110	€80
DS	£50	$90	€65
AP	£40	$75	€55

EMERSON, MICHAEL

SP	£50	$90	€65
DS	£40	$75	€55
AP	£30	$55	€40

ENGLUND, ROBERT

SP	£50	$90	€65
DS	£45	$85	€60
AP	£35	$65	€50

ESPISITO, JENNIFER

SP	£75	$135	€100
DS	£60	$110	€80
AP	£40	$75	€55

ESTEVEZ, EMILIO

SP	£75	$135	€100
DS	£60	$110	€80
AP	£40	$75	€55

EVANS, CHRIS

SP	£75	$135	€100
DS	£40	$75	€55
AP	£30	$55	€40

FAIRBANKS, DOUGLAS JR

SP	£75	$135	€100
DS	£125	$225	€165
AP	£40	$75	€55

FALCO, EDIE

SP	£50	$90	€65
DS	£45	$85	€60
AP	£30	$55	€40

FALK, PETER

SP	£50	$90	€65
DS	£40	$75	€55
AP	£30	$55	€40

FARMER, FRANCES

SP	£995	$1,770	€1,295
DS	£800	$1,425	€1,040
AP	£400	$715	€520

FARRELL, CHARLES

SP	£50	$90	€65
DS	£40	$75	€55
AP	£30	$55	€40

FARRELL, COLIN

SP	£75	$135	€100
DS	£60	$110	€80
AP	£40	$75	€55

FARRELL, MIKE

SP	£50	$90	€65
DS	£40	$75	€55
AP	£30	$55	€40

FARRELL, TERRY

SP	£50	$90	€65
DS	£40	$75	€55
AP	£30	$55	€40

FARROW, MIA

SP	£75	$135	€100
DS	£60	$110	€80
AP	£40	$75	€55

EVERETT, RUPERT

SP	£75	$135	€100
DS	£60	$110	€80
AP	£40	$75	€55

FAWCETT, FARRAH

SP	**£50**	$90	€65
DS	**£40**	$75	€55
AP	**£30**	$55	€40

FELDMAN, COREY
CHRIS BLACK MANAGEMENT

SP	**£75**	$135	€100
DS	**£60**	$110	€80
AP	**£40**	$75	€55

FELDMAN, MARTY

SP	**£550**	$980	€715
DS	**£490**	$875	€640
AP	**£395**	$705	€515

FELDON, BARBARA

SP	**£50**	$90	€65
DS	**£40**	$75	€55
AP	**£30**	$55	€40

FENN, SHERILYN

SP	**£50**	$90	€65
DS	**£40**	$75	€55
AP	**£30**	$55	€40

FIELD, SALLY

SP	**£75**	$135	€100
DS	**£60**	$110	€80
AP	**£50**	$90	€65

FIELDS, GRACIE

SP	**£60**	$110	€80
DS	**£45**	$85	€60
AP	**£25**	$45	€35

FIELDS, W C

SP	**£1,500**	$2,670	€1,950
DS	**£995**	$1,770	€1,295
AP	**£650**	$1,160	€845

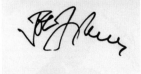

FIENNES, JOSEPH

SP	**£75**	$135	€100
DS	**£60**	$110	€80
AP	**£40**	$75	€55

FIENNES, RALPH

SP	**£85**	$155	€115
DS	**£60**	$110	€80
AP	**£40**	$75	€55

FINNEY, ALBERT

SP	**£50**	$90	€65
DS	**£40**	$75	€55
AP	**£30**	$55	€40

FIORENTINO, LINDA

SP	**£50**	$90	€65
DS	**£40**	$75	€55
AP	**£30**	$55	€40

FIRTH, COLIN

SP	£75	$135	€100
DS	£60	$110	€80
AP	£40	$75	€55

FISHBURNE, LAURENCE

SP	£75	$135	€100
DS	£60	$110	€80
AP	£40	$75	€55

FISHER, CARRIE

SP	£100	$180	€130
DS	£120	$215	€160
AP	£40	$75	€55

FITZGERALD, TARA

SP	£50	$90	€65
DS	£40	$75	€55
AP	£30	$55	€40

FLANAGAN, BUD

SP	£75	$135	€100
DS	£60	$110	€80
AP	£40	$75	€55

FLANERY, SEAN PATRICK

SP	£50	$90	€65
DS	£40	$75	€55
AP	£30	$55	€40

FLOCKHART, CALISTA

SP	£50	$90	€65
DS	£40	$75	€55
AP	£30	$55	€40

FLYNN, ERROL

SP	£1,250	$2,225	€1,625
DS	£650	$1,160	€845
AP	£350	$625	€455

FLYNN, JOE

SP	£50	$90	€65
DS	£40	$75	€55
AP	£30	$55	€40

FOLEY, SCOTT

SP	£50	$90	€65
DS	£40	$75	€55
AP	£30	$55	€40

FONDA, BRIDGET

SP	£50	$90	€65
DS	£40	$75	€55
AP	£30	$55	€40

FONDA, HENRY

SP	£650	$1,160	€845
DS	£550	$980	€715
AP	£225	$405	€295

FONDA, JANE

SP	£75	$135	€100
DS	£60	$110	€80
AP	£40	$75	€55

FONDA, PETER

SP	£75	$135	€100
DS	£60	$110	€80
AP	£40	$75	€55

FOSTER, BARRY

SP	£50	$90	€65
DS	£40	$75	€55
AP	£30	$55	€40

FOX, MICHAEL J.

SP	£50	$90	€65
DS	£40	$75	€55
AP	£30	$55	€40

FONTAINE, JOAN

SP	£75	$135	€100
DS	£60	$110	€80
AP	£30	$55	€40

FOSTER, JODIE

SP	£75	$135	€100
DS	£60	$110	€80
AP	£40	$75	€55

FOX, VIVICA A.

SP	£75	$135	€100
DS	£60	$110	€80
AP	£40	$75	€55

FORD, HARRISON

SP	£195	$350	€255
DS	£100	$180	€130
AP	£70	$125	€95

FOX, EMILIA

SP	£50	$90	€65
DS	£40	$75	€55
AP	£30	$55	€40

FOXX, JAMIE

SP	£75	$135	€100
DS	£60	$110	€80
AP	£40	$75	€55

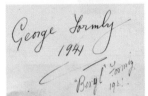

FORMBY, GEORGE

SP	£125	$225	€165
DS	£75	$135	€100
AP	£50	$90	€65

FORSYTHE, JOHN

SP	£75	$135	€100
DS	£60	$110	€80
AP	£45	$85	€60

FOX, MATTHEW

SP	£100	$180	€130
DS	£80	$145	€105
AP	£40	$75	€55

FRAKES, JONATHAN

SP	£75	$135	€100
DS	£60	$110	€80
AP	£40	$75	€55

Film, TV and Theatre

FRASER, BRENDAN

SP	£75	$135	€100
DS	£60	$110	€80
AP	£40	$75	€55

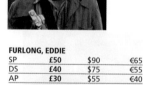

FROBE, GERT

SP	£200	$360	€260
DS	£150	$270	€195
AP	£80	$145	€105

FURLONG, EDDIE

SP	£50	$90	€65
DS	£40	$75	€55
AP	£30	$55	€40

FURST, STEPHEN

SP	£50	$90	€65
DS	£40	$75	€55
AP	£30	$55	€40

GABLE, CLARK

SP	£1,250	$2,225	€1,625
DS	£585	$1,045	€765
AP	£495	$885	€645

GACY, JOHN WAYNE

SP	£200	$360	€260
DS	£175	$315	€230
AP	£100	$180	€130

GAMBON, MICHAEL

SP	£100	$180	€130
DS	£80	$145	€105
AP	£50	$90	€65

GANDOLFINI, JAMES

SP	£75	$135	€100
DS	£60	$110	€80
AP	£40	$75	€55

GARCIA, ANDY

SP	£125	$225	€165
DS	£80	$145	€105
AP	£50	$90	€65

GARCIA, JORGE

SP	£50	$90	€65
DS	£40	$75	€55
AP	£30	$55	€40

GARDENIA, VINCENT

SP	£50	$90	€65
DS	£40	$75	€55
AP	£30	$55	€40

GARDNER, AVA

SP	£300	$535	€390
DS	£280	$500	€365
AP	£150	$270	€195

GAREIS, JENNIFER

SP	£50	$90	€65
DS	£40	$75	€55
AP	£30	$55	€40

GARLAND, JUDY

SP	£2,250	$4,005	€2,925
DS	£1,250	$2,225	€1,625
AP	£650	$1,160	€845

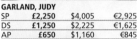

GARNER, JAMES

SP	£75	$135	€100
DS	£60	$110	€80
AP	£30	$55	€40

GAROFOLO, JANEANE

SP	£50	$90	€65
DS	£40	$75	€55
AP	£30	$55	€40

GARSON, GREER

SP	£100	$180	€130
DS	£70	$125	€95
AP	£50	$90	€65

GAYHEART, REBECCA

SP	£50	$90	€65
DS	£40	$75	€55
AP	£30	$55	€40

GELLAR, SARAH MICHELLE

SP	£75	$135	€100
DS	£60	$110	€80
AP	£40	$75	€55

GELLER, URI

SP	£50	$90	€65
DS	£40	$75	€55
AP	£30	$55	€40

GERARD, GIL

SP	£50	$90	€65
DS	£40	$75	€55
AP	£30	$55	€40

GERE, RICHARD

SP	£75	$135	€100
DS	£60	$110	€80
AP	£40	$75	€55

GERSON, BETTY LOU

SP	£50	$90	€65
DS	£40	$75	€55
AP	£30	$55	€40

GERVAIS, RICKY

SP	£85	$155	€115
DS	£60	$110	€80
AP	£40	$75	€55

GIBSON, MEL

SP	£195	$350	€255
DS	£120	$215	€160
AP	£80	$145	€105

GIELGUD, JOHN

SP	£150	$270	€195
DS	£90	$165	€120
AP	£50	$90	€65

GILBERT, MELISSA

SP	£50	$90	€65
DS	£40	$75	€55
AP	£30	$55	€40

GILFORD, JACK

SP	£50	$90	€65
DS	£40	$75	€55
AP	£30	$55	€40

GILLIAM, TERRY

SP	£50	$90	€65
DS	£40	$75	€55
AP	£30	$55	€40

GINGOLD, HERMIONE

SP	£50	$90	€65
DS	£40	$75	€55
AP	£30	$55	€40

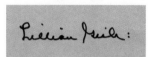

GISH, LILLIAN

SP	£45	$85	€60
DS	£35	$65	€50
AP	£25	$45	€35

GLASER, PAUL MICHAEL

SP	£50	$90	€65
DS	£40	$75	€55
AP	£30	$55	€40

GLESS, SHARON

SP	£50	$90	€65
DS	£40	$75	€55
AP	£30	$55	€40

GLOVER, DANNY

SP	£75	$135	€100
DS	£60	$110	€80
AP	£40	$75	€55

GLOVER, JULIAN

SP	£50	$90	€65
DS	£40	$75	€55
AP	£30	$55	€40

GOLDBERG, ADAM

SP	£50	$90	€65
DS	£40	$75	€55
AP	£30	$55	€40

GOLDBERG, WHOOPI

SP	£65	$120	€85
DS	£50	$90	€65
AP	£40	$75	€55

GOLDBLUM, JEFF

SP	£75	$135	€100
DS	£60	$110	€80
AP	£40	$75	€55

GOSSETT, LOUIS

SP	£50	$90	€65
DS	£40	$75	€55
AP	£30	$55	€40

GRAMMER, KELSEY

SP	£50	$90	€65
DS	£40	$75	€55
AP	£30	$55	€40

GOODING JR, CUBA

SP	£50	$90	€65
DS	£40	$75	€55
AP	£30	$55	€40

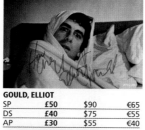

GOULD, ELLIOT

SP	£50	$90	€65
DS	£40	$75	€55
AP	£30	$55	€40

GOODMAN, JOHN

SP	£75	$135	€100
DS	£40	$75	€55
AP	£35	$65	€50

GRABLE, BETTY

SP	£200	$360	€260
DS	£180	$325	€235
AP	£150	$270	€195

GRANT, CARY

SP	£1,250	$2,225	€1,625
DS	£750	$1,335	€975
AP	£400	$715	€520

GORSHIN, FRANK

SP	£50	$90	€65
DS	£40	$75	€55
AP	£30	$55	€40

GRAHAM, HEATHER

SP	£75	$135	€100
DS	£60	$110	€80
AP	£40	$75	€55

GRANT, HUGH

SP	£50	$90	€65
DS	£40	$75	€55
AP	£30	$55	€40

GRASSLE, KAREN

SP	£50	$90	€65
DS	£40	$75	€55
AP	£30	$55	€40

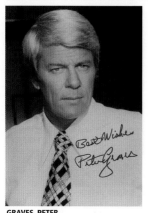

GRAVES, PETER

SP	£50	$90	€65
DS	£40	$75	€55
AP	£30	$55	€40

GRAY, CHARLES

SP	£125	$225	€165
DS	£110	$200	€145
AP	£60	$110	€80

GRAY, ERIN

SP	£50	$90	€65
DS	£40	$75	€55
AP	£30	$55	€40

GREEN, SETH

SP	£75	$135	€100
DS	£40	$75	€55
AP	£30	$55	€40

GREEN, TOM

SP	£75	$135	€100
DS	£60	$110	€80
AP	£40	$75	€55

GREENE, LORNE

SP	£250	$445	€325
DS	£175	$315	€230
AP	£75	$135	€100

GREENE, RICHARD

SP	£50	$90	€65
DS	£40	$75	€55
AP	£30	$55	€40

GREER, JANE

SP	£50	$90	€65
DS	£40	$75	€55
AP	£30	$55	€40

GRENFELL, JOYCE

SP	£50	$90	€65
DS	£40	$75	€55
AP	£30	$55	€40

GRIFFITHS, MELANIE

SP	£75	$135	€100
DS	£60	$110	€80
AP	£40	$75	€55

GRIFFITHS, RICHARD

SP	£50	$90	€65
DS	£40	$75	€55
AP	£30	$55	€40

GRINT, RUPERT

SP	£175	$315	€230
DS	£125	$225	€165
AP	£80	$145	€105

GUINNESS, ALEC

SP	£100	$180	€130
DS	£60	$110	€80
AP	£40	$75	€55

GUTTENBERG, STEVE

SP	£50	$90	€65
DS	£40	$75	€55
AP	£30	$55	€40

GWYNNE, FRED

SP	£300	$535	€390
DS	£250	$445	€325
AP	£150	$270	€195

GYLLENHAAL, JAKE

SP	£75	$135	€100
DS	£60	$110	€80
AP	£40	$75	€55

HACK, SHELLEY

SP	£50	$90	€65
DS	£40	$75	€55
AP	£30	$55	€40

HACKMAN, GENE

SP	£75	$135	€100
DS	£60	$110	€80
AP	£40	$75	€55

HALEY, JACK

SP	£395	$705	€515
DS	£195	$350	€255
AP	£250	$445	€325

HAMILL, MARK

SP	£100	$180	€130
DS	£90	$165	€120
AP	£50	$90	€65

HAMILTON, GEORGE

SP	£75	$135	€100
DS	£60	$110	€80
AP	£40	$75	€55

HAMILTON, LINDA

SP	£75	$135	€100
DS	£60	$110	€80
AP	£40	$75	€55

HAMILTON, MARGARET

SP	£250	$445	€325
DS	£225	$405	€295
AP	£125	$225	€165

HAMLIN, HARRY

SP	£50	$90	€65
DS	£40	$75	€55
AP	£30	$55	€40

HANCOCK, TONY

SP	£895	$1,595	€1,165
DS	£600	$1,070	€780
AP	£300	$535	€390

Film, TV and Theatre

HANDL, IRENE

SP	£50	$90	€65
DS	£40	$75	€55
AP	£30	$55	€40

HANKS, TOM

SP	£100	$180	€130
DS	£75	$135	€100
AP	£50	$90	€65

HANNAH, DARYL

SP	£75	$135	€100
DS	£60	$110	€80
AP	£40	$75	€55

HANNIGAN, ALYSON

SP	£75	$135	€100
DS	£60	$110	€80
AP	£40	$75	€55

HANSEN, GUNNAR

SP	£50	$90	€65
DS	£45	$85	€60
AP	£30	$55	€40

HARLOW, JEAN

SP	£11,000	$19,560	€14,300
DS	£9,000	$16,005	€11,700
AP	£4,000	$7,115	€5,200

HARMON, MARK

SP	£50	$90	€65
DS	£40	$75	€55
AP	£30	$55	€40

HAROLD, KATHRYN

SP	£50	$90	€65
DS	£40	$75	€55
AP	£30	$55	€40

HARRIS, JONATHAN

SP	£125	$225	€165
DS	£80	$145	€105
AP	£50	$90	€65

HARRIS, JULIE

SP	£45	$85	€60
DS	£40	$75	€55
AP	£30	$55	€40

HARRIS, KEITH

SP	£45	$85	€60
DS	£35	$65	€50
AP	£25	$45	€35

HARRIS, PHIL

SP	£45	$85	€60
DS	£35	$65	€50
AP	£25	$45	€35

HARRIS, RICHARD

SP	£100	$180	€130
DS	£80	$145	€105
AP	£50	$90	€65

HARRIS, SAM

SP	£50	$90	€65
DS	£40	$75	€55
AP	£30	$55	€40

HARRISON, LINDA

SP	£50	$90	€65
DS	£40	$75	€55
AP	£30	$55	€40

HARRISON, REX

SP	£150	$270	€195
DS	£120	$215	€160
AP	£40	$75	€55

HART, MELISSA JOAN

SP	£50	$90	€65
DS	£40	$75	€55
AP	£30	$55	€40

HARTNELL, WILLIAM

SP	£450	$805	€585
DS	£400	$715	€520
AP	£200	$360	€260

HARTNETT, JOSH

SP	£75	$135	€100
DS	£60	$110	€80
AP	£40	$75	€55

HATCHER, TERI

SP	£75	$135	€100
DS	£60	$110	€80
AP	£40	$75	€55

HAUER, RUTGER

SP	£75	$135	€100
DS	£60	$110	€80
AP	£40	$75	€55

HAVERS, NIGEL

SP	£40	$75	€55
DS	£35	$65	€50
AP	£30	$55	€40

HAWKE, ETHAN

SP	£75	$135	€100
DS	£60	$110	€80
AP	£40	$75	€55

HASSO, SIGNE

SP	£50	$90	€65
DS	£40	$75	€55
AP	£30	$55	€40

HAWN, GOLDIE

SP	£50	$90	€65
DS	£45	$85	€60
AP	£35	$65	€50

HAYES, ISAAC

SP	£150	$270	€195
DS	£120	$215	€160
AP	£75	$135	€100

HEATON, PATRICIA

SP	£50	$90	€65
DS	£40	$75	€55
AP	£30	$55	€40

HEDREN, TIPPI

SP	£100	$180	€130
DS	£80	$145	€105
AP	£50	$90	€65

HAWTHORNE, NIGEL

SP	£50	$90	€65
DS	£40	$75	€55
AP	£30	$55	€40

HAYSBERT, DENNIS

SP	£50	$90	€65
DS	£40	$75	€55
AP	£30	$55	€40

HAYWARD, SUSAN

SP	£275	$490	€360
DS	£250	$445	€325
AP	£125	$225	€165

Will Hay

HAY, WILL

SP	£350	$625	€455
DS	£300	$535	€390
AP	£200	$360	€260

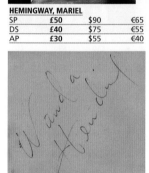

HEMINGWAY, MARIEL

SP	£50	$90	€65
DS	£40	$75	€55
AP	£30	$55	€40

HAYEK, SALMA

SP	£75	$135	€100
DS	£60	$110	€80
AP	£40	$75	€55

HEAD, ANTHONY

SP	£50	$90	€65
DS	£40	$75	€55
AP	£30	$55	€40

HENDRIX, WANDA

SP	£50	$90	€65
DS	£40	$75	€55
AP	£30	$55	€40

HENDRY, GLORIA

SP	£50	$90	€65
DS	£40	$75	€55
AP	£30	$55	€40

HENNER, MARILU

SP	£50	$90	€65
DS	£40	$75	€55
AP	£30	$55	€40

HENSTRIDGE, NATASHA

SP	£50	$90	€65
DS	£40	$75	€55
AP	£30	$55	€40

HEY, VIRGINIA

SP	£50	$90	€65
DS	£40	$75	€55
AP	£30	$55	€40

HENREID, PAUL

SP	£300	$535	€390
DS	£280	$500	€365
AP	£150	$270	€195

HEPBURN, AUDREY

SP	£995	$1,770	€1,295
DS	£450	$805	€585
AP	£300	$535	€390

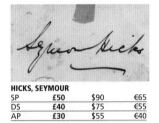

HICKS, SEYMOUR

SP	£50	$90	€65
DS	£40	$75	€55
AP	£30	$55	€40

HENSLEY, SHULER

SP	£50	$90	€65
DS	£40	$75	€55
AP	£30	$55	€40

HEPBURN, KATHARINE

SP	£1,000	$1,780	€1,300
DS	£350	$625	€455
AP	£295	$525	€385

HIGGINS, JOEL

SP	£50	$90	€65
DS	£40	$75	€55
AP	£30	$55	€40

HENSON, JIM

SP	£275	$490	€360
DS	£225	$405	€295
AP	£150	$270	€195

HESTON, CHARLTON

SP	£50	$90	€65
DS	£40	$75	€55
AP	£30	$55	€40

HILL, BENNY

SP	£75	$135	€100
DS	£60	$110	€80
AP	£40	$75	€55

HILTON, PARIS

SP	**£75**	$135	€100
DS	**£60**	$110	€80
AP	**£40**	$75	€55

HINES, GREGORY

SP	**£50**	$90	€65
DS	**£40**	$75	€55
AP	**£30**	$55	€40

HIRD, THORA

SP	**£50**	$90	€65
DS	**£40**	$75	€55
AP	**£30**	$55	€40

HIRSCH, JUDD

SP	**£50**	$90	€65
DS	**£40**	$75	€55
AP	**£30**	$55	€40

HITCHCOCK, ALFRED

SP	**£2,000**	$3,560	€2,600
DS	**£1,500**	$2,670	€1,950
AP	**£1,250**	$2,225	€1,625

HOBSON, VALERIE

SP	**£50**	$90	€65
DS	**£40**	$75	€55
AP	**£30**	$55	€40

HOFFMAN, DUSTIN

SP	**£75**	$135	€100
DS	**£60**	$110	€80
AP	**£40**	$75	€55

HOLDEN, AMANDA

SP	**£50**	$90	€65
DS	**£40**	$75	€55
AP	**£30**	$55	€40

HOLLOWAY, STANLEY

SP	**£50**	$90	€65
DS	**£40**	$75	€55
AP	**£30**	$55	€40

HOLM, IAN

SP	**£75**	$135	€100
DS	**£60**	$110	€80
AP	**£40**	$75	€55

HOLMES, KATIE

SP	**£85**	$155	€115
DS	**£60**	$110	€80
AP	**£40**	$75	€55

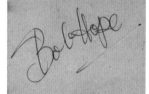

HOPE, BOB

SP	**£175**	$315	€230
DS	**£125**	$225	€165
AP	**£80**	$145	€105

HOPKINS, ANTHONY

SP	£75	$135	€100
DS	£60	$110	€80
AP	£40	$75	€55

HOPKINS, BRUCE

SP	£75	$135	€100
DS	£60	$110	€80
AP	£40	$75	€55

HOPKINS, MIRIAM

SP	£60	$110	€80
DS	£50	$90	€65
AP	£40	$75	€55

HOPPER, DENNIS

SP	£50	$90	€65
DS	£40	$75	€55
AP	£30	$55	€40

HORROCKS, JANE

SP	£50	$90	€65
DS	£40	$75	€55
AP	£30	$55	€40

HOUSTON, DONALD

SP	£45	$85	€60
DS	£35	$65	€50
AP	£25	$45	€35

HOWARD, RON

SP	£75	$135	€100
DS	£60	$110	€80
AP	£40	$75	€55

HOWARD, TREVOR

SP	£75	$135	€100
DS	£60	$110	€80
AP	£45	$85	€60

HOWERD, FRANKIE

SP	£150	$270	€195
DS	£125	$225	€165
AP	£80	$145	€105

HU, KELLY

SP	£50	$90	€65
DS	£40	$75	€55
AP	£30	$55	€40

HUDD, ROY

SP	£45	$85	€60
DS	£35	$65	€50
AP	£25	$45	€35

HUDSON, KATE

SP	£75	$135	€100
DS	£60	$110	€80
AP	£40	$75	€55

HUDSON, ROCK

SP	£75	$135	€100
DS	£60	$110	€80
AP	£40	$75	€55

HUGHES, HOWARD

SP	£2,950	$5,245	€3,835
DS	£1,500	$2,670	€1,950
AP	£1,250	$2,225	€1,625

HULCE, TOM

SP	£50	$90	€65
DS	£40	$75	€55
AP	£30	$55	€40

HUNTER, KIM

SP	£50	$90	€65
DS	£40	$75	€55
AP	£30	$55	€40

HUSTON, JOHN

SP	£50	$90	€65
DS	£40	$75	€55
AP	£30	$55	€40

HURLEY, ELIZABETH

SP	£75	$135	€100
DS	£60	$110	€80
AP	£40	$75	€55

HUTTON, LAUREN

SP	£50	$90	€65
DS	£40	$75	€55
AP	£30	$55	€40

HUTTON, TIMOTHY

SP	£50	$90	€65
DS	£40	$75	€55
AP	£30	$55	€40

HUNT, HELEN

SP	£75	$135	€100
DS	£60	$110	€80
AP	£40	$75	€55

HURT, JOHN

SP	£50	$90	€65
DS	£40	$75	€55
AP	£30	$55	€40

HYDE PIERCE, DAVID

SP	£60	$110	€80
DS	£45	$85	€60
AP	£35	$65	€50

HUNTER, HOLLY

SP	£50	$90	€65
DS	£40	$75	€55
AP	£30	$55	€40

HUSSEY, OLIVIA

SP	£50	$90	€65
DS	£40	$75	€55
AP	£30	$55	€40

INMAN, JOHN

SP	£45	$85	€60
DS	£35	$65	€50
AP	£25	$45	€35

IRELAND, JILL

SP	£50	$90	€65
DS	£40	$75	€55
AP	£30	$55	€40

IRONS, JEREMY

SP	£75	$135	€100
DS	£60	$110	€80
AP	£40	$75	€55

IRVING, AMY

SP	£50	$90	€65
DS	£40	$75	€55
AP	£30	$55	€40

JACKMAN, HUGH

SP	£75	$135	€100
DS	£60	$110	€80
AP	£40	$75	€55

JACKSON, GLENDA

SP	£50	$90	€65
DS	£40	$75	€55
AP	£30	$55	€40

JACKSON, SAMUEL. L

SP	£75	$135	€100
DS	£60	$110	€80
AP	£40	$75	€55

JACKSON, VICTORIA

SP	£50	$90	€65
DS	£40	$75	€55
AP	£30	$55	€40

JACOBI, DEREK

SP	£50	$90	€65
DS	£40	$75	€55
AP	£30	$55	€40

JACQUES, HATTIE

SP	£300	$535	€390
DS	£250	$445	€325
AP	£175	$315	€230

JAGGER, BIANCA

SP	£250	$445	€325
DS	£200	$360	€260
AP	£150	$270	€195

JAMES, JOHN

SP	£50	$90	€65
DS	£40	$75	€55
AP	£30	$55	€40

JAMES, SID

SP	£750	$1,335	€975
DS	£500	$890	€650
AP	£300	$535	€390

JANE, THOMAS

SP	£50	$90	€65
DS	£40	$75	€55
AP	£30	$55	€40

JANNEY, ALLISON

SP	£50	$90	€65
DS	£40	$75	€55
AP	£30	$55	€40

JANSSEN, FAMKE

SP	£50	$90	€65
DS	£40	$75	€55
AP	£30	$55	€40

JASON, DAVID

SP	£250	$445	€325
DS	£225	$405	€295
AP	£150	$270	€195

JOHANSSON, SCARLETT

SP	£150	$270	€195
DS	£110	$200	€145
AP	£60	$110	€80

JOHNS, GLYNIS

SP	£50	$90	€65
DS	£40	$75	€55
AP	£30	$55	€40

JOHNSON, DON

SP	£50	$90	€65
DS	£40	$75	€55
AP	£30	$55	€40

JOHNSTON, KRISTEN

SP	£75	$135	€100
DS	£60	$110	€80
AP	£40	$75	€55

JOLIE, ANGELINA

SP	£150	$270	€195
DS	£80	$145	€105
AP	£60	$110	€80

JOLSON, AL

SP	£350	$625	€455
DS	£200	$360	€260
AP	£125	$225	€165

JONES, GRIFFITH

SP	£50	$90	€65
DS	£40	$75	€55
AP	£30	$55	€40

JONES, TOMMY LEE

SP	£50	$90	€65
DS	£40	$75	€55
AP	£30	$55	€40

JONES, VINNIE

SP	£50	$90	€65
DS	£40	$75	€55
AP	£30	$55	€40

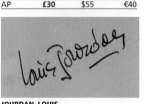

JOURDAN, LOUIS

SP	£75	$135	€100
DS	£60	$110	€80
AP	£50	$90	€65

JOVOVICH, MILLA

SP	£50	$90	€65
DS	£40	$75	€55
AP	£30	$55	€40

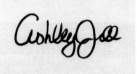

JUDD, ASHLEY

SP	£50	$90	€65
DS	£35	$65	€50
AP	£30	$55	€40

JUDGE, MIKE

SP	£75	$135	€100
DS	£60	$110	€80
AP	£40	$75	€55

KACZMAREK, JANE

SP	£50	$90	€65
DS	£40	$75	€55
AP	£30	$55	€40

KAHN, MADELEINE

SP	£50	$90	€65
DS	£40	$75	€55
AP	£30	$55	€40

KARLOFF, BORIS

SP	£1,500	$2,670	€1,950
DS	£975	$1,735	€1,270
AP	£750	$1,335	€975

KAVNER, JULIE

SP	£100	$180	€130
DS	£80	$145	€105
AP	£50	$90	€65

KAYE, DANNY

SP	£250	$445	€325
DS	£225	$405	€295
AP	£200	$360	€260

KEATON, BUSTER

SP	£250	$445	€325
DS	£225	$405	€295
AP	£750	$1,335	€975

KEATON, MICHAEL

SP	£125	$225	€165
DS	£110	$200	€145
AP	£50	$90	€65

KEEL, HOWARD

SP	£50	$90	€65
DS	£40	$75	€55
AP	£30	$55	€40

KEITEL, HARVEY

SP	£50	$90	€65
DS	£40	$75	€55
AP	£30	$55	€40

KELLER, MARTHE

SP	£50	$90	€65
DS	£40	$75	€55
AP	£30	$55	€40

KELLY, GENE

SP	£500	$890	€650
DS	£450	$805	€585
AP	£250	$445	€325

KELLY, GRACE

SP	£1,000	$1,780	€1,300
DS	£750	$1,335	€975
AP	£350	$625	€455

KELLY, MOIRA

SP	£50	$90	€65
DS	£40	$75	€55
AP	£30	$55	€40

KENDALL, KAY

SP	£175	$315	€230
DS	£125	$225	€165
AP	£75	$135	€100

KENT, JEAN

SP	£50	$90	€65
DS	£40	$75	€55
AP	£30	$55	€40

KERR, DEBORAH

SP	£75	$135	€100
DS	£65	$120	€85
AP	£50	$90	€65

KERSHNER, IRVIN

SP	£50	$90	€65
DS	£40	$75	€55
AP	£30	$55	€40

KIDDER, MARGOT

SP	£50	$90	€65
DS	£40	$75	€55
AP	£30	$55	€40

KIDMAN, NICOLE

SP	£100	$180	€130
DS	£60	$110	€80
AP	£40	$75	€55

KILMER, VAL

SP	£75	$135	€100
DS	£60	$110	€80
AP	£40	$75	€55

KIM, YUNJIN

SP	£75	$135	€100
DS	£60	$110	€80
AP	£40	$75	€55

KING, CAMMIE

SP	£50	$90	€65
DS	£40	$75	€55
AP	£30	$55	€40

KING, JAIME

SP	£50	$90	€65
DS	£40	$75	€55
AP	£30	$55	€40

KINGSLEY, BEN

SP	£75	$135	€100
DS	£60	$110	€80
AP	£40	$75	€55

KINSKI, KLAUS

SP	£475	$845	€620
DS	£375	$670	€490
AP	£200	$360	€260

KINSKI, NASTASSJA

SP	£75	$135	€100
DS	£60	$110	€80
AP	£40	$75	€55

KITT, EARTHA

SP	£75	$135	€100
DS	£60	$110	€80
AP	£40	$75	€55

KLEIN, CHRIS

SP	£50	$90	€65
DS	£40	$75	€55
AP	£30	$55	€40

KLINE, KEVIN

SP	£50	$90	€65
DS	£40	$75	€55
AP	£30	$55	€40

KNIGHT, ESMOND

SP	£50	$90	€65
DS	£40	$75	€55
AP	£30	$55	€40

KNIGHT, SHIRLEY

SP	£45	$85	€60
DS	£40	$75	€55
AP	£30	$55	€40

KNIGHTLEY, KEIRA

SP	£125	$225	€165
DS	£80	$145	€105
AP	£60	$110	€80

Film, TV and Theatre

KNOXVILLE, JOHNNY

SP	£75	$135	€100
DS	£60	$110	€80
AP	£40	$75	€55

KOENIG, WALTER

SP	£50	$90	€65
DS	£40	$75	€55
AP	£30	$55	€40

KOSSOFF, DAVID

SP	£50	$90	€65
DS	£40	$75	€55
AP	£30	$55	€40

KRAKOWSKI, JANE

SP	£50	$90	€65
DS	£40	$75	€55
AP	£30	$55	€40

KRISTOFFERSON, KRIS

SP	£50	$90	€65
DS	£40	$75	€55
AP	£30	$55	€40

KUDROW, LISA

SP	£75	$135	€100
DS	£60	$110	€80
AP	£50	$90	€65

KUNIS, MILA

SP	£40	$75	€55
DS	£35	$65	€50
AP	£30	$55	€40

KURTZ, GARY

SP	£50	$90	€65
DS	£40	$75	€55
AP	£30	$55	€40

KUTCHER, ASHTON

SP	£75	$135	€100
DS	£60	$110	€80
AP	£40	$75	€55

LACEY, CATHERINE

SP	£150	$270	€195
DS	£120	$215	€160
AP	£75	$135	€100

LADD, CHERYL

SP	£50	$90	€65
DS	£40	$75	€55
AP	£30	$55	€40

LAHR, BERT

SP	£9,500	$16,890	€12,350
DS	£1,500	$2,670	€1,950
AP	£1,250	$2,225	€1,625

166-27   LORENZO LAMAS stars as Chilly D, an ambitious
entertainer who makes a rapid rise into the
fast life uptown in New World Pictures'
energetic musical fantasy "BODY ROCK."

LAMAS, LORENZO

SP	£50	$90	€65
DS	£40	$75	€55
AP	£30	$55	€40

LANCASTER, BURT

SP	£295	$525	€385
DS	£150	$270	€195
AP	£100	$180	€130

ELSA LANCHESTER
Vic-Wells Shakespeare Co.
photo by Dorothy Wilding

LANCHESTER, ELSA

SP	£225	$405	€295
DS	£120	$215	€160
AP	£80	$145	€105

LANDON, MICHAEL

SP	£350	$625	€455
DS	£300	$535	€390
AP	£160	$285	€210

LANE, DIANE

SP	£50	$90	€65
DS	£40	$75	€55
AP	£30	$55	€40

LANGE, JESSICA

SP	£50	$90	€65
DS	£40	$75	€55
AP	£30	$55	€40

LANSBURY, ANGELA

SP	£75	$135	€100
DS	£60	$110	€80
AP	£40	$75	€55

LARNER, ELIZABETH

SP	£50	$90	€65
DS	£40	$75	€55
AP	£30	$55	€40

LARSON, JACK

SP	£50	$90	€65
DS	£40	$75	€55
AP	£30	$55	€40

LARTER, ALI

SP	£75	$135	€100
DS	£60	$110	€80
AP	£40	$75	€55

LAUGHTON, CHARLES

SP	£350	$625	€455
DS	£250	$445	€325
AP	£200	$360	€260

To ANDREW, WITH BEST WISHES,
1929

LAUREL, STAN

SP	£1,250	$2,225	€1,625
DS	£875	$1,560	€1,140
AP	£650	$1,160	€845

LAURIE, PIPER

SP	£50	$90	€65
DS	£40	$75	€55
AP	£30	$55	€40

Film, TV and Theatre

LAW, JUDE

SP	£50	$90	€65
DS	£40	$75	€55
AP	£30	$55	€40

LAWSON, DENIS

SP	£50	$90	€65
DS	£40	$75	€55
AP	£30	$55	€40

LE MESURIER, JOHN

SP	£350	$625	€455
DS	£225	$405	€295
AP	£200	$360	€260

LAWLESS, LUCY

SP	£75	$135	€100
DS	£60	$110	€80
AP	£40	$75	€55

LAZENBY, GEORGE

SP	£75	$135	€100
DS	£60	$110	€80
AP	£40	$75	€55

LEARY, DENIS

SP	£50	$90	€65
DS	£40	$75	€55
AP	£30	$55	€40

LAWRENCE, GERTRUDE

SP	£75	$135	€100
DS	£65	$120	€85
AP	£40	$75	€55

LEDGER, HEATH

SP	£350	$625	€455
DS	£300	$535	€390
AP	£200	$360	€260

LE BLANC, MATT

SP	£75	$135	€100
DS	£60	$110	€80
AP	£40	$75	€55

LEE, BRANDON

SP	£495	$885	€645
DS	£350	$625	€455
AP	£175	$315	€230

Heath Ledger

Heath Andrew Ledger was born in Perth, Australia on April 4th 1979. He studied at Guildford Grammar, Perth until he turned 17, when he decided to pack up and search for stardom in Sydney. Ledger struggled until 1997 when he was cast in a low budget film, *Blackrock*. He then appeared in Australian TV shows *Sweet* and *Home and Away*. Ledger continued to appear briefly in films until he was cast in *Two Hands* and *10 Things I Hate About You* in 1999.

From there Ledger appeared in *The Patriot*, *Monster's Ball* and *A Knights Tale*, but it was not until 2005 that Heath got the break he really deserved, when he was cast for a lead role alongside Jake Gyllenhaal in *Brokeback Mountain*. He was nominated for an Oscar and a BAFTA and made a household name. He was then cast as *The Joker* in the 2008 Batman film *The Dark Night*. Shockingly on 22nd January 2008, before the release of the film, Ledger was found dead in his apartment in Manhattan with a bottle of prescription sleeping pills nearby.

Heath started as a teen heart-throb but quickly moved on to be recognised as one of Hollywood's most talented actors.

LEE, CHRISTOPHER

SP	£225	$405	€295
DS	£120	$215	€160
AP	£60	$110	€80

LEE, GYPSY ROSE

SP	£150	$270	€195
DS	£100	$180	€130
AP	£75	$135	€100

LEE, JASON

SP	£50	$90	€65
DS	£40	$75	€55
AP	£30	$55	€40

LEE, SHERYL

SP	£75	$135	€100
DS	£60	$110	€80
AP	£40	$75	€55

LEGUIZAMO, JOHN

SP	£75	$135	€100
DS	£60	$110	€80
AP	£40	$75	€55

LEHMANN, BEATRIX

SP	£50	$90	€65
DS	£40	$75	€55
AP	£30	$55	€40

LEIGH, JANET

SP	£125	$225	€165
DS	£100	$180	€130
AP	£60	$110	€80

LEMAT, PAUL

SP	£50	$90	€65
DS	£40	$75	€55
AP	£30	$55	€40

LEMMON, JACK

SP	£50	$90	€65
DS	£40	$75	€55
AP	£30	$55	€40

LEPARMENTIER, RICHARD

SP	£50	$90	€65
DS	£40	$75	€55
AP	£30	$55	€40

LEIGH, VIVIEN

SP	£1,500	$2,670	€1,950
DS	£675	$1,205	€880
AP	£375	$670	€490

LEWIS, DANIEL DAY

SP	£75	$135	€100
DS	£60	$110	€80
AP	£40	$75	€55

Film, TV and Theatre

LEWIS, JULIETTE

SP	£75	$135	€100
DS	£60	$110	€80
AP	£40	$75	€55

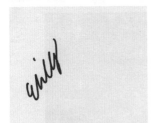

LILLARD, MATTHEW

SP	£50	$90	€65
DS	£40	$75	€55
AP	£30	$55	€40

LILLY, EVANGELINE

SP	£75	$135	€100
DS	£60	$110	€80
AP	£40	$75	€55

LIOTTA, RAY

SP	£50	$90	€65
DS	£40	$75	€55
AP	£30	$55	€40

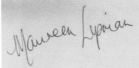

LIPMAN, MAUREEN

SP	£50	$90	€65
DS	£40	$75	€55
AP	£30	$55	€40

LISTER, MOIRA

SP	£50	$90	€65
DS	£40	$75	€55
AP	£30	$55	€40

LITHGOW, JOHN

SP	£50	$90	€65
DS	£40	$75	€55
AP	£35	$65	€50

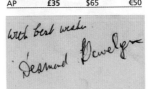

LLEWELYN, DESMOND

SP	£50	$90	€65
DS	£40	$75	€55
AP	£30	$55	€40

PETER FALK and EMILY LLOYD star as a hot-tempered father-daughter duo who manage to outsmart both the mob and the law in Warner Bros.' new comedy 'Cookie'.

LLOYD, EMILY

SP	£50	$90	€65
DS	£40	$75	€55
AP	£30	$55	€40

LLOYD, HAROLD

SP	£450	$805	€585
DS	£350	$625	€455
AP	£200	$360	€260

LLOYD, HAROLD (JR)

SP	£75	$135	€100
DS	£60	$110	€80
AP	£40	$75	€55

LLOYD, JAKE

SP	£50	$90	€65
DS	£40	$75	€55
AP	£30	$55	€40

LLOYD, MARIE JR

SP	£50	$90	€65
DS	£40	$75	€55
AP	£30	$55	€40

LOCKLEAR, HEATHER

SP	£50	$90	€65
DS	£40	$75	€55
AP	£30	$55	€40

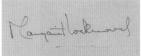

LOCKWOOD, MARGARET

SP	£50	$90	€65
DS	£40	$75	€55
AP	£30	$55	€40

LOGAN, DANIEL

SP	£50	$90	€65
DS	£40	$75	€55
AP	£30	$55	€40

LOHAN, LINDSAY

SP	£50	$90	€65
DS	£40	$75	€55
AP	£30	$55	€40

LOHMAN, ALISON

SP	£50	$90	€65
DS	£40	$75	€55
AP	£30	$55	€40

LOHR, MARIE

SP	£50	$90	€65
DS	£40	$75	€55
AP	£30	$55	€40

LOKEN, KRISTANNA

SP	£50	$90	€65
DS	£40	$75	€55
AP	£30	$55	€40

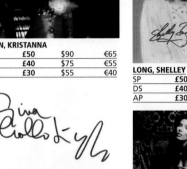

LOLLOBRIGIDA, GINA

SP	£75	$135	€100
DS	£60	$110	€80
AP	£40	$75	€55

LOM, HERBERT

SP	£75	$135	€100
DS	£60	$110	€80
AP	£45	$85	€60

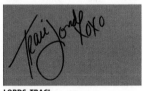

LONDON, JULIE

SP	£75	$135	€100
DS	£60	$110	€80
AP	£40	$75	€55

LONG, SHELLEY

SP	£50	$90	€65
DS	£40	$75	€55
AP	£30	$55	€40

LONGORIA, EVA

SP	£75	$135	€100
DS	£60	$110	€80
AP	£50	$90	€65

LOOS, ANITA

SP	£50	$90	€65
DS	£40	$75	€55
AP	£30	$55	€40

LORDS, TRACI

SP	£50	$90	€65
DS	£40	$75	€55
AP	£30	$55	€40

LOREN, SOPHIA

SP	£195	$350	€255
DS	£150	$270	€195
AP	£100	$180	€130

LORRE, PETER

SP	**£350**	$625	€455
DS	**£325**	$580	€425
AP	**£295**	$525	€385

LOUIS-DREYFUS, JULIA

SP	**£50**	$90	€65
DS	**£40**	$75	€55
AP	**£30**	$55	€40

LOVE, BESSIE

SP	**£50**	$90	€65
DS	**£40**	$75	€55
AP	**£30**	$55	€40

LOWE, ARTHUR

SP	**£300**	$535	€390
DS	**£250**	$445	€325
AP	**£150**	$270	€195

LOWE, ROB

SP	**£50**	$90	€65
DS	**£40**	$75	€55
AP	**£30**	$55	€40

LOWELL, CAREY

SP	**£100**	$180	€130
DS	**£80**	$145	€105
AP	**£50**	$90	€65

LUCAS, GEORGE

SP	**£175**	$315	€230
DS	**£80**	$145	€105
AP	**£60**	$110	€80

LUCAS, JOSH

SP	**£50**	$90	€65
DS	**£40**	$75	€55
AP	**£30**	$55	€40

LUCAS, MATT

SP	**£75**	$135	€100
DS	**£60**	$110	€80
AP	**£40**	$75	€55

LUGOSI, BELA

SP	**£1,250**	$2,225	€1,625
DS	**£650**	$1,160	€845
AP	**£495**	$885	€645

LUI, LUCY

SP	**£85**	$155	€115
DS	**£60**	$110	€80
AP	**£40**	$75	€55

LYNCH, DAVID

SP	**£50**	$90	€65
DS	**£40**	$75	€55
AP	**£30**	$55	€40

LYONNE, NATASHA

SP	£75	$135	€100
DS	£60	$110	€80
AP	£40	$75	€55

MACCHIO, RALPH

SP	£50	$90	€65
DS	£40	$75	€55
AP	£30	$55	€40

MACGRAW, ALI

SP	£50	$90	€65
DS	£40	$75	€55
AP	£30	$55	€40

MACLACHLAN, KYLE

SP	£50	$90	€65
DS	£40	$75	€55
AP	£30	$55	€40

MACLAINE, SHIRLEY

SP	£75	$135	€100
DS	£60	$110	€80
AP	£40	$75	€55

MACNAUGHTON, ROBERT

SP	£50	$90	€65
DS	£40	$75	€55
AP	£30	$55	€40

MACNEE, PATRICK

SP	£100	$180	€130
DS	£80	$145	€105
AP	£50	$90	€65

MACY, WILLIAM H

SP	£50	$90	€65
DS	£40	$75	€55
AP	£30	$55	€40

MADSEN, MICHAEL

SP	£75	$135	€100
DS	£60	$110	€80
AP	£40	$75	€55

MAGUIRE, TOBEY

SP	£125	$225	€165
DS	£80	$145	€105
AP	£60	$110	€80

MAHONEY, JOHN

SP	£50	$90	€65
DS	£40	$75	€55
AP	£30	$55	€40

MAJORS, LEE

SP	£50	$90	€65
DS	£40	$75	€55
AP	£30	$55	€40

MAKO

SP	£75	$135	€100
DS	£60	$110	€80
AP	£40	$75	€55

MAKOARE, LAWRENCE

SP	£75	$135	€100
DS	£60	$110	€80
AP	£40	$75	€55

MALDEN, KARL

SP	£50	$90	€65
DS	£40	$75	€55
AP	£30	$55	€40

MALKOVICH, JOHN

SP	£50	$90	€65
DS	£40	$75	€55
AP	£30	$55	€40

MANE, TYLER

SP	£50	$90	€65
DS	£40	$75	€55
AP	£30	$55	€40

MANNING, KATY

SP	£65	$120	€85
DS	£50	$90	€65
AP	£40	$75	€55

MANSFIELD, JAYNE

SP	£775	$1,380	€1,010
DS	£500	$890	€650
AP	£175	$315	€230

MARCEAU, SOPHIE

SP	£75	$135	€100
DS	£60	$110	€80
AP	£40	$75	€55

MARCIL, VANESSA

SP	£50	$90	€65
DS	£40	$75	€55
AP	£30	$55	€40

MAREN, JERRY

SP	£75	$135	€100
DS	£60	$110	€80
AP	£40	$75	€55

MARGRET, ANN

SP	£50	$90	€65
DS	£40	$75	€55
AP	£30	$55	€40

MARGULIES, JULIANNA

SP	£50	$90	€65
DS	£40	$75	€55
AP	£30	$55	€40

MARSDEN, JAMES

SP	£50	$90	€65
DS	£40	$75	€55
AP	£30	$55	€40

MARSHALL, PENNY

SP	£50	$90	€65
DS	£40	$75	€55
AP	£30	$55	€40

MARSTERS, JAMES

SP	£50	$90	€65
DS	£40	$75	€55
AP	£30	$55	€40

MARTIN, DEAN

SP	£350	$625	€455
DS	£250	$445	€325
AP	£115	$205	€150

MARTIN, JILL

SP	£125	$225	€165
DS	£100	$180	€130
AP	£75	$135	€100

MARTIN, MARY

SP	£50	$90	€65
DS	£40	$75	€55
AP	£30	$55	€40

MARTIN, MILLICENT

SP	£50	$90	€65
DS	£40	$75	€55
AP	£30	$55	€40

MARTIN, STEVE

SP	£100	$180	€130
DS	£70	$125	€95
AP	£50	$90	€65

MARTINELLI, ELSA

SP	£50	$90	€65
DS	£40	$75	€55
AP	£30	$55	€40

MARVIN, LEE

SP	£695	$1,240	€905
DS	£500	$890	€650
AP	£300	$535	€390

MARX, CHICO

SP	£650	$1,160	€845
DS	£625	$1,115	€815
AP	£595	$1,060	€775

MARX, GROUCHO

SP	£1,250	$2,225	€1,625
DS	£1,000	$1,780	€1,300
AP	£650	$1,160	€845

MARX, ZEPPO

SP	£1,250	$2,225	€1,625
DS	£750	$1,335	€975
AP	£400	$715	€520

MASKELL, VIRGINIA

SP	£50	$90	€65
DS	£40	$75	€55
AP	£30	$55	€40

MASON, JACKIE

SP	£75	$135	€100
DS	£60	$110	€80
AP	40s		#VALUE!

MASON, JAMES

SP	£225	$405	€295
DS	£200	$360	€260
AP	£100	$180	€130

ROMANTIC FULFILLMENT — Marsha Mason stars as an unlucky-in-love New York stage performer who finds romantic fulfilment in Neil Simon's "The Goodbye Girl." A Ray Stark Production of A Herbert Ross Film for Warner Bros. release. Richard Dreyfuss also stars in the film produced by Ray Stark and directed by Herbert Ross from the original screenplay by Neil Simon.

MASON, MARSHA

SP	**£50**	$90	€65
DS	**£40**	$75	€55
AP	**£30**	$55	€39

MASSEY, ANNA

SP	**£50**	$90	€65
DS	**£40**	$75	€55
AP	**£30**	$55	€39

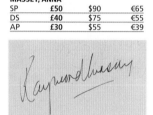

MASSEY, RAYMOND

SP	**£45**	$85	€60
DS	**£35**	$65	€50
AP	**£25**	$45	€33

MASTERSON, DANNY

SP	**£50**	$90	€65
DS	**£40**	$75	€55
AP	**£30**	$55	€39

MATTHAU, WALTER

SP	**£50**	$90	€65
DS	**£40**	$75	€55
AP	**£30**	$55	€39

MATTHEWS, JESSIE

SP	**£75**	$135	€100
DS	**£60**	$110	€80
AP	**£30**	$55	€39

MAXWELL, LOIS

SP	**£75**	$135	€100
DS	**£60**	$110	€80
AP	**£40**	$75	€52

MAYALL, RIK

SP	**£75**	$135	€100
DS	**£60**	$110	€80
AP	**£40**	$75	€52

MAYER, DINA

SP	**£50**	$90	€65
DS	**£40**	$75	€55
AP	**£30**	$55	€39

MAYHEW, PETER

SP	**£75**	$135	€100
DS	**£60**	$110	€80
AP	**£40**	$75	€52

MAZAR, DEBI

SP	**£75**	$135	€100
DS	**£60**	$110	€80
AP	**£40**	$75	€52

MCBRIDE, MARTINA

SP	**£75**	$135	€100
DS	**£60**	$110	€80
AP	**£40**	$75	€52

MCCALLUM, DAVID

SP	**£50**	$90	€65
DS	**£40**	$75	€55
AP	**£30**	$55	€39

MCCARTHY, ANDREW

SP	**£50**	$90	€65
DS	**£40**	$75	€55
AP	**£30**	$55	€39

MCCOY, SYLVESTER

SP	£50	$90	€65
DS	£40	$75	€55
AP	£30	$55	€39

MCDANIEL, HATTIE

SP	£1,500	$2,670	€1,950
DS	£750	$1,335	€975
AP	£500	$890	€650

MCDERMOTT, DYLAN

SP	£50	$90	€65
DS	£40	$75	€55
AP	£30	$55	€39

MCDIARMID, IAN

SP	£50	$90	€65
DS	£40	$75	€55
AP	£30	$55	€39

MCDOWELL, ANDIE

SP	£50	$90	€65
DS	£40	$75	€55
AP	£30	$55	€39

MCDOWELL, MALCOLM

SP	£175	$315	€230
DS	£160	$285	€210
AP	£75	$135	€98

MCDOWELL, RODDY

SP	£50	$90	€65
DS	£40	$75	€55
AP	£30	$55	€39

MCEWAN, GERALDINE

SP	£50	$90	€65
DS	£40	$75	€55
AP	£30	$55	€39

MCGOOHAN, PATRICK

SP	£175	$315	€230
DS	£120	$215	€160
AP	£65	$120	€85

MCGOVERN, ELIZABETH

SP	£50	$90	€65
DS	£40	$75	€55
AP	£30	$55	€39

MCGOWAN, ROSE

SP	£85	$155	€115
DS	£60	$110	€80
AP	£40	$75	€52

MCGRAW, ALI

SP	£75	$135	€100
DS	£60	$110	€80
AP	£40	$75	€52

MCGREGOR, EWAN

SP	£75	$135	€100
DS	£60	$110	€80
AP	£40	$75	€52

MCKEE, LONETTE

SP	£50	$90	€65
DS	£40	$75	€55
AP	£30	$55	€39

MCLACHLAN, KYLE

SP	£50	$90	€65
DS	£40	$75	€55
AP	£30	$55	€39

MCGUIRE, DOROTHY

SP	£50	$90	€65
DS	£40	$75	€55
AP	£30	$55	€39

MCKELLEN, IAN

SP	£50	$90	€65
DS	£40	$75	€55
AP	£30	$55	€39

MCQUEEN, BUTTERFLY

SP	£350	$625	€455
DS	£300	$535	€390
AP	£160	$285	€208

MCQUEEN, STEVE

SP	£3,500	$6,225	€4,550
DS	£1,950	$3,470	€2,535
AP	£1,750	$3,115	€2,275

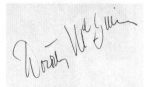

MCKEAN, MICHAEL

SP	£75	$135	€100
DS	£60	$110	€80
AP	£40	$75	€52

MCKENNA, VIRGINIA

SP	£45	$85	€60
DS	£35	$65	€50
AP	£25	$45	€33

Steve McQueen

Terence Steven McQueen was born March 24th 1930 in Beech Grove, Indiana. McQueen had a troubled youth, spent in gangs. He was sent to a reform school where he began to mature, and in 1947 McQueen joined the United States Marine Corps where he served until 1950, when he was honorably discharged.

In 1952 McQueen began studying acting and to help fund his education he started motorcycle racing. Before long he was winning races and bought himself a used Harley Davidson, whilst earning himself $100 in winnings.

McQueen landed his film debut in *Somebody Up There Likes Me* and made a Broadway appearance in *A Hatful of Rain* in 1955. He made his first real break through, not in a film but in a TV show called *Wanted: Dead or Alive* in 1958. Aged 29, McQueen was starring alongside Frank Sinatra in *Never So Few*, and in 1963 was cast in *The Magnificent Seven* & *The Great Escape*.

McQueen started struggling in a long fight against cancer and in 1980 completed his last two films, *Tom Horn* and *The Hunter*, but at the age of 50, McQueen died on 7th November 1980.

McQueen is still considered as an icon of popular culture.

MEANEY, COLM

SP	£50	$90	€65
DS	£40	$75	€55
AP	£30	$55	€39

MESSENGER, MELINDA

SP	£100	$180	€130
DS	£80	$145	€105
AP	£60	$110	€78

MILANO, ALYSSA

SP	£50	$90	€65
DS	£40	$75	€55
AP	£30	$55	€39

MENDES, EVA

SP	£75	$135	€100
DS	£60	$110	€80
AP	£40	$75	€52

MESSING, DEBRA

SP	£50	$90	€65
DS	£40	$75	€55
AP	£30	$55	€39

MILFORD, PENELOPE

SP	£50	$90	€65
DS	£40	$75	€55
AP	£30	$55	€39

MEWES, JASON

SP	£75	$135	€100
DS	£60	$110	€80
AP	£40	$75	€52

MEREDITH, BURGESS

SP	£50	$90	€65
DS	£40	$75	€55
AP	£30	$55	€39

MERIWETHER, LEE

SP	£50	$90	€65
DS	£40	$75	€55
AP	£30	$55	€39

MILLAND, RAY

SP	£250	$445	€325
DS	£125	$225	€165
AP	£85	$155	€111

MIDLER, BETTE

SP	£50	$90	€65
DS	£45	$85	€60
AP	£35	$65	€46

MILLER, ANN

SP	£50	$90	€65
DS	£40	$75	€55
AP	£30	$55	€39

Film, TV and Theatre

MILLER, JOHNNY LEE

SP	£50	$90	€65
DS	£35	$65	€50
AP	£30	$55	€39

MILLS, HAYLEY

SP	£50	$90	€65
DS	£40	$75	€55
AP	£30	$55	€39

MINNELLI, LIZA

SP	£250	$445	€325
DS	£225	$405	€295
AP	£125	$225	€163

MILLER, ROGER

SP	£50	$90	€65
DS	£40	$75	€55
AP	£30	$55	€39

MILLS, JOHN

SP	£50	$90	€65
DS	£40	$75	€55
AP	£30	$55	€39

MIRANDA, CARMEN

SP	£500	$890	€650
DS	£450	$805	€585
AP	£300	$535	€390

MILLER, SIENNA

SP	£75	$135	€100
DS	£60	$110	€80
AP	£40	$75	€52

MILLS, JULIET

SP	£50	$90	€65
DS	£40	$75	€55
AP	£30	$55	€39

MIRREN, HELEN

SP	£175	$315	€230
DS	£125	$225	€165
AP	£75	$135	€98

MILLER, WENTWORTH

SP	£100	$180	€130
DS	£80	$145	€105
AP	£60	$110	€78

MINEO, SAL

SP	£250	$445	€325
DS	£375	$670	€490
AP	£175	$315	€228

MITCHUM, ROBERT

SP	£395	$705	€515
DS	£375	$670	€490
AP	£125	$225	€163

MODINE, MATTHEW

SP	£50	$90	€65
DS	£40	$75	€55
AP	£30	$55	€39

MOL, GRETCHEN

SP	£50	$90	€65
DS	£40	$75	€55
AP	£30	$55	€39

MOLINA, ALFRED

SP	£50	$90	€65
DS	£40	$75	€55
AP	£30	$55	€39

MONROE, MARILYN

SP	£18,500	$32,895	€24,050
DS	£8,000	$14,225	€10,400
AP	£5,500	$9,780	€7,150

MOODY, RON

SP	£75	$135	€100
DS	£60	$110	€80
AP	£40	$75	€52

MOORE, DEMI

SP	£125	$225	€165
DS	£110	$200	€145
AP	£60	$110	€78

MOORE, DUDLEY

SP	£50	$90	€65
DS	£40	$75	€55
AP	£30	$55	€39

MOORE, JULIANNE

SP	£100	$180	€130
DS	£80	$145	€105
AP	£50	$90	€65

MOORE, KIERON

SP	£50	$90	€65
DS	£40	$75	€55
AP	£30	$55	€39

MOORE, ROGER

SP	£300	$535	€390
DS	£280	$500	€365
AP	£150	$270	€195

MOORE, TERRY

SP	£50	$90	€65
DS	£40	$75	€55
AP	£30	$55	€39

MOOREHEAD, AGNES

SP	£175	$315	€230
DS	£150	$270	€195
AP	£90	$165	€117

MOREAU, JEANNE

SP	£50	$90	€65
DS	£40	$75	€55
AP	£30	$55	€39

MORECAMBE, ERIC

SP	£75	$135	€100
DS	£60	$110	€80
AP	£40	$75	€52

MORRISSEY, DAVID

SP	£50	$90	€65
DS	£40	$75	€55
AP	£30	$55	€39

MORTENSEN, VIGGO

SP	£100	$180	€130
DS	£75	$135	€100
AP	£50	$90	€65

MR T

SP	£75	$135	€100
DS	£60	$110	€80
AP	£40	$75	€52

MULGREW, KATE

SP	£50	$90	€65
DS	£40	$75	€55
AP	£30	$55	€39

MUNRO, CAROLINE

SP	£50	$90	€65
DS	£40	$75	€55
AP	£30	$55	€39

MURCIANO, ENRIQUE

SP	£50	$90	€65
DS	£40	$75	€55
AP	£30	$55	€39

MURPHY, AUDIE

SP	£750	$1,335	€975
DS	£600	$1,070	€780
AP	£350	$625	€455

MURPHY, BRITTANY

SP	£75	$135	€100
DS	£60	$110	€80
AP	£40	$75	€52

MURPHY, EDDIE

SP	£75	$135	€100
DS	£60	$110	€80
AP	£40	$75	€52

MURRAY, BILL

SP	£75	$135	€100
DS	£60	$110	€80
AP	£40	$75	€52

MYERS, MIKE

SP	£75	$135	€100
DS	£60	$110	€80
AP	£40	$75	€52

NADER, MICHAEL

SP	£50	$90	€65
DS	£40	$75	€55
AP	£30	$55	€39

NAKAJIMA, HARUO

SP	£50	$90	€65
DS	£40	$75	€55
AP	£30	$55	€39

NEAGLE, ANNA

SP	£60	$110	€80
DS	£45	$85	€60
AP	£30	$55	€39

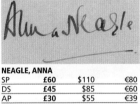

NEESON, LIAM

SP	£100	$180	€130
DS	£80	$145	€105
AP	£50	$90	€65

NEILL, SAM

SP	£50	$90	€65
DS	£40	$75	€55
AP	£30	$55	€39

NESBIT, DERREN

SP	£50	$90	€65
DS	£40	$75	€55
AP	£30	$55	€39

NEUWIRTH, BEBE

SP	£50	$90	€65
DS	£40	$75	€55
AP	£30	$55	€39

NEWHART, BOB

SP	£50	$90	€65
DS	£40	$75	€55
AP	£30	$55	€39

NEWMAN, PAUL

SP	£850	$1,515	€1,105
DS	£1,000	$1,780	€1,300
AP	£495	$885	€644

NEWMAR, JULIE

SP	£50	$90	€65
DS	£40	$75	€55
AP	£30	$55	€39

NEWTON JOHN, OLIVIA

SP	£195	$350	€255
DS	£125	$225	€165
AP	£70	$125	€91

NEWTON, THANDIE

SP	£60	$110	€80
DS	£45	$85	€60
AP	£35	$65	€46

NEY, MARIE

SP	£45	$85	€60
DS	£30	$55	€40
AP	£25	$45	€33

NICHOLS, NICHELLE

SP	£75	$135	€100
DS	£60	$110	€80
AP	£40	$75	€52

NICHOLSON, JACK

SP	£175	$315	€230
DS	£60	$110	€80
AP	£40	$75	€52

NIGHY, BILL

SP	£75	$135	€100
DS	£60	$110	€80
AP	£40	$75	€52

NIMOY, LEONARD

SP	£75	$135	€100
DS	£60	$110	€80
AP	£40	$75	€52

NIXON, CYNTHIA

SP	£75	$135	€100
DS	£60	$110	€80
AP	£40	$75	€52

NOBLE, JOHN

SP	£50	$90	€65
DS	£40	$75	€55
AP	£30	$55	€39

NORELL, PAUL

SP	£50	$90	€65
DS	£40	$75	€55
AP	£30	$55	€39

NORRIS, CHUCK

SP	£50	$90	€65
DS	£40	$75	€55
AP	£30	$55	€39

NORTON, GRAHAM

SP	£50	$90	€65
DS	£40	$75	€55
AP	£30	$55	€39

NOVAK, KIM

SP	£200	$360	€260
DS	£180	$325	€235
AP	£100	$180	€130

NOVARRO, RAMON

SP	£50	$90	€65
DS	£40	$75	€55
AP	£30	$55	€39

NOVELLO, IVOR

SP	£75	$135	€100
DS	£50	$90	€65
AP	£40	$75	€52

O'BRIEN, RICHARD

SP	£50	$90	€65
DS	£40	$75	€55
AP	£30	$55	€39

O'CONNOR, GLYNNIS

SP	£50	$90	€65
DS	£40	$75	€55
AP	£30	$55	€39

O'HARA, MAUREEN

SP	£85	$155	€115
DS	£75	$135	€100
AP	£60	$110	€78

O'KEEFE, MICHAEL

SP	£50	$90	€65
DS	£40	$75	€55
AP	£30	$55	€39

OLDMAN, GARY

SP	£75	$135	€100
DS	£60	$110	€80
AP	£40	$75	€52

OLIVER, VIC

SP	£45	$85	€60
DS	£35	$65	€50
AP	£25	$45	€33

OLIVIER, LAURENCE

SP	£300	$535	€390
DS	£280	$500	€365
AP	£150	$270	€195

O'NEAL, TATUM

SP	£40	$75	€55
DS	£35	$65	€50
AP	£30	$55	€39

ONTKEAN, MICHAEL

SP	£50	$90	€65
DS	£40	$75	€55
AP	£30	$55	€39

O'ROURKE, HEATHER

SP	£250	$445	€325
DS	£270	$485	€355
AP	£200	$360	€260

OSMENT, HALEY JOEL

SP	£50	$90	€65
DS	£40	$75	€55
AP	£30	$55	€39

O'TOOLE, PETER

SP	£75	$135	€100
DS	£60	$110	€80
AP	£40	$75	€52

OWEN, CLIVE

SP	£75	$135	€100
DS	£60	$110	€80
AP	£40	$75	€52

Film, TV and Theatre

OZ, FRANK

SP	£50	$90	€65
DS	£40	$75	€55
AP	£30	$55	€39

PACINO, AL

SP	£150	$270	€195
DS	£100	$180	€130
AP	£80	$145	€104

PAGET, DEBRA

SP	£100	$180	€130
DS	£80	$145	€105
AP	£50	$90	€65

PALANCE, JACK

SP	£50	$90	€65
DS	£40	$75	€55
AP	£30	$55	€39

PALIN, MICHAEL

SP	£75	$135	€100
DS	£60	$110	€80
AP	£40	$75	€52

PAQUIN, ANNA

SP	£50	$90	€65
DS	£40	$75	€55
AP	£30	$55	€39

PALK, ANNA

SP	£50	$90	€65
DS	£40	$75	€55
AP	£30	$55	€39

PALMER, BETSY

SP	£75	$135	€100
DS	£60	$110	€80
AP	£40	$75	€52

PARK, RAY

SP	£50	$90	€65
DS	£40	$75	€55
AP	£30	$55	€39

PARKER, SARAH JESSICA

SP	£85	$155	€115
DS	£60	$110	€80
AP	£40	$75	€52

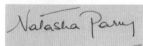

PARRY, NATASHA

SP	£50	$90	€65
DS	£40	$75	€55
AP	£30	$55	€39

PALTROW, GWYNNETH

SP	£125	$225	€165
DS	£80	$145	€105
AP	£50	$90	€65

PATRICK, BUTCH

SP	£75	$135	€100
DS	£60	$110	€80
AP	£40	$75	€52

PAXTON, BILL

SP	£75	$135	€100
DS	£60	$110	€80
AP	£40	$75	€52

PECK, GREGORY

SP	£300	$535	€390
DS	£280	$500	€365
AP	£150	$270	€195

PENN, SEAN

SP	£50	$90	€65
DS	£40	$75	€55
AP	£30	$55	€39

PEPPARD, GEORGE

SP	£50	$90	€65
DS	£40	$75	€55
AP	£30	$55	€39

PERABO, PIPER

SP	£50	$90	€65
DS	£40	$75	€55
AP	£30	$55	€39

PERLMAN, RHEA

SP	£50	$90	€65
DS	£40	$75	€55
AP	£30	$55	€39

PERRINE, VALERIE

SP	£50	$90	€65
DS	£40	$75	€55
AP	£30	$55	€39

PERRY, MATTHEW

SP	£75	$135	€100
DS	£60	$110	€80
AP	£40	$75	€52

PERTWEE, BILL

SP	£50	$90	€65
DS	£40	$75	€55
AP	£30	$55	€39

PERTWEE, JON

SP	£100	$180	€130
DS	£75	$135	€100
AP	£30	$55	€39

PESCI, JOE

SP	£50	$90	€65
DS	£40	$75	€55
AP	£30	$55	€39

PESCOW, DONNA

SP	£50	$90	€65
DS	£40	$75	€55
AP	£30	$55	€39

Film, TV and Theatre

PETERS, BERNADETTE

SP	£50	$90	€65
DS	£40	$75	€55
AP	£30	$55	€39

PFEIFFER, MICHELLE

SP	£75	$135	€100
DS	£60	$110	€80
AP	£40	$75	€52

PHILBIN, REGIS

SP	£50	$90	€65
DS	£40	$75	€55
AP	£30	$55	€39

PHILLIPPE, RYAN

SP	£75	$135	€100
DS	£60	$110	€80
AP	£40	$75	€52

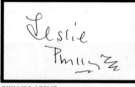

PHILLIPS, LESLIE

SP	£45	$85	€60
DS	£35	$65	€50
AP	£25	$45	€33

PHILLIPS, LOU DIAMOND

SP	£50	$90	€65
DS	£40	$75	€55
AP	£30	$55	€39

PHOENIX, JOAQUIN

SP	£75	$135	€100
DS	£60	$110	€80
AP	£40	$75	€52

PHOENIX, RIVER

SP	£750	$1,335	€975
DS	£500	$890	€650
AP	£450	$805	€585

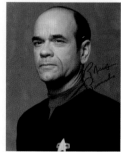

PICARDO, ROBERT

SP	£50	$90	€65
DS	£40	$75	€55
AP	£30	$55	€39

PAUL PICERNI

PICERNI, PAUL

SP	£50	$90	€65
DS	£40	$75	€55
AP	£30	$55	€39

PICKETT, CINDY

SP	£50	$90	€65
DS	£40	$75	€55
AP	£30	$55	€39

PICKFORD, MARY

SP	£75	$135	€100
DS	£60	$110	€80
AP	£45	$85	€59

PIGOTT SMITH, TIM

SP	£50	$90	€65
DS	£40	$75	€55
AP	£30	$55	€39

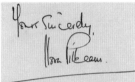

PILBEAM, NOVA

SP	£75	$135	€100
DS	£60	$110	€80
AP	£40	$75	€52

PITT, BRAD

SP	£75	$135	€100
DS	£60	$110	€80
AP	£40	$75	€52

PITT, INGRID

SP	£85	$155	€115
DS	£75	$135	€100
AP	£45	$85	€59

PLUMMER, AMANDA

SP	£50	$90	€65
DS	£40	$75	€55
AP	£30	$55	€39

PLUMMER, CHRISTOPHER

SP	£45	$85	€60
DS	£40	$75	€55
AP	£30	$55	€39

POLLARD, SU

SP	£50	$90	€65
DS	£40	$75	€55
AP	£30	$55	€39

POLO, TERI

SP	£50	$90	€65
DS	£40	$75	€55
AP	£30	$55	€39

PORTMAN, NATALIE

SP	£100	$180	€130
DS	£80	$145	€105
AP	£50	$90	€65

POSTGATE, OLIVER

SP	£100	$180	€130
DS	£80	$145	€105
AP	£50	$90	€65

POSTLETHWAITE, PETE

SP	£50	$90	€65
DS	£40	$75	€55
AP	£30	$55	€39

POWELL, WILLIAM

SP	£195	$350	€255
DS	£180	$325	€235
AP	£95	$170	€124

POWER, TYRONE

SP	£75	$135	€100
DS	£60	$110	€80
AP	£40	$75	€52

POWERS, STEFANIE

SP	£75	$135	€100
DS	£60	$110	€80
AP	£40	$75	€52

PREPON, LAURA

SP	£50	$90	€65
DS	£40	$75	€55
AP	£30	$55	€39

PRESLEY, ELVIS

SP	£4,500	$8,005	€5,850
DS	£4,500	$8,005	€5,850
AP	£2,000	$3,560	€2,600

PRESLEY, PRISCILLA

SP	£75	$135	€100
DS	£60	$110	€80
AP	£40	$75	€52

PRESSLEY, JAMIE

SP	£50	$90	€65
DS	£40	$75	€55
AP	£30	$55	€39

PRICE, VINCENT

SP	£195	$350	€255
DS	£180	$325	€235
AP	£95	$170	€124

PRIESTLEY, JASON

SP	£100	$180	€130
DS	£80	$145	€105
AP	£50	$90	€65

PRINZE JR, FREDDIE

SP	£50	$90	€65
DS	£45	$85	€60
AP	£40	$75	€52

PROCTER, EMILY

SP	£75	$135	€100
DS	£60	$110	€80
AP	£40	$75	€52

PROVOST, JON

SP	£75	$135	€100
DS	£60	$110	€80
AP	£40	$75	€52

PROWSE, DAVE

SP	£75	$135	€100
DS	£60	$110	€80
AP	£40	$75	€52

PRYCE, JONATHAN

SP	£75	$135	€100
DS	£60	$110	€80
AP	£40	$75	€52

PULLMAN, BILL

SP	£75	$135	€100
DS	£60	$110	€80
AP	£40	$75	€52

QUAID, DENNIS

SP	£50	$90	€65
DS	£40	$75	€55
AP	£30	$55	€39

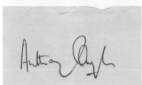

QUAYLE, ANTHONY

SP	£45	$85	€60
DS	£35	$65	€50
AP	£25	$45	€33

QUINN, AIDAN

SP	£50	$90	€65
DS	£40	$75	€55
AP	£30	$55	€39

QUINN, ANTHONY

SP	£250	$445	€325
DS	£225	$405	€295
AP	£125	$225	€163

RADCLIFFE, DANIEL

SP	£695	$1,240	€905
DS	£650	$1,160	€845
AP	£350	$625	€455

RAE, CHARLOTTE

SP	£50	$90	€65
DS	£40	$75	€55
AP	£30	$55	€39

RAFT, GEORGE

SP	£250	$445	€325
DS	£150	$270	€195
AP	£90	$165	€117

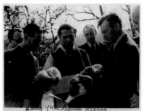

RAINS, CLAUDE

SP	£395	$705	€515
DS	£375	$670	€490
AP	£190	$340	€247

RAMBO, DACK

SP	£50	$90	€65
DS	£40	$75	€55
AP	£30	$55	€39

RANDALL, TONY

SP	£50	$90	€65
DS	£40	$75	€55
AP	£30	$55	€39

Film, TV and Theatre

RATHBONE, BASIL

SP	£475	$845	€620
DS	£450	$805	€585
AP	£225	$405	€293

REDGRAVE, VANESSA

SP	£80	$145	€105
DS	£65	$120	€85
AP	£50	$90	€65

REID, TARA

SP	£50	$90	€65
DS	£40	$75	€55
AP	£30	$55	€39

REEVE, CHRISTOPHER

SP	£450	$805	€585
DS	£195	$350	€255
AP	£100	$180	€130

RAYE, MARTHA

SP	£50	$90	€65
DS	£40	$75	€55
AP	£30	$55	€39

REILLY, JOHN C.

SP	£50	$90	€65
DS	£40	$75	€55
AP	£30	$55	€39

REA, STEPHEN

SP	£75	$135	€100
DS	£60	$110	€80
AP	£40	$75	€52

REEVES, KEANU

SP	£75	$135	€100
DS	£60	$110	€80
AP	£40	$75	€52

REINHOLD, JUDGE

SP	£50	$90	€65
DS	£40	$75	€55
AP	£30	$55	€39

REDFORD, ROBERT

SP	£175	$315	€230
DS	£160	$285	€210
AP	£85	$155	€111

REEVES, STEVE

SP	£75	$135	€100
DS	£60	$110	€80
AP	£40	$75	€52

REINKING, ANN

SP	£50	$90	€65
DS	£40	$75	€55
AP	£30	$55	€39

REMICK, LEE

SP	£50	$90	€65
DS	£40	$75	€55
AP	£30	$55	€39

REYNOLDS, RYAN

SP	£50	$90	€65
DS	£40	$75	€55
AP	£30	$55	€39

RICHARDS, DENISE

SP	£50	$90	€65
DS	£40	$75	€55
AP	£30	$55	€39

REMINI, LEAH

SP	£75	$135	€100
DS	£60	$110	€80
AP	£40	$75	€52

RHYS DAVIES, JOHN

SP	£50	$90	€65
DS	£40	$75	€55
AP	£30	$55	€39

RICHARDSON, NATASHA

SP	£50	$90	€65
DS	£40	$75	€55
AP	£30	$55	€39

RENO, JEAN

SP	£75	$135	€100
DS	£60	$110	€80
AP	£40	$75	€52

RIBISI, GIOVANNI

SP	£75	$135	€100
DS	£60	$110	€80
AP	£40	$75	€52

RICHARDSON, RALPH

SP	£225	$405	€295
DS	£150	$270	€195
AP	£75	$135	€98

REYNOLDS, DEBBIE

SP	£50	$90	€65
DS	£40	$75	€55
AP	£30	$55	€39

RICCI, CHRISTINA

SP	£75	$135	€100
DS	£60	$110	€80
AP	£40	$75	€52

RIEFENSTAHL, LENI

SP	£450	$805	€585
DS	£375	$670	€490
AP	£250	$445	€325

RIGG, DIANA

SP	£125	$225	€165
DS	£175	$315	€230
AP	£80	$145	€104

ROBERT, PATRICK

SP	£50	$90	€65
DS	£40	$75	€55
AP	£30	$55	€39

ROBERTSON, CLIFF

SP	£50	$90	€65
DS	£40	$75	€55
AP	£30	$55	€39

ROBEY, GEORGE

SP	£45	$85	€60
DS	£35	$65	€50
AP	£25	$45	€33

RIVERS, JOAN

SP	£50	$90	€65
DS	£40	$75	€55
AP	£30	$55	€39

ROBERTS, ERIC

SP	£50	$90	€65
DS	£40	$75	€55
AP	£30	$55	€39

ROBINSON, EDWARD G

SP	£450	$805	€585
DS	£350	$625	€455
AP	£150	$270	€195

ROBARDS, JASON

SP	£50	$90	€65
DS	£40	$75	€55
AP	£30	$55	€39

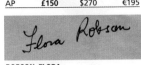

ROBSON, FLORA

SP	£50	$90	€65
DS	£40	$75	€55
AP	£30	$55	€39

ROBERTS, JULIA

SP	£75	$135	€100
DS	£60	$110	€80
AP	£40	$75	€52

ROBBINS, THOMAS

SP	£50	$90	€65
DS	£40	$75	€55
AP	£30	$55	€39

ROBERTS, TANYA

SP	£50	$90	€65
DS	£40	$75	€55
AP	£30	$55	€39

ROCKER, ROXIE

SP	£50	$90	€65
DS	£40	$75	€55
AP	£30	$55	€39

RODDENBERRY, GENE

SP	£300	$535	€390
DS	£280	$500	€365
AP	£150	$270	€195

RODRIGUEZ, ADAM

SP	£50	$90	€65
DS	£40	$75	€55
AP	£30	$55	€39

RODRIGUEZ, MICHELLE

SP	£75	$135	€100
DS	£60	$110	€80
AP	£40	$75	€52

ROGERS, GINGER

SP	£375	$670	€490
DS	£350	$625	€455
AP	£175	$315	€228

ROGERS, MIMI

SP	£45	$85	€60
DS	£40	$75	€55
AP	£30	$55	€39

ROMERO, CESAR

SP	£50	$90	€65
DS	£40	$75	€55
AP	£30	$55	€39

ROMIJN-STAMOS, REBECCA

SP	£50	$90	€65
DS	£40	$75	€55
AP	£30	$55	€39

ROONEY, MICKEY

SP	£50	$90	€65
DS	£40	$75	€55
AP	£30	$55	€39

ROSELINI, ISABELLA

SP	£75	$135	€100
DS	£60	$110	€80
AP	£50	$90	€65

ROSENBAUM, MICHAEL

SP	£50	$90	€65
DS	£40	$75	€55
AP	£30	$55	€39

ROSS, KATHERINE

SP	£250	$445	€325
DS	£225	$405	€295
AP	£125	$225	€163

ROTH, TIM

SP	£50	$90	€65
DS	£40	$75	€55
AP	£35	$65	€46

ROUNDTREE, RICHARD

SP	£50	$90	€65
DS	£45	$85	€60
AP	£40	$75	€52

RUSSELL, KURT

SP	£75	$135	€100
DS	£60	$110	€80
AP	£40	$75	€52

RYAN, MEG

SP	£75	$135	€100
DS	£60	$110	€80
AP	£35	$65	€46

ROURKE, MICKY

SP	£75	$135	€100
DS	£60	$110	€80
AP	£40	$75	€52

RUSSELL, ROSALIND

SP	£50	$90	€65
DS	£40	$75	€55
AP	£30	$55	€39

RYDER, WINONA

SP	£75	$135	€100
DS	£60	$110	€80
AP	£40	$75	€52

RUSH, GEOFFREY

SP	£75	$135	€100
DS	£60	$110	€80
AP	£40	$75	€52

RUSSELL, THERESA

SP	£75	$135	€100
DS	£60	$110	€80
AP	£40	$75	€52

SABATO, ANTONIO (JR)

SP	£50	$90	€65
DS	£40	$75	€55
AP	£30	$55	€39

RUSSELL, JANE

SP	£250	$445	€325
DS	£125	$225	€165
AP	£80	$145	€104

RUSSO, RENE

SP	£50	$90	€65
DS	£40	$75	€55
AP	£30	$55	€39

SABU

SP	£50	$90	€65
DS	£40	$75	€55
AP	£30	$55	€39

SACHS, LEONARD

SP	£100	$180	€130
DS	£75	$135	€100
AP	£50	$90	€65

SAKATA, HAROLD

SP	£600	$1,070	€780
DS	£495	$885	€645
AP	£300	$535	€390

EMMA SAMMS

SAMMS, EMMA

SP	£50	$90	€65
DS	£40	$75	€55
AP	£30	$55	€39

SANDERS, GEORGE

SP	£250	$445	€325
DS	£160	$285	€210
AP	£80	$145	€104

SANDLER, ADAM

SP	£50	$90	€65
DS	£40	$75	€55
AP	£30	$55	€39

SARANDON, SUSAN

SP	£75	$135	€100
DS	£60	$110	€80
AP	£40	$75	€52

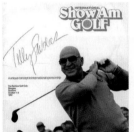

SAVALAS, TELLY

SP	£50	$90	€65
DS	£40	$75	€55
AP	£30	$55	€39

SAWALHA, JULIA

SP	£40	$75	€55
DS	£35	$65	€50
AP	£30	$55	€39

SCHELL, MARIA

SP	£50	$90	€65
DS	£40	$75	€55
AP	£30	$55	€39

SCHIFFER, CLAUDIA

SP	£100	$180	€130
DS	£80	$145	€105
AP	£50	$90	€65

SCHNEIDER, ROB

SP	£45	$85	€60
DS	£40	$75	€55
AP	£30	$55	€39

SCHWARZENEGGER, ARNOLD

SP	£100	$180	€130
DS	£60	$110	€80
AP	£45	$85	€59

SCHWIMMER, DAVID

SP	£50	$90	€65
DS	£45	$85	€60
AP	£40	$75	€52

SCIORRA, ANNABELLA

SP	£50	$90	€65
DS	£40	$75	€55
AP	£30	$55	€39

SCOTT CAAN

SP	£50	$90	€65
DS	£40	$75	€55
AP	£30	$55	€39

SCOTT THOMAS, KRISTIN

SP	£50	$90	€65
DS	£40	$75	€55
AP	£30	$55	€39

SCOTT, CAMPBELL

SP	£50	$90	€65
DS	£40	$75	€55
AP	£30	$55	€39

SCOTT, JANETTE

SP	£50	$90	€65
DS	£40	$75	€55
AP	£30	$55	€39

SCOTT, SEANN WILLIAM

SP	£50	$90	€65
DS	£40	$75	€55
AP	£30	$55	€39

SEAGAL, STEVEN

SP	£75	$135	€100
DS	£60	$110	€80
AP	£40	$75	€52

SECOMBE, HARRY

SP	£75	$135	€100
DS	£60	$110	€80
AP	£40	$75	€52

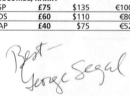

SEGAL, GEORGE

SP	£50	$90	€65
DS	£40	$75	€55
AP	£30	$55	€39

SEINFIELD, JERRY

SP	£50	$90	€65
DS	£40	$75	€55
AP	£30	$55	€39

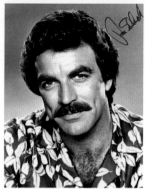

SELLECK, TOM

SP	£50	$90	€65
DS	£40	$75	€55
AP	£30	$55	€39

SELLERS, PETER

SP	£175	$315	€230
DS	£125	$225	€165
AP	£80	$145	€104

SERKIS, ANDY

SP	£100	$180	€130
DS	£60	$110	€80
AP	£40	$75	€52

SEVIGNY, CHLOE

SP	£50	$90	€65
DS	£40	$75	€55
AP	£30	$55	€39

SEWELL, RUFUS

SP	£40	$75	€55
DS	£35	$65	€50
AP	£30	$55	€39

SHARIF, OMAR

SP	£75	$135	€100
DS	£60	$110	€80
AP	£40	$75	€52

SHARPE, CORNELIA

SP	£50	$90	€65
DS	£40	$75	€55
AP	£30	$55	€39

SHATNER, WILLIAM

SP	£75	$135	€100
DS	£60	$110	€80
AP	£40	$75	€52

SHEARD, MICHAEL

SP	£45	$85	€60
DS	£40	$75	€55
AP	£30	$55	€39

SHEEN, CHARLIE

SP	£50	$90	€65
DS	£40	$75	€55
AP	£30	$55	€39

SHEEN, MARTIN

SP	£50	$90	€65
DS	£40	$75	€55
AP	£30	$55	€39

SHEPHERD, ELIZABETH

SP	£100	$180	€130
DS	£75	$135	€100
AP	£50	$90	€65

SHER, ANTHONY

SP	£45	$85	€60
DS	£35	$65	€50
AP	£25	$45	€33

SHIELDS, BROOKE

SP	£75	$135	€100
DS	£40	$75	€55
AP	£30	$55	€39

SHOTTER, WINIFRED

SP	£50	$90	€65
DS	£40	$75	€55
AP	£30	$55	€39

SILVERS, PHIL

SP	£795	$1,415	€1,035
DS	£450	$805	€585
AP	£250	$445	€325

SILVERSTONE, ALICIA

SP	£75	$135	€100
DS	£60	$110	€80
AP	£40	$75	€52

SIM, ALASTAIR

SP	£150	$270	€195
DS	£120	$215	€160
AP	£85	$155	€111

SIMMONS, JEAN

SP	£50	$90	€65
DS	£40	$75	€55
AP	£30	$55	€39

SINATRA, FRANK

SP	£1,500	$2,670	€1,950
DS	£1,000	$1,780	€1,300
AP	£875	$1,560	€1,138

SINGER, LORI

SP	£50	$90	€65
DS	£40	$75	€55
AP	£30	$55	€39

SIRTIS, MARINA

SP	£50	$90	€65
DS	£40	$75	€55
AP	£30	$55	€39

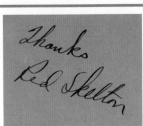

SKELTON, RED

SP	£50	$90	€65
DS	£40	$75	€55
AP	£30	$55	€39

SLADEN, ELISABETH

SP	£45	$85	€60
DS	£40	$75	€55
AP	£30	$55	€39

SLATER, CHRISTIAN

SP	£65	$120	€85
DS	£40	$75	€55
AP	£30	$55	€39

SLATER, HELEN

SP	£50	$90	€65
DS	£40	$75	€55
AP	£30	$55	€39

SMART, AMY

SP	£50	$90	€65
DS	£40	$75	€55
AP	£30	$55	€39

SMITH, ANNA NICOLE

SP	£450	$805	€585
DS	£300	$535	€390
AP	£200	$360	€260

SMITH, JACLYN

SP	£50	$90	€65
DS	£40	$75	€55
AP	£30	$55	€39

SMITH, MAGGIE

SP	£85	$155	€115
DS	£60	$110	€80
AP	£40	$75	€52

SMITH, WILL

SP	£100	$180	€130
DS	£60	$110	€80
AP	£40	$75	€52

SOBIESKI, LEELEE

SP	£65	$120	€85
DS	£40	$75	€55
AP	£30	$55	€39

SORVINO, MIRA

SP	£50	$90	€65
DS	£40	$75	€55
AP	£30	$55	€39

SPACEK, SISSY

SP	£75	$135	€100
DS	£40	$75	€55
AP	£30	$55	€39

SOMERS, SUZANNE

SP	£50	$90	€65
DS	£40	$75	€55
AP	£30	$55	€39

SORVINO, PAUL

SP	£50	$90	€65
DS	£40	$75	€55
AP	£30	$55	€39

SPACEY, KEVIN

SP	£75	$135	€100
DS	£60	$110	€80
AP	£40	$75	€52

SOMMER, ELKE

SP	£50	$90	€65
DS	£40	$75	€55
AP	£30	$55	€39

SOTO, TALISA

SP	£45	$85	€60
DS	£40	$75	€55
AP	£30	$55	€39

SPELLING, TORI

SP	£50	$90	€65
DS	£40	$75	€55
AP	£30	$55	€39

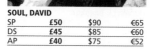

SOUL, DAVID

SP	£50	$90	€65
DS	£45	$85	€60
AP	£40	$75	€52

SORBO, KEVIN

SP	£50	$90	€65
DS	£40	$75	€55
AP	£30	$55	€39

SPIELBERG, STEVEN

SP	£100	$180	€130
DS	£80	$145	€105
AP	£50	$90	€65

SPINER, BRENT

SP	£50	$90	€65
DS	£40	$75	€55
AP	£30	$55	€39

STAMOS, JOHN

SP	£60	$110	€80
DS	£40	$75	€55
AP	£30	$55	€39

STEIGER, ROD

SP	£50	$90	€65
DS	£40	$75	€55
AP	£30	$55	€39

STACK, ROBERT

SP	£50	$90	€65
DS	£40	$75	€55
AP	£30	$55	€39

STAMP, TERENCE

SP	£50	$90	€65
DS	£40	$75	€55
AP	£30	$55	€39

STEVENS, STELLA

SP	£50	$90	€65
DS	£40	$75	€55
AP	£30	$55	€39

STAHL, NICK

SP	£75	$135	€100
DS	£60	$110	€80
AP	£40	$75	€52

STANTON, HARRY DEAN

SP	£50	$90	€65
DS	£40	$75	€55
AP	£30	$55	€39

STEWART, JAMES

SP	£995	$1,770	€1,295
DS	£775	$1,380	€1,010
AP	£250	$445	€325

STALLONE, SYLVESTER

SP	£175	$315	€230
DS	£90	$165	€120
AP	£60	$110	€78

STANWYCK, BARBARA

SP	£175	$315	€230
DS	£150	$270	€195
AP	£45	$85	€59

STEWART, PATRICK

SP	£50	$90	€65
DS	£40	$75	€55
AP	£30	$55	€39

STILES, JULIA

SP	£75	$135	€100
DS	£60	$110	€80
AP	£40	$75	€52

STILLER, BEN

SP	£75	$135	€100
DS	£60	$110	€80
AP	£40	$75	€52

STONE, OLIVER

SP	£75	$135	€100
DS	£60	$110	€80
AP	£40	$75	€52

STONE, SHARON

SP	£75	$135	€100
DS	£60	$110	€80
AP	£40	$75	€52

STREEP, MERYL

SP	£75	$135	€100
DS	£60	$110	€80
AP	£40	$75	€52

STREISAND, BARBRA

SP	£575	$1,025	€750
DS	£375	$670	€490
AP	£260	$465	€338

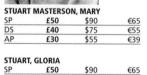

STUART MASTERSON, MARY

SP	£50	$90	€65
DS	£40	$75	€55
AP	£30	$55	€39

STUART, GLORIA

SP	£50	$90	€65
DS	£40	$75	€55
AP	£30	$55	€39

STUBBS, UNA

SP	£50	$90	€65
DS	£40	$75	€55
AP	£30	$55	€39

SUCHET, DAVID

SP	£50	$90	€65
DS	£40	$75	€55
AP	£30	$55	€39

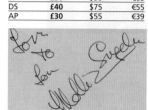

SUGDEN, MOLLIE

SP	£50	$90	€65
DS	£40	$75	€55
AP	£30	$55	€39

SUTHERLAND, DONALD

SP	£75	$135	€100
DS	£45	$85	€60
AP	£35	$65	€46

SUTHERLAND, JOAN

SP	£75	$135	€100
DS	£60	$110	€80
AP	£40	$75	€52

SUTHERLAND, KIEFER

SP	£100	$180	€130
DS	£80	$145	€105
AP	£50	$90	€65

Film, TV and Theatre

SUVARI, MENA

SP	£60	$110	€80
DS	£50	$90	€65
AP	£40	$75	€52

SWAIN, DOMINIQUE

SP	£50	$90	€65
DS	£40	$75	€55
AP	£30	$55	€39

SWANK, HILARY

SP	£75	$135	€100
DS	£60	$110	€80
AP	£40	$75	€52

SWANSON, GLORIA

SP	£200	$360	€260
DS	£180	$325	€235
AP	£100	$180	€130

SWAYZE, PATRICK

SP	£150	$270	€195
DS	£90	$165	€120
AP	£60	$110	€78

SWEENEY, CLAIRE

SP	£50	$90	€65
DS	£40	$75	€55
AP	£30	$55	€39

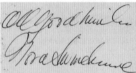

SWINBURNE, NORA

SP	£50	$90	€65
DS	£40	$75	€55
AP	£30	$55	€39

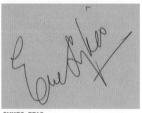

SYKES, ERIC

SP	£150	$270	€195
DS	£100	$180	€130
AP	£75	$135	€98

SYMONS, EMILY

SP	£50	$90	€65
DS	£40	$75	€55
AP	£30	$55	€39

TAKEI, GEORGE

SP	£75	$135	€100
DS	£60	$110	€80
AP	£40	$75	€52

TANDY, JESSICA

SP	£50	$90	€65
DS	£40	$75	€55
AP	£30	$55	€39

TARANTINO, QUENTIN

SP	£75	$135	€100
DS	£60	$110	€80
AP	£40	$75	€52

Bien amicalement,

Jacques TATI

TATI, JACQUES

SP	£1,000	$1,780	€1,300
DS	£675	$1,205	€880
AP	£375	$670	€488

TAYLOR THOMAS, JONATHAN

SP	£45	$85	€60
DS	£40	$75	€55
AP	£30	$55	€39

TAYLOR, ELIZABETH

SP	£795	$1,415	€1,035
DS	£650	$1,160	€845
AP	£575	$1,025	€748

TAYLOR, ROBERT

SP	£45	$85	€60
DS	£35	$65	€50
AP	£25	$45	€33

TEMPLE, SHIRLEY

SP	£750	$1,335	€975
DS	£450	$805	€585
AP	£395	$705	€514

TERRY, ELLEN

SP	£300	$535	€390
DS	£280	$500	€365
AP	£150	$270	€195

THERON, CHARLIZE

SP	£75	$135	€100
DS	£60	$110	€80
AP	£40	$75	€52

THOMAS, HENRY

SP	£100	$180	€130
DS	£80	$145	€105
AP	£50	$90	€65

THOMAS, MARLO

SP	£50	$90	€65
DS	£40	$75	€55
AP	£30	$55	€39

THOMAS, SEAN PATRICK

SP	£50	$90	€65
DS	£40	$75	€55
AP	£30	$55	€39

THOMAS, TERRY

SP	£50	$90	€65
DS	£40	$75	€55
AP	£30	$55	€39

THOMPSON, EMMA

SP	£85	$155	€115
DS	£60	$110	€80
AP	£40	$75	€52

THOMPSON, LEA

SP	£45	$85	€60
DS	£40	$75	€55
AP	£30	$55	€39

THORNDIKE, SYBIL

SP	£50	$90	€65
DS	£40	$75	€55
AP	£30	$55	€39

THORNTON, BILLY BOB

SP	£75	$135	€100
DS	£60	$110	€80
AP	£40	$75	€52

THURMAN, UMA

SP	£150	$270	€195
DS	£80	$145	€105
AP	£60	$110	€78

TILLY, JENNIFER

SP	£75	$135	€100
DS	£50	$90	€65
AP	£40	$75	€52

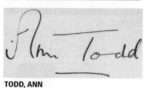

TILTON, CHARLENE

SP	£45	$85	€60
DS	£40	$75	€55
AP	£30	$55	€39

TODD, ANN

SP	£50	$90	€65
DS	£40	$75	€55
AP	£30	$55	€39

TODD, RICHARD

SP	£50	$90	€65
DS	£40	$75	€55
AP	£25	$45	€33

TOMEI, MARISA

SP	£75	$135	€100
DS	£60	$110	€80
AP	£40	$75	€52

The Royle Family

TOMLINSON, RICKY

SP	£50	$90	€65
DS	£40	$75	€55
AP	£30	$55	€39

TRACY, SPENCER

SP	£975	$1,735	€1,270
DS	£350	$625	€455
AP	£250	$445	€325

TRAVOLTA, JOHN

SP	£75	$135	€100
DS	£60	$110	€80
AP	£40	$75	€52

TREJO, DANNY

SP	£50	$90	€65
DS	£40	$75	€55
AP	£30	$55	€39

TRIPPLEHORN, JEANNE

SP	£50	$90	€65
DS	£40	$75	€55
AP	£30	$55	€39

TROUGHTON, PATRICK

SP	£275	$490	€360
DS	£250	$445	€325
AP	£125	$225	€163

TROYER, VERN

SP	£50	$90	€65
DS	£40	$75	€55
AP	£30	$55	€39

TROYER, VERNE

SP	£40	$75	€55
DS	£35	$65	€50
AP	£30	$55	€39

TUCCI, STANLEY

SP	£40	$75	€55
DS	£35	$65	€50
AP	£30	$55	€39

TUCKER, SOPHIE

SP	£50	$90	€65
DS	£40	$75	€55
AP	£30	$55	€39

TUDOR-POLE, EDWARD

SP	£50	$90	€65
DS	£40	$75	€55
AP	£30	$55	€39

TURKEL, ANN

SP	£50	$90	€65
DS	£40	$75	€55
AP	£30	$55	€39

TURNER, KATHLEEN

SP	£50	$90	€65
DS	£40	$75	€55
AP	£30	$55	€39

TURTURRO, NICHOLAS

SP	£50	$90	€65
DS	£40	$75	€55
AP	£30	$55	€39

TYLER, LIV

SP	£75	$135	€100
DS	£60	$110	€80
AP	£40	$75	€52

ULRICH, SKEET

SP	£50	$90	€65
DS	£40	$75	€55
AP	£30	$55	€39

URICH, ROBERT

SP	£50	$90	€65
DS	£40	$75	€55
AP	£30	$55	€39

USTINOV, PETER

SP	£100	$180	€130
DS	£80	$145	€105
AP	£50	$90	€65

Film, TV and Theatre

VALANCE, HOLLY

SP	£75	$135	€100
DS	£60	$110	€80
AP	£40	$75	€52

VALENTINO, RUDOLPH

SP	£2,000	$3,560	€2,600
DS	£1,500	$2,670	€1,950
AP	£950	$1,690	€1,235

VAN DOREN, MAMIE

SP	£75	$135	€100
DS	£60	$110	€80
AP	£40	$75	€52

VAN DYKE, DICK

SP	£75	$135	€100
DS	£60	$110	€80
AP	£40	$75	€52

VAUGHAN, NORMAN

SP	£45	$85	€60
DS	£40	$75	€55
AP	£30	$55	€39

VAUGHN, ROBERT

SP	£75	$135	€100
DS	£60	$110	€80
AP	£40	$75	€52

VAUGHN, VINCE

SP	£75	$135	€100
DS	£60	$110	€80
AP	£40	$75	€52

VEGAS, JOHNNY

SP	£75	$135	€100
DS	£60	$110	€80
AP	£50	$90	€65

VINCENT, JAN MICHAEL

SP	£50	$90	€65
DS	£40	$75	€55
AP	£30	$55	€39

VOIGHT, JON

SP	£60	$110	€80
DS	£40	$75	€55
AP	£30	$55	€39

VON SYDOW, MAX

SP	£50	$90	€65
DS	£40	$75	€55
AP	£30	$55	€39

VOSLOO, ARNOLD

SP	£40	$75	€55
DS	£35	$65	€50
AP	£30	$55	€39

WAGNER, JACK

SP	£40	$75	€55
DS	£35	$65	€50
AP	£30	$55	€39

WAHLBERG, MARK

SP	£60	$110	€80
DS	£40	$75	€55
AP	£30	$55	€39

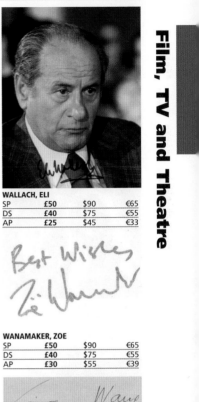

WALLACH, ELI

SP	£50	$90	€65
DS	£40	$75	€55
AP	£25	$45	€33

WAGNER, LINDSAY

SP	£50	$90	€65
DS	£40	$75	€55
AP	£30	$55	€39

WAITE, RALPH

SP	£45	$85	€60
DS	£40	$75	€55
AP	£30	$55	€39

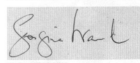

WANAMAKER, ZOE

SP	£50	$90	€65
DS	£40	$75	€55
AP	£30	$55	€39

WAGNER, NATASHA GREGSON

SP	£50	$90	€65
DS	£40	$75	€55
AP	£30	$55	€39

WALKEN, CHRISTOPHER

SP	£50	$90	€65
DS	£40	$75	€55
AP	£30	$55	€39

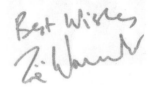

WANG, CILLI

SP	£50	$90	€65
DS	£40	$75	€55
AP	£30	$55	€39

WARD, BURT

SP	£50	$90	€65
DS	£40	$75	€55
AP	£30	$55	€39

WARD, GEORGINA

SP	£50	$90	€65
DS	£40	$75	€55
AP	£30	$55	€39

WAGNER, ROBERT

SP	£50	$90	€65
DS	£40	$75	€55
AP	£25	$45	€33

WALKER, PAUL

SP	£50	$90	€65
DS	£40	$75	€55
AP	£30	$55	€39

WARNER, JACK

SP	£50	$90	€65
DS	£40	$75	€55
AP	£30	$55	€39

WARREN, ESTELLA

SP	£50	$90	€65
DS	£40	$75	€55
AP	£30	$55	€39

WASHINGTON, DENZEL

SP	£75	$135	€100
DS	£60	$110	€80
AP	£40	$75	€52

WATERS, JOHN

SP	£40	$75	€55
DS	£35	$65	€50
AP	£30	$55	€39

WATSON, EMMA

SP	£150	$270	€195
DS	£100	$180	€130
AP	£70	$125	€91

WATTERS, MARLYS

SP	£50	$90	€65
DS	£40	$75	€55
AP	£30	$55	€39

WAYANS, DAMON

SP	£50	$90	€65
DS	£40	$75	€55
AP	£30	$55	€39

WAYNE, JOHN

SP	£1,500	$2,670	€1,950
DS	£3,950	$7,025	€5,135
AP	£995	$1,770	€1,294

WEAVER, SIGOURNEY

SP	£75	$135	€100
DS	£60	$110	€80
AP	£50	$90	€65

WEAVING, HUGO

SP	£50	$90	€65
DS	£40	$75	€55
AP	£30	$55	€39

WEISSMULLER, JOHNNY

SP	£500	$890	€650
DS	£350	$625	€455
AP	£250	$445	€325

WEISZ, RACHEL

SP	£75	$135	€100
DS	£45	$85	€60
AP	£35	$65	€46

WELCH, ELISABETH

SP	£50	$90	€65
DS	£40	$75	€55
AP	£30	$55	€39

WEST, ADAM

SP	£75	$135	€100
DS	£60	$110	€80
AP	£40	$75	€52

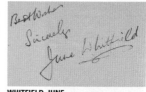

WHITFIELD, JUNE

SP	£50	$90	€65
DS	£40	$75	€55
AP	£30	$55	€39

WHITNEY, GRACE LEE

SP	£45	$85	€60
DS	£40	$75	€55
AP	£30	$55	€39

WEST, MAE

SP	£500	$890	€650
DS	£400	$715	€520
AP	£300	$535	€390

WELCH, RAQUEL

SP	£125	$225	€165
DS	£80	$145	€105
AP	£50	$90	€65

WELCH, TAHNEE

SP	£50	$90	€65
DS	£40	$75	€55
AP	£30	$55	€39

WHATELEY, KEVIN

SP	£45	$85	€60
DS	£40	$75	€55
AP	£30	$55	€39

WILD, JACK

SP	£40	$75	€55
DS	£35	$65	€50
AP	£30	$55	€39

WILDER, GENE

SP	£100	$180	€130
DS	£75	$135	€100
AP	£50	$90	€65

WELLER, PETER

SP	£50	$90	€65
DS	£40	$75	€55
AP	£30	$55	€39

WELLES, ORSON

SP	£1,250	$2,225	€1,625
DS	£1,000	$1,780	€1,300
AP	£750	$1,335	€975

WHITEHOUSE, PAUL

SP	£50	$90	€65
DS	£40	$75	€55
AP	£30	$55	€39

WILLIAM SCOTT, SEANN

SP	£50	$90	€65
DS	£40	$75	€55
AP	£30	$55	€39

WILLIAMS, ROBIN

SP	£75	$135	€100
DS	£60	$110	€80
AP	£50	$90	€65

WILLIAMS, BILLY DEE

SP	£45	$85	€60
DS	£40	$75	€55
AP	£30	$55	€39

WILSON, OWEN

SP	£60	$110	€80
DS	£40	$75	€55
AP	£30	$55	€39

WILLIAMS, ESTHER

SP	£50	$90	€65
DS	£40	$75	€55
AP	£30	$55	€39

WILLIAMS, STEPHANIE

SP	£50	$90	€65
DS	£40	$75	€55
AP	£30	$55	€39

WILSON, PETA

SP	£50	$90	€65
DS	£40	$75	€55
AP	£30	$55	€39

WILLIS, BRUCE

SP	£60	$110	€80
DS	£40	$75	€55
AP	£30	$55	€39

WILLIAMS, KENNETH

SP	£100	$180	€130
DS	£80	$145	€105
AP	£50	$90	€65

WILSON, LOIS

SP	£150	$270	€195
DS	£120	$215	€160
AP	£75	$135	€98

WINCOTT, MICHAEL

SP	£50	$90	€65
DS	£40	$75	€55
AP	£30	$55	€39

WILLIAMS, MICHELLE

SP	£50	$90	€65
DS	£40	$75	€55
AP	£30	$55	€39

WILSON, MARA

SP	£50	$90	€65
DS	£40	$75	€55
AP	£30	$55	€39

WINDSOR, BARBARA

SP	£50	$90	€65
DS	£40	$75	€55
AP	£30	$55	€39

WINKLER, HENRY

SP	£50	$90	€65
DS	£40	$75	€55
AP	£30	$55	€39

WINNER, MICHAEL

SP	£50	$90	€65
DS	£40	$75	€55
AP	£30	$55	€39

WINSLET, KATE

SP	£75	$135	€100
DS	£60	$110	€80
AP	£40	$75	€52

WINSTONE, RAY

SP	£75	$135	€100
DS	£60	$110	€80
AP	£40	$75	€52

WINTERS, SHELLEY

SP	£75	$135	€100
DS	£60	$110	€80
AP	£45	$85	€59

WISDOM, NORMAN

SP	£75	$135	€100
DS	£60	$110	€80
AP	£40	$75	€52

WISEMAN, JOSEPH

SP	£125	$225	€165
DS	£110	$200	€145
AP	£60	$110	€78

WITHERS, GOOGIE

SP	£50	$90	€65
DS	£40	$75	€55
AP	£30	$55	€39

WITHERSPOON, REESE

SP	£50	$90	€65
DS	£40	$75	€55
AP	£30	$55	€39

WOOD, ELIJAH

SP	£150	$270	€195
DS	£120	$215	€160
AP	£65	$120	€85

WOOD, EVAN RACHEL

SP	£50	$90	€65
DS	£40	$75	€55
AP	£30	$55	€39

WOOD, LANA

SP	£100	$180	€130
DS	£80	$145	€105
AP	£50	$90	€65

WOOD, NATALIE

SP	£650	$1,160	€845
DS	£450	$805	€585
AP	£225	$405	€293

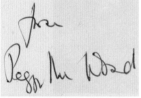

WOOD, PEGGY ANN

SP	£50	$90	€65
DS	£40	$75	€55
AP	£30	$55	€39

WOODHOUSE, BARBARA

SP	£50	$90	€65
DS	£40	$75	€55
AP	£30	$55	€39

WOODS, JAMES

SP	£40	$75	€55
DS	£35	$65	€50
AP	£30	$55	€39

WOPAT, TOM

SP	£45	$85	€60
DS	£40	$75	€55
AP	£30	$55	€39

WRAY, FAY

SP	£275	$490	€360
DS	£150	$270	€195
AP	£75	$135	€98

WRIGHT, TERESA

SP	£50	$90	€65
DS	£40	$75	€55
AP	£30	$55	€39

WUHRER, KARI

SP	£50	$90	€65
DS	£40	$75	€55
AP	£30	$55	€39

WYNYARD, DIANA

SP	£50	$90	€65
DS	£40	$75	€55
AP	£30	$55	€39

YEOH, MICHELLE

SP	£50	$90	€65
DS	£40	$75	€55
AP	£30	$55	€39

YORK, SUSANNA

SP	£125	$225	€165
DS	£110	$200	€145
AP	£60	$110	€78

YOUNG, ALAN

SP	£50	$90	€65
DS	£40	$75	€55
AP	£30	$55	€39

YOUNG, BURT

SP	£50	$90	€65
DS	£40	$75	€55
AP	£30	$55	€39

YOUNG, ROBERT

SP	£50	$90	€65
DS	£40	$75	€55
AP	£30	$55	€39

ZELLWEGER, RENEE

SP	£75	$135	€100
DS	£60	$110	€80
AP	£40	$75	€52

ZIMBALIST, STEPHANIE

SP	£50	$90	€65
DS	£40	$75	€55
AP	£30	$55	€39

ZADORA, PIA

SP	£50	$90	€65
DS	£40	$75	€55
AP	£30	$55	€39

ZETA JONES, CATHERINE

SP	£75	$135	€100
DS	£60	$110	€80
AP	£40	$75	€52

ZINNEMANN, FRED

SP	£50	$90	€65
DS	£40	$75	€55
AP	£25	$45	€33

ZETTERLING, MAI

SP	£50	$90	€65
DS	£40	$75	€55
AP	£30	$55	€39

ZANE, BILLY

SP	£45	$85	€60
DS	£40	$75	€55
AP	£30	$55	€39

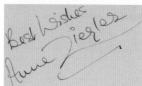

ZIEGLER, ANNE

SP	£50	$90	€65
DS	£40	$75	€55
AP	£30	$55	€39

Film, TV and Theatre

Literature

Collecting literary autographs can be a fascinating hobby. As this particular occupation lends itself towards the written form of communication, most authors are quite prolific during their lifetime, therefore it is not unusual to find a lot of very personal letters available for sale. These letters, as well as manuscripts or typescripts of works have extraordinary research value and very often go from private hands to libraries and archives. For a true literature and book lover there is nothing more intriguing than finding a personal letter or acquiring a typescript Nobel Prize speech written by a favourite author.

As always in autograph collecting, the value of the item will depend on the medium used. In this case signed books, particularly limited or first editions, bear a particularly high value. In very high demand also are handwritten poems bearing hand corrections. Items relating to a body of work or comments on/ about it are in high demand, as well as letters including comments on a particular book, poem or play. Autographed material which refers to personal matters or events which influenced the work of the author or refer to a particular era in their professional lives will bear higher value than payment receipts, Christmas card, etc. Signed photographs of authors are always very popular for their display possibilities.

It is good for the collector to learn about the most important works of the author and to know his first, last and most widely published texts. A lot of those with interest in literature start their collection with material written by Charles Dickens or Mark Twain. Other popular names include Oscar Wilde, Ernest Hemingway and Rudyard Kipling.

This area of collecting can be seen as a good field for investors as some unique items can generate very high prices. The best example is very popular J.K. Rowling, whose handwritten and hand drawn *The Tales of Beedle the Bard* realised £2,000,000 in a 2007 Sotheby's sale.

AMIS, KINGSLEY

SP	£90	$160	€115
DS	£70	$125	€90
AP	£50	$90	€65

ANDERSEN, HANS CHRISTIAN

SP	£5,950	$10,545	€7,315
DS	£4,500	$7,975	€5,530
AP	£3,500	$6,205	€4,305

ARMSTRONG, ANTHONY

SP	£75	$135	€95
DS	£60	$110	€75
AP	£30	$55	€40

AUDEN, W.H

SP	£250	$445	€310
DS	£195	$350	€240
AP	£165	$295	€205

AWDREY, REVD. W

SP	*		
DS	£225	$400	€280
AP	£175	$315	€220

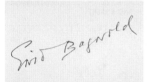

BAGNOLD, ENID

SP	£75	$135	€95
DS	£50	$90	€65
AP	£30	$55	€40

BAINBRIDGE, BERYL

SP	£100	$180	€125
DS	£75	$135	€95
AP	£50	$90	€65

BALDWIN, JAMES

SP	£75	$135	€95
DS	£50	$90	€65
AP	£30	$55	€40

BALZAC, HONORE DE

SP	*		
DS	£2,500	$4,430	€3,075
AP	£1,750	$3,105	€2,155

BARRIE, J M

SP	£850	$1,510	€1,045
DS	£750	$1,330	€925
AP	£400	$710	€495

BECKETT, SAMUEL

SP	£995	$1,765	€1,225
DS	£550	$975	€680
AP	*		

BENCHLEY, PETER

SP	£100	$180	€125
DS	£75	$135	€95
AP	£50	$90	€65

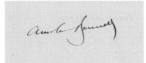

BENNETT, ARNOLD

SP	£75	$135	€95
DS	£60	$110	€75
AP	£45	$80	€60

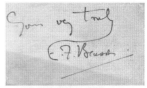

BENSON, EDWARD FREDRICK

SP	£75	$135	€95
DS	£65	$120	€80
AP	£50	$90	€65

BESANT, WALTER

SP	£75	$135	€95
DS	£65	$120	€80
AP	£50	$90	€65

BETJEMAN, JOHN

SP	£450	$800	€555
DS	£395	$700	€490
AP	£295	$525	€365

BLACKMORE, RICHARD D

SP	£125	$225	€155
DS	£95	$170	€120
AP	£75	$135	€95

BLEASDALE, ALAN

SP	£75	$135	€95
DS	£45	$80	€60
AP	£30	$55	€40

BLYTON, ENID

SP	£750	$1,330	€925
DS	£475	$845	€585
AP	£325	$580	€400

BOND, MICHAEL

SP	£50	$90	€65
DS	£40	$75	€50
AP	£30	$55	€40

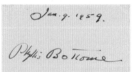

BOTTOME, PHYLLIS

SP	£75	$135	€95
DS	£50	$90	€65
AP	£30	$55	€40

BOWEN, ELIZABETH

SP	£75	$135	€95
DS	£50	$90	€65
AP	£30	$55	€40

BRETT HARTE, FRANCIS

SP	£90	$160	€115
DS	£75	$135	€95
AP	£50	$90	€65

BRONTE, CHARLOTTE

SP	£7,500	$13,290	€9,215
DS	£5,500	$9,745	€6,760
AP	£4,250	$7,530	€5,225

BROWN, DAN

SP	£550	$975	€680
DS	£450	$800	€555
AP	£300	$535	€370

BROWNING, ROBERT

SP	£2,950	$5,230	€3,625
DS	£1,250	$2,215	€1,540
AP	£650	$1,155	€800

BRUNA, DICK

SP	£50	$90	€65
DS	£45	$80	€60
AP	£30	$55	€40

BUCHAN, JOHN

SP	£90	$160	€115
DS	£75	$135	€95
AP	£50	$90	€65

BULWER, HENRY LYTTON

SP	£95	$170	€120
DS	£75	$135	€95
AP	£50	$90	€65

BURNAND, FRANCIS

SP	£75	$135	€95
DS	£50	$90	€65
AP	£30	$55	€40

BURNS, ROBERT

SP	*		
DS	£1,500	$2,660	€1,845
AP	£1,250	$2,215	€1,540

BURROUGHS, WILLIAM

SP	£300	$535	€370
DS	£225	$400	€280
AP	£150	$270	€185

BYRON, LORD

SP	*		
DS	£3,500	$6,205	€4,305
AP	£1,950	$3,455	€2,400

CAMERON, JAMES

SP	£100	$180	€125
DS	£75	$135	€95
AP	£50	$90	€65

CAPOTE, TRUMAN

SP	£1,250	$2,215	€1,540
DS	£875	$1,555	€1,080
AP	£550	$975	€680

CARTER, ANGELA

SP	£75	$135	€95
DS	£60	$110	€75
AP	£40	$75	€50

CHRISTIE, AGATHA

SP	£650	$1,155	€800
DS	£500	$890	€615
AP	£395	$700	€490

CLARKE, ARTHUR C

SP	£300	$535	€370
DS	£225	$400	€280
AP	£150	$270	€185

COCTEAU, JEAN

SP	£750	$1,330	€925
DS	£650	$1,155	€800
AP	£500	$890	€615

COLLINS, WILKIE

SP	£495	$880	€610
DS	£395	$700	€490
AP	£195	$350	€240

CONAN DOYLE, ARTHUR

SP	£2,500	$4,430	€3,075
DS	£1,500	$2,660	€1,845
AP	£1,200	$2,130	€1,475

CONRAD, JOSEPH

SP	£1,250	$2,215	€1,540
DS	£950	$1,685	€1,170
AP	£775	$1,375	€955

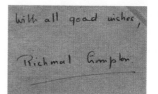

CRISP, QUENTIN

SP	£95	$170	€120
DS	£75	$135	€95
AP	£30	$55	€40

CROMPTON, RICHMAL

SP	*		
DS	£150	$270	€185
AP	£100	$180	€125

DAHL, ROALD

SP	£350	$625	€435
DS	£275	$490	€340
AP	£200	$355	€250

DE LA MARE, WALTER

SP	*		
DS	£125	$225	€155
AP	£75	$135	€95

DE LA ROCHE, MAZO

SP	£75	$135	€95
DS	£50	$90	€65
AP	£30	$55	€40

DE SADE, MARQUIS

SP	*		
DS	£1,750	$3,105	€2,155
AP	£1,250	$2,215	€1,540

DICKENS, CHARLES

SP	£12,500	$22,145	€15,360
DS	£3,500	$6,205	€4,305
AP	£2,250	$3,990	€2,765

DR SEUSS

SP	£350	$625	€435
DS	£495	$880	€610
AP	£175	$315	€220

DUMAS, ALEXANDRE (Father)

SP	*		
DS	£850	$1,510	€1,045
AP	£350	$625	€435

Ian Fleming

Ian Fleming will forever be remembered as the man who introduced the world to James Bond, but it wasn't until Fleming was 44 that the first Bond novel hit the bookshelves. What came before this in Fleming's life, however, was pivotal to the creation of the man who would become known simply as 007.

Following an education at Eton and in Austria, Fleming joined Reuters as a journalist, during which time he excelled in covering a Russian spy trial. Despite this, he left journalism behind to pursue the riches of the banking world soon after. Fleming eventually tired of banking and in 1939 joined British Naval Intelligence. This role not only greatly furthered his understanding of the risk and complexity of espionage but also his flair for well-structured and creative writing.

Despite his late introduction to being a published author, Fleming was relatively prolific – managing to write 15 Bond stories before his death in 1964. In this time he also penned *Chitty Chitty Bang Bang* for his son Caspar. The Bond legacy continues after Fleming's death – both in film adaptations and in print with several authors commissioned to write continuation of the Bond story.

DUMAS, ALEXANDRE (Son)

SP	*		
DS	£350	$625	€435
AP	£225	$400	€280

ELIOT, GEORGE

SP	*		
DS	£950	$1,685	€1,170
AP	£650	$1,155	€800

ELIOT, T.S.

SP	*		
DS	£695	$1,235	€855
AP	£350	$625	€435

FARJEON, ELEANOR

SP	£75	$135	€95
DS	£50	$90	€65
AP	£30	$55	€40

FAULKNER, WILLIAM

SP	*		
DS	£995	$1,765	€1,225
AP	£695	$1,235	€855

FERBER, EDNA

SP	£75	$135	€95
DS	£50	$90	€65
AP	£30	$55	€40

FITZGERALD, F. SCOTT

SP	*		
DS	£3,500	$6,205	€4,305
AP	£1,750	$3,105	€2,155

FLEMING, IAN

SP	£4,950	$8,770	€6,085
DS	£2,500	$4,430	€3,075
AP	£1,250	$2,215	€1,540

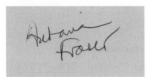

FRASER, ANTONIA

SP	£75	$135	€95
DS	£50	$90	€65
AP	£30	$55	€40

GILBERT, W.S.

SP	£450	$800	€555
DS	£395	$700	€490
AP	£295	$525	€365

GINSBERG, ALLEN

SP	£350	$625	€435
DS	£795	$1,410	€980
AP	£200	$355	€250

GOLDING, WILLIAM

SP	£180	$320	€225
DS	£120	$215	€150
AP	£80	$145	€100

GREENE, GRAHAM

SP	£550	$975	€680
DS	£450	$800	€555
AP	£375	$665	€465

HALEY, ALEX

SP	£350	$625	€435
DS	£295	$525	€365
AP	£175	$315	€220

HARDY, THOMAS

SP	£1,250	$2,215	€1,540
DS	£795	$1,410	€980
AP	£450	$800	€555

HALLAM, HENRY

SP	£95	$170	€120
DS	£75	$135	€95
AP	£50	$90	€65

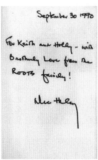

HEMINGWAY, ERNEST

SP	£4,950	$8,770	€6,085
DS	£3,500	$6,205	€4,305
AP	£1,950	$3,455	€2,400

HERGE

SP	*		
DS	£1,500	$2,660	€1,845
AP	£995	$1,765	€1,225

HESSE, HERMANN

SP	£995	$1,765	€1,225
DS	£695	$1,235	€855
AP	£450	$800	€555

HOLMES, OLIVER WENDELL

SP	£400	$710	€495
DS	£300	$535	€370
AP	£200	$355	€250

HUGO, VICTOR

SP	*		
DS	£795	$1,410	€980
AP	£425	$755	€525

HUNTER, WILLIAM WILSON

SP	£75	$135	€95
DS	£45	$80	€60
AP	£30	$55	€40

Literature

HUXLEY, ALDOUS
SP	£550	$975	€680
DS	£495	$880	€610
AP	£350	$625	€435

JAMES, HENRY
SP	*		
DS	£1,250	$2,215	€1,540
AP	£950	$1,685	€1,170

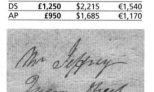

JEFFREY, FRANCIS
SP	£125	$225	€155
DS	£95	$170	€120
AP	£75	$135	€95

JENKINS, ELIZABETH
SP	£75	$135	€95
DS	£45	$80	€60
AP	£30	$55	€40

JOHNS, W.E
SP	£225	$400	€280
DS	£150	$270	€185
AP	£100	$180	€125

KELLER, HELEN
SP	£450	$800	€555
DS	£295	$525	€365
AP	£195	$350	€240

KESEY, KEN
SP	£275	$490	€340
DS	£225	$400	€280
AP	£195	$350	€240

KING, STEPHEN
SP	*		
DS	£775	$1,375	€955
AP	£350	$625	€435

LAWRENCE, D.H
SP	*		
DS	£1,500	$2,660	€1,845
AP	£950	$1,685	€1,170

LEAR, EDWARD
SP	*		
DS	*		
AP	£325	$580	€400

LEE, HARPER
SP	£650	$1,155	€800
DS	£500	$890	€615
AP	£350	$625	€435

KIPLING, RUDYARD
SP	£2,500	$4,430	€3,075
DS	£1,500	$2,660	€1,845
AP	£450	$800	€555

LEWIS, C.S
SP	*		
DS	£2,950	$5,230	€3,625
AP	£2,250	$3,990	€2,765

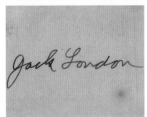

LONDON, JACK

SP	**£1,750**	$3,105	€2,155
DS	**£1,200**	$2,130	€1,475
AP	**£850**	$1,510	€1,045

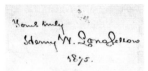

LONGFELLOW, HENRY W

SP	**£1,500**	$2,660	€1,845
DS	**£895**	$1,590	€1,100
AP	**£650**	$1,155	€800

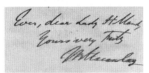

LOOS, ANITA

SP	**£125**	$225	€155
DS	**£90**	$160	€115
AP	**£50**	$90	€65

MACAULAY, THOMAS BABINGTON

SP		*	
DS	**£100**	$180	€125
AP	**£50**	$90	€65

MANN, THOMAS

SP	**£850**	$1,510	€1,045
DS	**£795**	$1,410	€980
AP	**£500**	$890	€615

MARQUEZ, GABRIEL GARCIA

SP	**£295**	$525	€365
DS	**£350**	$625	€435
AP	**£175**	$315	€220

MARSH, NGAIO

SP	**£100**	$180	€125
DS	**£80**	$145	€100
AP	**£50**	$90	€65

MAUGHAM, W. SOMERSET

SP	**£395**	$700	€490
DS	**£350**	$625	€435
AP	**£275**	$490	€340

MILLER, ARTHUR

SP	**£295**	$525	€365
DS	**£250**	$445	€310
AP	**£100**	$180	€125

MILLER, HENRY

SP	**£650**	$1,155	€800
DS	**£595**	$1,055	€735
AP	**£450**	$800	€555

MITCHELL, MARGARET

SP		*	
DS	**£1,500**	$2,660	€1,845
AP	**£650**	$1,155	€800

MITFORD, JESSICA

SP	**£175**	$315	€220
DS	**£150**	$270	€185
AP	**£100**	$180	€125

MITFORD, NANCY

SP	**£250**	$445	€310
DS	**£250**	$445	€310
AP	**£150**	$270	€185

MURDOCH, IRIS

SP	**£100**	$180	€125
DS	**£200**	$355	€250
AP	**£80**	$145	€100

NIN, ANAIS

SP	£450	$800	€555
DS	£525	$935	€650
AP	£200	$355	€250

ORWELL, GEORGE

SP	*		
DS	£1,725	$3,060	€2,120
AP	*		

POSTGATE, OLIVER

SP	£85	$155	€105
DS	£65	$120	€80
AP	£50	$90	€65

POTTER, BEATRIX (HELEN)

SP	*		
DS	£4,500	$7,975	€5,530
AP	£3,000	$5,315	€3,690

PRAED, WINTHROP

SP	*		
DS	£75	$135	€95
AP	£45	$80	€60

PRIESTLEY, J.B

SP	£100	$180	€125
DS	£100	$180	€125
AP	£80	$145	€100

PRITCHETT, SIR VICTOR SAWDEN

SP	£75	$135	€95
DS	£50	$90	€65
AP	£30	$55	€40

RAND, AYN

SP	*		
DS	£3,250	$5,760	€3,995
AP	£1,750	$3,105	€2,155

RATTIGAN, TERENCE

SP	£75	$135	€95
DS	£100	$180	€125
AP	£30	$55	€40

ROGERS, SAMUEL

SP	*		
DS	£75	$135	€95
AP	£30	$55	€40

ROSE, REGINALD

SP	£75	$135	€95
DS	£50	$90	€65
AP	£30	$55	€40

ROWLING, J K

SP	£1,950	$3,455	€2,400
DS	£1,750	$3,105	€2,155
AP	£750	$1,330	€925

RUSHDIE, SALMAN

SP	£125	$225	€155
DS	£175	$315	€220
AP	£100	$180	€125

SAYERS, DOROTHY L.

SP	£225	$400	€280
DS	£275	$490	€340
AP	£75	$135	€95

SCOTT, WALTER

SP	*		
DS	£695	$1,235	€855
AP	£375	$665	€465

SHAW, GEORGE BERNARD

SP	£1,250	$2,215	€1,540
DS	£995	$1,765	€1,225
AP	£500	$890	€615

SHELLEY, PERCY BYSSHE

SP	*		
DS	£2,950	$5,230	€3,625
AP	£1,250	$2,215	€1,540

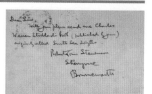

SHEPARD, ERNEST.H

SP	£1,500	$2,660	€1,845
DS	£2,950	$5,230	€3,625
AP	£575	$1,020	€710

SOLZHENITSYN, ALEXANDER

SP	£995	$1,765	€1,225
DS	£1,250	$2,215	€1,540
AP	£550	$975	€680

SPAIN, NANCY

SP	£75	$135	€95
DS	£50	$90	€65
AP	£30	$55	€40

STEVENSON, ROBERT LOUIS

SP	*		
DS	£2,500	$4,430	€3,075
AP	£1,250	$2,215	€1,540

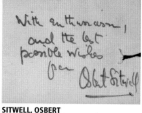

SITWELL, OSBERT

SP	*		
DS	£75	$135	€95
AP	£45	$80	€60

SPENDER, STEPHEN

SP	£90	$160	€115
DS	£75	$135	€95
AP	£50	$90	€65

STREATFIELD, MARY NOEL

SP	£75	$135	€95
DS	£45	$80	€60
AP	£35	$65	€45

SITWELL, SACHEVERELL

SP	£60	$110	€75
DS	£45	$80	€60
AP	£30	$55	€40

SPILLANE, MICKEY

SP	£80	$145	€100
DS	£70	$125	€90
AP	£50	$90	€65

STRINDBERG, AUGUST

SP	£3,950	$7,000	€4,855
DS	£3,500	$6,205	€4,305
AP	£2,500	$4,430	€3,075

SMITH, SAMUEL FRANCIS

SP	£3,500	$6,205	€4,305
DS	£2,950	$5,230	€3,625
AP	£2,250	$3,990	€2,765

Shadowmancer

SMITH, SYDNEY

SP	£150	$270	€185
DS	£100	$180	€125
AP	£80	$145	€100

STEINBECK, JOHN

SP	£1,950	$3,455	€2,400
DS	£1,750	$3,105	€2,155
AP	£895	$1,590	€1,100

TAYLOR, G.P.

SP	*		
DS	£750	$1,330	€925
AP	£350	$625	€435

Literature

BARON TENNYSON

TENNYSON, ALFRED LORD

SP	£1,250	$2,215	€1,540
DS	£595	$1,055	€735
AP	£350	$625	€435

THACKERAY, WILLIAM

SP	*		
DS	£850	$1,510	€1,045
AP	£500	$890	€615

THOMAS, DYLAN

SP	*		
DS	£3,500	$6,205	€4,305
AP	£1,750	$3,105	€2,155

TOLKIEN, J. R. R.

SP	*		
DS	£3,750	$6,645	€4,610
AP	£2,250	$3,990	€2,765

TOLSTOY, LEO

SP	£7,950	$14,085	€9,770
DS	£3,500	$6,205	€4,305
AP	£2,500	$4,430	€3,075

TRAVERS, P.L

SP	£100	$180	€125
DS	£120	$215	€150
AP	£60	$110	€75

TWAIN, MARK

SP	£4,500	$7,975	€5,530
DS	£3,950	$7,000	€4,855
AP	£1,950	$3,455	€2,400

VERNE, JULES

SP	£2,500	$4,430	€3,075
DS	£1,250	$2,215	€1,540
AP	£900	$1,595	€1,110

Leo Tolstoy

Widely regarded as one of the greatest authors of all time, Leo Tolstoy was born into an aristocratic Russian family in 1828. Tolstoy enjoyed a fruitful career as a novelist, playwright and philosophical essayist but he will be most fondly remembered for his two grandest and most extensive works, War and Peace and Anna Karenina. Critical acclaim of Tolstoy remains strong almost a century after his death, with the aforementioned texts named first and third respectively in Time Magazine's *Greatest Novels of All Time* in 2007.

His works were renowned for their realistic depiction of 19th Century Russian life and also for their vastness, both in terms of the scale and content. For example, War and Peace includes a staggering 580 characters and includes settings as diverse as Napoleon's headquarters and the Russian battlefields. The complexity of Tolstoy's writing seems only to echo the nature of his own mind, in which he battled inner conflict on the subjects of religion, morality and wealth despite an open appreciation of the wholeness of life.

Tolstoy's writing inspired not only his literary peers but also Gandhi, with whom he had long-running correspondence. His legacy in the literary world is unquestionable, and as the writer of *the greatest novel of all time*, his stature remains huge in the 21st Century.

"If the world could write by itself, it would write like Tolstoy." – Isaak Babel

Literature

Oscar Wilde

Born in Dublin in 1854, Oscar Wilde is regarded as one of the greatest playwrights and wits of the Victorian era. Prior to his fame Wilde was an excellent student, being awarded a double first from Magdalen College, Oxford where he became a part of the Aesthetic movement. The movement's principle of *art for art's sake* would later form a fitting summary of Wilde's life.

In his only novel, The Picture of Dorian Gray, Wilde focuses on the alluring nature of male physical beauty, a subject whose decadence seemed to befit his own lifestyle. Ultimately it was this lifestyle, noted for Wilde's flamboyant dress, wit and dandyish behaviour that elevated him to the status of celebrity just as much as his writing ability.

Between 1892 and 1895 Wilde enthralled the theatrical world with three of his most popular works – Lady Windermere's Fan, An *Ideal Husband* and *The Importance of Being Earnest* – each a comedic satire on Victorian society.

Wilde's later life was marred with controversy, ultimately resulting in his imprisonment in 1895 for *gross indecency*, a punishment he served for almost two years. Three years later, following a life of opulence, Wilde tragically died penniless in a Paris hotel, aged just 46. Fortunately we are still able to revel in the luxury of his poetry and prose.

VON TRAPP, MARIA

SP	£350	$625	€435
DS	£295	$525	€365
AP	£150	$270	€185

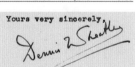

WAUGH, EVELYN

SP	£150	$270	€185
DS	*		
AP	£100		$180	€125

WELLS, H. G.

SP	£1,250	$2,215	€1,540
DS	£750	$1,330	€925
AP	£450	$800	€555

WEST, REBECCA

SP	£350	$625	€435
DS	£275	$490	€340
AP	£150	$270	€185

WHEATLEY, DENNIS

SP	£150	$270	€185
DS	£100	$180	€125
AP	£50	$90	€65

WILDE, OSCAR

SP	£3,500	$6,205	€4,305
DS	£3,000	$5,315	€3,690
AP	£1,750	$3,105	€2,155

WILLIAMS, TENNESSEE

SP	£495	$880	€610
DS	£450	$800	€555
AP	£350	$625	€435

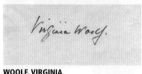

WOOLF, VIRGINIA

SP	*		
DS	£4,950	$8,770	€6,085
AP	£1,750	$3,105	€2,155

WORDSWORTH, WILLIAM

SP	*		
DS	£2,950	$5,230	€3,625
AP	£3,950	$7,000	€4,855

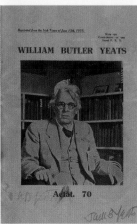

YEATS, WILLIAM BUTLER

SP	£4,000	$7,090	€4,915
DS	£3,000	$5,315	€3,690
AP	£1,200	$2,130	€1,475

YOUNG, C.M

SP	£80	$145	€100
DS	£60	$110	€75
AP	£40	$75	€50

ZOLA, EMILE

SP	£950	$1,685	€1,170
DS	£450	$800	€555
AP	£395	$700	€490

Military

Napoleon once said "Soldiers usually win the battles and generals get the credit for them." This, of course, is very true; after all it is not called the 7th Cavalry's last stand, the battle instead, bears the name of a certain George A Custer. As a result of this it is the general's signatures which often attract the highest prices, particularly if they achieved fame through great victory or, even better, great notoriety.

However, interest in military philography extends beyond simply those in charge. Military men and women who fought with distinction provide an amazing wealth of material, and their stories often far outweigh the general's in terms of courage and valour. Signatures from the likes of the Dambuster bomber crews, those who fought in the trenches of the Somme or even gulf war veterans, are all hugely popular and offer an affordable way of entering this field.

Ever popular are the great leaders from Napoleonic times, the American civil war and the two world wars. It is possible to build a themed collection around events in history, featuring leaders and soldiers from both sides of the divide. In this way one can document the conflict in the vivid personal way that only autographs can.

ATOMIC BOMB: ENOLA GAY & BOCK'S CAR

SP	*		
DS	£2,950	$5,195	€3,675
AP	£1,950	$3,435	€2,430

MOSQUITO AIRCRAFT MUSEUM
Salisbury Hall,
St. Albans Hertfordshire

BADER, DOUGLAS

SP	£250	$445	€315
DS	£225	$400	€285
AP	£150	$265	€190

BATTENBERG, PRINCE LOUIS

SP	£175	$310	€220
DS	£125	$225	€160
AP	£90	$160	€115

BONAPARTE, NAPOLEON

SP	*		
DS	£3,250	$5,725	€4,050
AP	£2,000	$3,525	€2,495

CAMBRIDGE, GEORGE - DUKE OF

SP	*		
DS	£100	$180	€125
AP	£80	$145	€100

CARDIGAN, JAMES THOMAS BRUDENELL

SP	*		
DS	£795	$1,400	€995
AP	£450	$795	€565

Yours sincerely,

Odette Hallowes.

CHURCHILL, ODETTE

SP	£250	$445	€315
DS	£195	$345	€245
AP	£100	$180	€125

A. Cleaver
607 SQDN.

CLEAVER, SID

SP	£125	$225	€160
DS	£90	$160	€115
AP	£60	$110	€75

CODRINGTON, EDWARD

SP	*		
DS	£95	$170	€120
AP	£75	$135	€95

CROMWELL, OLIVER

SP	*		
DS	£7,500	$13,205	€9,340
AP	£4,950	$8,715	€6,165

CUSTER, GEORGE A.

SP	*		
DS	£5,000	$8,805	€6,230
AP	£3,250	$5,725	€4,050

DAMBUSTERS

SP	*		
DS	*		
AP	£3,950	$6,955	€4,920

DE GAULLE, CHARLES

SP	£750	$1,325	€935
DS	£950	$1,675	€1,185
AP	£450	$795	€565

EARL ROBERTS

SP	£395	$700	€495
DS	£295	$520	€370
AP	£225	$400	€285

GAMBIER, JAMES

SP	£100	$180	€125
DS	£80	$145	€100
AP	£60	$110	€75

HADDOCK, SIR RICHARD

SP	*		
DS	£175	$310	€220
AP	£150	$265	€190

HESS, RUDOLPH

SP	£1,750	$3,085	€2,180
DS	£1,450	$2,555	€1,810
AP	£995	$1,755	€1,240

Jhr sehr ergebener

HIMMLER, HEINRICH

SP	£3,750	$6,605	€4,670
DS	£2,950	$5,195	€3,675
AP	£1,950	$3,435	€2,430

KITCHENER, LORD HORATIO HUBERT

SP	£650	$1,145	€810
DS	£395	$700	€495
AP	£195	$345	€245

Montgomery of El Alamein

Field Marshal Bernard Law Montgomery, is the most famous of Britain's WW2 generals. He was affectionately known as Monty by his men and was the instigator to one of Britain's most important victories in the fight against Hitler.

Born 17th November 1887, Montgomery was injured early in the First World War when a bullet passed through his left lung. The injury was so bad that the medics ordered his grave to be dug before Monty showed some of his famous tenacity and pulled through. He served the rest of WWI as a staff officer before embarking on various postings between the wars.

In 1942 Monty had his finest moment. The beleaguered British Eighth army in Egypt was all that stood between Rommel and the Suez Canal; the main gateway to the oil rich Middle East.

Monty revitalized the troops and on the 23rd October 1942 launched a huge offensive against the Axis lines at El Alamein. A dawn bombardment by 9 miles of British artillery and operation *"Light foot"*, the slowly but surely advance by sappers across the extensive mine fields, saw Axis troops retreat after only a matter of days. This was the first big victory on land made by Britain and marked a turning point in the war as a whole.

LAWRENCE, T.E

SP	£3,950	$6,955	€4,920
DS	£3,500	$6,165	€4,360
AP	£2,750	$4,845	€3,425

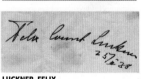

LUCKNER, FELIX

SP	£95	$170	€120
DS	£75	$135	€95
AP	£50	$90	€65

MACARTHUR, DOUGLAS

SP	£395	$700	€495
DS	£325	$575	€405
AP	£225	$400	€285

MESSERSCHMITT, WILLY

SP	£250	$445	€315
DS	£150	$265	€190
AP	£100	$180	€125

MONTGOMERY OF ALAMEIN

SP	£995	$1,755	€1,240
DS	£395	$700	€495
AP	£225	$400	€285

MUSSOLINI, BENITO

SP	£2,750	$4,845	€3,425
DS	£975	$1,720	€1,215
AP	£650	$1,145	€810

NELSON, VISCOUNT ADMIRAL HORATIO

SP		*	
DS	£9,500	$16,725	€11,835
AP	£4,500	$7,925	€5,605

MOUNTBATTEN, LORD LOUIS

SP	£475	$840	€595
DS	£275	$485	€345
AP	£200	$355	€250

PATTON, GEORGE S.

SP	£4,950	$8,715	€6,165
DS	£2,950	$5,195	€3,675
AP	£1,950	$3,435	€2,430

ROMMEL, ERWIN

SP	£2,750	$4,845	€3,425
DS	£1,750	$3,085	€2,180
AP	£1,500	$2,645	€1,870

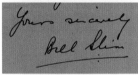

SLIM, WILLIAM JOSEPH

SP	£150	$265	€190
DS	£100	$180	€125
AP	£75	$135	€95

Horatio Nelson

Born on the 29th September 1758, Horatio was the sixth of eleven children. He joined the navy at only twelve but quickly rose through the ranks and at only 20 became a Captain. He married Frances Nisbet (Fanny) in 1787, whilst on service in the West Indies but returned soon after to England, only to be quickly frustrated he was not at sea.

Having lost both his right eye and his right hand in combat against the French and Spanish Navy, Nelson went on to command during the Napoleonic wars where he gained his real legacy. The battle of the Nile saw Nelson destroy the French fleet and establish an overland route to India. It was a famous victory and one which propelled him into the public imagination.

Soon after this, whilst in Naples, Nelson met the second woman in his life, Emma, Lady Hamilton. They fell in love and openly had a son together outside of wedlock.

In 1805 he commanded the British fleet at the battle of Trafalgar. During the first few hours of engagement Nelson was hit in the spine by a French sniper. He continued to command the British fleet for the next three hours until he died in the arms of his adjutant.

SMUTS, JAN CHRISTIAAN

SP	£150	$265	€190
DS	£120	$215	€150
AP	£80	$145	€100

VON HINDENBURG, PAUL

SP	£2,950	$5,195	€3,675
DS	£1,500	$2,645	€1,870
AP	£750	$1,325	€935

WELLINGTON, DUKE OF

SP	£750	$1,325	€935
DS	£575	$1,015	€720
AP	£375	$665	€470

Music

The great singers, composers and musicians will never be forgotten. Collecting signatures and manuscripts of the world's premier composers has always been popular, even though the material is scarce and the prices high. However, collecting music autographs and memorabilia is not restricted to handwritten material alone. Performances have been recorded for the enjoyment of future generations and signed media such as records, CDs, videos and tapes are in very high demand.

The interest in this area of collecting can be attributed to the music's universal appeal. You need not speak the language to understand and appreciate a country's musical heritage. This applies to classical as well as contemporary and pop music. Interestingly, many musicians themselves are collectors of music memorabilia!

As mentioned earlier, music manuscripts and autographs can generate very high prices. Most collectors remember the 1977 Christie's sale of an autographed letter from Mozart to his wife Constanze for at the time an astounding $25,500. Today this letter would probably fetch 15 times as much.

So what does a collector need to know and watch out for?

Firstly, the most collectable items in the area of classical music are manuscripts, original musical compositions in all forms (from sketch to the final version) and musical quotations commonly given out by composers. Such material is usually very scarce as institutional libraries and museums continue to dominate this area of collecting for research reasons. The content is usually paramount, followed by scarcity, condition and length. Everyone who has interest in this field dreams about acquiring manuscripts at Mozart, Bach or Beethoven level, but as the prices are usually unachievable for an average collector, they can still enjoy autographed material from other composers at more affordable prices.

Very popular are photographs signed by performers (whether opera or jazz). Unforgettable Louis Armstrong, Duke Ellington, Nellie Melba, Enrico Caruso, and Maria Callas are always in high demand and attract a lot of interest.

Autographs of more contemporary figures command much more affordable prices. When possible, collectors prefer to acquire signatures in person to guarantee their authenticity, however an artist's limited availability reduces the chances of obtaining it. Illegible, 'rushed' signatures as well as unusual variations of autographs are common in this field which makes the authentication process even more difficult. The market is also flooded with forgeries and it is essential that the autographs are obtained via a recognised dealer.

Although so much more recent, this market is driven by the

most popular entertainers, which can command very high prices. The Beatles, Elvis Presley, the Rolling Stones and Madonna have proven to be a great investment asset and their values constantly increase. Forgeries are commonly encountered as those signatures command the highest values in this area of collecting and can generate a good profit.

Other than legends, the most popular entertainers of the day seem to be in high demand. Popular forms include CDs, guitars, handwritten lyrics, concert programmes, etc. Signatures of the first line-up of a group seem to be preferred by collectors.

Collecting music autographs and memorabilia is usually driven by passion, sentiment and personal interest, and it can give a collector great pleasure. This area of collecting is filled with treasures!

MUSICAL ARTISTS

ABDUL, PAULA

SP	£50	$90	€65
DS	£40	$75	€50
AP	£30	$55	€40

AGUILERA, CHRISTINA

SP	£75	$135	€95
DS	£60	$110	€75
AP	£45	$80	€55

AMOS, TORI

SP	£50	$90	€65
DS	£40	$75	€50
AP	£30	$55	€40

ADAMS, BRYAN

SP	£50	$90	€65
DS	£40	$75	€50
AP	£30	$55	€40

ADLER, RICHARD

SP	£50	$90	€65
DS	£40	$75	€50
AP	£30	$55	€40

ALLEN, LILY

SP	£75	$135	€95
DS	£50	$90	€65
AP	£35	$65	€45

ANDERSSON, BENNY

SP	£175	$310	€215
DS	£125	$225	€155
AP	£100	$180	€125

PETER ANDRE

ANDRE, PETER

SP	£40	$75	€50
DS	£25	$45	€35
AP	£15	$30	€20

APPLEBY, KIM

SP	£30	$55	€40
DS	£20	$35	€25
AP	£15	$30	€20

BAKER, JOSEPHINE

SP	£1,000	$1,775	€1,230
DS	£500	$890	€615
AP	£375	$665	€465

ANT, ADAM

SP	£50	$90	€65
DS	£40	$75	€50
AP	£30	$55	€40

ARMSTRONG, BILLIE JOE

SP	£75	$135	€95
DS	£50	$90	€65
AP	£35	$65	€45

BALL, MICHAEL

SP	£50	$90	€65
DS	£30	$55	€40
AP	£20	$35	€25

ANTHONY, MARC

SP	£75	$135	€95
DS	£50	$90	€65
AP	£35	$65	€45

ARMSTRONG, LOUIS

SP	£650	$1,155	€800
DS	£550	$975	€680
AP	£375	$665	€465

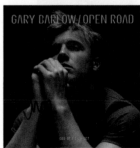

GARY BARLOW/OPEN ROAD

BARLOW, GARY

SP	£30	$55	€40
DS	£20	$35	€25
AP	£15	$30	€20

APPLE, FIONA

SP	£50	$90	€65
DS	£40	$75	€50
AP	£30	$55	€40

BAILEY RAE, CORINNE

SP	£75	$135	€95
DS	£50	$90	€65
AP	£35	$65	€45

BART, LIONEL

SP	£70	$125	€90
DS	£60	$110	€75
AP	£50	$90	€65

BASSEY, SHIRLEY

SP	£100	$180	€125
DS	£75	$135	€95
AP	£50	$90	€65

BEGA, LOU

SP	£60	$110	€75
DS	£40	$75	€50
AP	£30	$55	€40

BETMEAD, JON

SP	£60	$110	€75
DS	£40	$75	€50
AP	£25	$45	€35

BEYONCE

SP	£75	$135	€95
DS	£50	$90	€65
AP	£30	$55	€40

BECK

SP	£50	$90	€65
DS	£40	$75	€50
AP	£30	$55	€40

BENATAR, PAT

SP	£50	$90	€65
DS	£40	$75	€50
AP	£30	$55	€40

BJORK

SP	£50	$90	€65
DS	£40	$75	€50
AP	£40	$75	€50

BECKHAM, VICTORIA

SP	£75	$135	€95
DS	£60	$110	€75
AP	£50	$90	€65

BERRY, CHUCK

SP	£75	$135	€95
DS	£60	$110	€75
AP	£50	$90	€65

BLACK, CILLA

SP	£30	$55	€40
DS	£20	$35	€25
AP	£15	$30	€20

BEDINGFIELD, NATASHA

SP	£75	$135	€95
DS	£50	$90	€65
AP	£35	$65	€45

BEST, PETE

SP	£150	$270	€185
DS	£130	$230	€160
AP	£70	$125	€90

BLIGE, MARY J

SP	£85	$155	€105
DS	£55	$100	€70
AP	£35	$65	€45

BLUNT, JAMES

SP	**£75**	$135	€95
DS	**£60**	$110	€75
AP	**£40**	$75	€50

MARC BOLAN

BOLAN, MARC

SP	**£1,500**	$2,660	€1,845
DS	**£1,250**	$2,215	€1,540
AP	**£550**	$975	€680

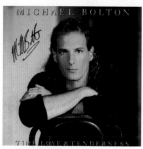

MICHAEL BOLTON

TIME, LOVE & TENDERNESS

BOLTON, MICHAEL

SP	**£50**	$90	€65
DS	**£35**	$65	€45
AP	**£20**	$35	€25

BON JOVI, JON

SP	**£75**	$135	€95
DS	**£60**	$110	€75
AP	**£40**	$75	€50

BONO, SONNY

SP	**£175**	$310	€215
DS	**£160**	$285	€200
AP	**£75**	$135	€95

BOONE, PAT

SP	**£60**	$110	€75
DS	**£50**	$90	€65
AP	**£40**	$75	€50

BOWIE, DAVID

SP	**£150**	$270	€185
DS	**£100**	$180	€125
AP	**£100**	$180	€125

BOY GEORGE

SP	**£35**	$65	€45
DS	**£20**	$35	€25
AP	**£15**	$30	€20

BRAGG, BILLY

SP	**£55**	$100	€70
DS	**£40**	$75	€50
AP	**£25**	$45	€35

BROWN, BOBBY

SP	**£80**	$145	€100
DS	**£70**	$125	€90
AP	**£50**	$90	€65

BROWN, JAMES

SP	**£150**	$270	€185
DS	**£100**	$180	€125
AP	**£75**	$135	€95

BROWN, MELANIE

SP	**£75**	$135	€95
DS	**£60**	$110	€75
AP	**£50**	$90	€65

BROWNE, JACKSON

SP	**£75**	$135	€95
DS	**£65**	$115	€80
AP	**£50**	$90	€65

BRUCE, JACK

SP	£75	$135	€95
DS	£65	$115	€80
AP	£50	$90	€65

CARLISLE, BELINDA

SP	£50	$90	€65
DS	£40	$75	€50
AP	£30	$55	€40

CASSIDY, DAVID

SP	£50	$90	€65
DS	£40	$75	€50
AP	£30	$55	€40

BUNTON, EMMA

SP	£65	$115	€80
DS	£50	$90	€65
AP	£40	$75	€50

BUSH, KATE

SP	£125	$225	€155
DS	£80	$145	€100
AP	£60	$110	€75

CARLISLE, ELSIE

SP	£35	$65	€45
DS	£25	$45	€35
AP	£15	$30	€20

CARPENTER, KAREN

SP	£650	$1,155	€800
DS	£475	$845	€585
AP	£350	$620	€430

CHER

SP	£75	$135	€95
DS	£60	$110	€75
AP	£40	$75	€50

BYRNE, NICKY

SP	£75	$135	€95
DS	£50	$90	€65
AP	£30	$55	€40

CHERRY, NENEH

SP	£50	$90	€65
DS	£40	$75	€50
AP	£30	$55	€40

CAREY, MARIAH

SP	£100	$180	€125
DS	£85	$155	€105
AP	£50	$90	€65

CASH, JOHNNY

SP	£300	$535	€370
DS	£200	$355	€250
AP	£90	$160	€115

CHISHOLM, MELANIE

SP	£75	$135	€95
DS	£50	$90	€65
AP	£40	$75	€50

CHURCH, CHARLOTTE

SP	£100	$180	€125
DS	£85	$155	€105
AP	£50	$90	€65

CLAPTON, ERIC

SP	£175	$310	€215
DS	£80	$145	€100
AP	£50	$90	€65

CLARK, DAVE

SP	£95	$170	€120
DS	£70	$125	€90
AP	£50	$90	€65

CLARKSON, KELLY

SP	£75	$135	€95
DS	£50	$90	€65
AP	£30	$55	€40

CLINE, PATSY

SP	£3,000	$5,315	€3,690
DS	£2,750	$4,875	€3,380
AP	£1,750	$3,100	€2,150

CLOONEY, ROSEMARY

SP	£50	$90	€65
DS	£40	$75	€50
AP	£30	$55	€40

COCHRAN, EDDIE

SP	£1,250	$2,215	€1,540
DS	£1,000	$1,775	€1,230
AP	£600	$1,065	€740

COCKER, JOE

SP	£50	$90	€65
DS	£40	$75	€50
AP	£30	$55	€40

COHEN, LEONARD

SP	£650	$1,155	€800
DS	£350	$620	€435
AP	£200	$355	€250

COLLINS, PHIL

SP	£100	$180	€125
DS	£65	$115	€80
AP	£40	$75	€50

COODER, RY

SP	£75	$135	€95
DS	£65	$115	€80
AP	£50	$90	€65

COOPER, ALICE

SP	£75	$135	€95
DS	£65	$115	€80
AP	£40	$75	€50

COSTELLO, ELVIS

SP	£75	$135	€95
DS	£50	$90	€65
AP	£30	$55	€40

COYLE, NADINE

SP	£95	$170	€120
DS	£70	$125	€90
AP	£50	$90	€65

CROSBY, DAVID

SP	£125	$225	€155
DS	£100	$180	€125
AP	£75	$135	€95

CROW, SHERYL

SP	£75	$135	€95
DS	£60	$110	€75
AP	£40	$75	€50

CRUISE, JULIE

SP	£35	$65	€45
DS	£25	$45	€35
AP	£15	$30	€20

DALTREY, ROGER

SP	£75	$135	€95
DS	£65	$115	€80
AP	£40	$75	€50

DARIN, BOBBY

SP	£475	$845	€585
DS	£400	$710	€495
AP	£200	$355	€250

DAVIES, RAY

SP	£25	$45	€35
DS	£15	$30	€20
AP	£10	$20	€15

DAVIS JR, SAMMY

SP	£495	$880	€610
DS	£400	$710	€495
AP	£250	$445	€310

DAVIS, MILES

SP	£495	$880	€610
DS	£450	$800	€555
AP	£250	$445	€310

DIAMOND, NEIL

SP	£50	$90	€65
DS	£40	$75	€50
AP	£30	$55	€40

DIDO

SP	£90	$160	€115
DS	£80	$145	€100
AP	£40	$75	€50

DION, CELINE

SP	£120	$215	€150
DS	£80	$145	€100
AP	£50	$90	€65

DOMINO, FATS

SP	£75	$135	€95
DS	£60	$110	€75
AP	£35	$65	€45

DURST, FRED

SP	£75	$135	€95
DS	£50	$90	€65
AP	£40	$75	€50

DYLAN, BOB

SP	£1,250	$2,215	€1,540
DS	£1,750	$3,100	€2,155
AP	£775	$1,375	€955

EASTON, SHEENA

SP	£75	$135	€95
DS	£65	$115	€80
AP	£40	$75	€50

EGAN, KIAN

SP	£75	$135	€95
DS	£50	$90	€65
AP	£30	$55	€40

ELLIS BEXTOR, SOPHIE

SP	£50	$90	€65
DS	£40	$75	€50
AP	£30	$55	€40

EMINEM

SP	£75	$135	€95
DS	£65	$115	€80
AP	£40	$75	€50

ESTEFAN, GLORIA

SP	£75	$135	€95
DS	£60	$110	€75
AP	£40	$75	€50

ESTELLE

SP	£75	$135	€95
DS	£50	$90	€65
AP	£30	$55	€40

EVE

SP	£75	$135	€95
DS	£50	$90	€65
AP	£30	$55	€40

FAITH, ADAM

SP	£150	$270	€185
DS	£130	$230	€160
AP	£80	$145	€100

FAITHFULL, MARIANNE

SP	£150	$270	€185
DS	£130	$230	€160
AP	£90	$160	€115

FALTSKOG, AGNETHA

SP	£150	$270	€185
DS	£100	$180	€125
AP	£65	$115	€80

FERGIE

SP	£75	$135	€95
DS	£50	$90	€65
AP	£30	$55	€40

Bryan Ferry

FERRY, BRYAN

SP	£150	$270	€185
DS	£130	$230	€160
AP	£40	$75	€50

FRAMPTON, PETER

SP	£50	$90	€65
DS	£40	$75	€50
AP	£30	$55	€40

FRANKLIN, ARETHA

SP	£200	$355	€250
DS	£100	$180	€125
AP	£60	$110	€75

FURTADO, NELLY

SP	£50	$90	€65
DS	£40	$75	€50
AP	£30	$55	€40

GABRIELLE

SP	£85	$155	€105
DS	£65	$115	€80
AP	£50	$90	€65

GALLAGHER, NOEL

SP	£125	$225	€155
DS	£80	$145	€100
AP	£50	$90	€65

GARCIA, JERRY

SP	£675	$1,200	€830
DS	£600	$1,065	€740
AP	£300	$535	€370

GARFUNKEL, ART

SP	£85	$155	€105
DS	£75	$135	€95
AP	£50	$90	€65

GARLAND, JUDY

SP	£2,250	$3,990	€2,765
DS	£1,750	$3,100	€2,155
AP	£500	$890	€615

MARVIN GAYE

GAYE, MARVIN

SP	£1,200	$2,130	€1,475
DS	£1,000	$1,775	€1,230
AP	£600	$1,065	€740

David Gray   iht

GRAY, DAVID

SP	£75	$135	€95
DS	£65	$115	€80
AP	£40	$75	€50

GRAY, MACY

SP	£50	$90	€65
DS	£40	$75	€50
AP	£30	$55	€40

GROHL, DAVE

SP	£175	$310	€215
DS	£150	$270	€185
AP	£100	$180	€125

GUTHRIE, ARLO

SP	£150	$270	€185
DS	£130	$230	€160
AP	£70	$125	€90

HAGGARD, MERLE

SP	£50	$90	€65
DS	£40	$75	€50
AP	£30	$55	€40

HALEY, BILL

SP	£750	$1,330	€925
DS	£700	$1,245	€865
AP	£300	$535	€370

HALEY, JACK

SP	£400	$710	€495
DS	£200	$355	€250
AP	£130	$230	€160

HALLIWELL, GERI

SP	£50	$90	€65
DS	£50	$90	€65
AP	£40	$75	€50

HARDING, SARAH

SP	£75	$135	€95
DS	£60	$110	€75
AP	£50	$90	€65

HARRISON, GEORGE

SP	£2,000	$3,545	€2,460
DS		*	
AP	£1,500	$2,660	€1,845

HARRY, DEBBIE

SP	£75	$135	€95
DS	£65	$115	€80
AP	£40	$75	€50

EAST 17

HARVEY, BRIAN

SP	£60	$110	€75
DS	£50	$90	€65
AP	£30	$55	€40

HEALY, FRAN

SP	£80	$145	€100
DS	£70	$125	€90
AP	£40	$75	€50

THE JIMI HENDRIX EXPERIENCE

HENDRIX, JIMI

SP	£2,500	$4,430	€3,075
DS	*		
AP	£1,750	$3,100	€2,150

HILL, LAURYN

SP	£50	$90	€65
DS	£40	$75	€50
AP	£30	$55	€40

HOGAN, BROOKE

SP	£75	$135	€95
DS	£45	$80	€55
AP	£30	$55	€40

HOLIDAY, BILLIE

SP	£3,500	$6,200	€4,300
DS	£2,000	$3,545	€2,460
AP	£1,500	$2,660	€1,845

HOLLY, BUDDY

SP	£2,500	$4,430	€3,075
DS	£1,750	$3,100	€2,150
AP	£1,000	$1,775	€1,230

HOOKER, JOHN LEE

SP	£175	$310	€215
DS	£160	$285	€200
AP	£50	$90	€65

HOUSTON, WHITNEY

SP	£100	$180	€125
DS	£80	$145	€100
AP	£75	$135	€95

HUCKNALL, MICK

SP	£50	$90	€65
DS	£40	$75	€50
AP	£30	$55	€40

HYNDE, CHRISSIE

SP	£50	$90	€65
DS	£40	$75	€50
AP	£30	$55	€40

ICE T

SP	£75	$135	€95
DS	£60	$110	€75
AP	£40	$75	€50

IDOL, BILLY

SP	£100	$180	€125
DS	£85	$155	€105
AP	£60	$110	€75

IGLESIAS, ENRIQUE

SP	£80	$145	€100
DS	£70	$125	€90
AP	£40	$75	€50

IGLESIAS, JULIO

SP	£75	$135	€95
DS	£65	$115	€80
AP	£40	$75	€50

JAGGER, MICK

SP	£180	$320	€225
DS	£125	$225	€155
AP	£80	$145	€100

JAY KAY

SP	£75	$135	€95
DS	£65	$115	€80
AP	£50	$90	€65

JACKSON, JANET

SP	£50	$90	€65
DS	£40	$75	€50
AP	£30	$55	€40

JAMELIA

SP	£50	$90	€65
DS	£35	$65	€45
AP	£30	$55	€40

JEWEL

SP	£50	$90	€65
DS	£40	$75	€50
AP	£30	$55	€40

JACKSON, LATOYA

SP	£75	$135	€95
DS	£65	$115	€80
AP	£40	$75	€50

JACKSON, MICHAEL

SP	£300	$535	€370
DS	£260	$465	€320
AP	£225	$400	€280

Michael Jackson

Michael Joseph Jackson, son of Joseph and Katherine was born in Gary, Indiana on 29th August 1958. Michael was born into a large family consisting of Rebbie, Jackie, Tito, Jermaine, La Toya, Marlon, Michael, Randy and Janet. In 1962 Jackie, Tito and Jermaine were performing under the direction of their father. The following year, Marlon and Michael joined their brothers to form the Jackson 5 where Michael quickly established himself as an awe-inspiring, energetic performer.

The Jackson 5 signed with Motown Records in 1968 and released their debut single *"I Want You Back"* in October 1969. *"ABC"*, *"The Love You Save"* and *"I'll Be There"* followed and were all number one hits in the 70's.

Jackson soon launched his solo career and with the help of Quincy Jones released *"Off the wall"* (1979), which gave Jackson four top ten singles. He then proceeded to make four more top selling albums, *"Thriller"* (1982), *"Bad"* (1987), *"Dangerous"* (1991) and *"History"* (1995).

Michael, now in his 50's, has been proclaimed the *King of Pop* and one of the world's most famous men.

JOEL, BILLY

SP	£60	$110	€75
DS	£50	$90	€65
AP	£30	$55	€40

JOHN, ELTON

SP	£150	$270	€185
DS	£130	$230	€160
AP	£75	$135	€95

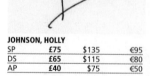

JOHNSON, HOLLY

SP	£75	$135	€95
DS	£65	$115	€80
AP	£40	$75	€50

JOLSON, AL

SP	£350	$620	€430
DS	£220	$390	€270
AP	£150	$270	€185

JONES, GLORIA

SP	£200	$355	€250
DS	£150	$270	€185
AP	£100	$180	€125

JONES, NORAH

SP	£75	$135	€95
DS	£60	$110	€75
AP	£30	$55	€40

JONES, PAUL

SP	£50	$90	€65
DS	£40	$75	€50
AP	£30	$55	€40

JONES, STEVE

SP	£60	$110	€75
DS	£50	$90	€65
AP	£30	$55	€40

JONES, TOM

SP	£75	$135	€95
DS	£65	$115	€80
AP	£30	$55	€40

JOPLIN, JANIS

SP	£4,500	$7,975	€5,530
DS	£3,500	$6,200	€4,300
AP	£2,200	$3,900	€2,705

JUDD, NAOMI

SP	£50	$90	€65
DS	£45	$80	€55
AP	£40	$75	€50

JUDD, WYNONNA

SP	£50	$90	€65
DS	£45	$80	€55
AP	£40	$75	€50

KIMBALL, CHEYENNE

SP	£75	$135	€95
DS	£45	$80	€55
AP	£30	$55	€40

KING, B.B

SP	£150	$270	€185
DS	£120	$215	€150
AP	£75	$135	€95

KRAMER, BILLY J

SP	£75	$135	€95
DS	£50	$90	€65
AP	£30	$55	€40

KEATING, RONAN

SP	£80	$145	€100
DS	£70	$125	€90
AP	£50	$90	€65

KITT, EARTHA

SP	£50	$90	€65
DS	£40	$75	€50
AP	£30	$55	€40

KRAVITZ, LENNY

SP	£50	$90	€65
DS	£40	$75	€50
AP	£30	$55	€40

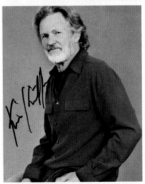

KEYS, ALICIA

SP	£50	$90	€65
DS	£40	$75	€50
AP	£30	$55	€40

KLASS, MYLEENE

SP	£75	$135	€95
DS	£45	$80	€55
AP	£30	$55	€40

KRISTOFFERSON, KRIS

SP	£75	$135	€95
DS	£45	$80	€55
AP	£30	$55	€40

k.d. lang

LANG, KD

SP	£50	$90	€65
DS	£40	$75	€50
AP	£30	$55	€40

LANG, THOMAS

SP	£30	$55	€40
DS	£20	$35	€25
AP	£15	$30	€20

LAUPER, CYNDI

SP	£75	$135	€95
DS	£60	$110	€75
AP	£40	$75	€50

LAVIGNE, AVRIL

SP	£75	$135	€95
DS	£50	$90	€65
AP	£40	$75	€50

LEMAR

SP	£75	$135	€95
DS	£65	$115	€80
AP	£40	$75	€50

LENNON, JOHN

SP		*	
DS	£10,000	$17,715	€12,290
AP	£5,950	$10,540	€7,315

LENNON, JULIAN

SP	£70	$125	€90
DS	£50	$90	€65
AP	£35	$65	€45

LENNON, SEAN

SP	£75	$135	€95
DS	£65	$115	€80
AP	£50	$90	€65

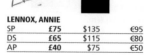

LENNOX, ANNIE

SP	£75	$135	€95
DS	£65	$115	€80
AP	£40	$75	€50

LESTER, KETTY

SP	£75	$135	€95
DS	£65	$115	€80
AP	£50	$90	€65

LEWIS, HUEY

SP	£95	$170	€120
DS	£70	$125	€90
AP	£50	$90	€65

LEWIS, JERRY

SP	£450	$800	€555
DS	£300	$535	€370
AP	£200	$355	€250

LIBERACE

SP	£250	$445	€310
DS	£150	$270	€185
AP	£100	$180	€125

LIL KIM

SP	£100	$180	€125
DS	£65	$115	€80
AP	£40	$75	€50

LITTLE RICHARD

SP	£200	$355	€250
DS	£150	$270	€185
AP	£75	$135	€95

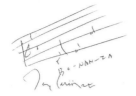

LIVINGSTON, JAY

SP	£60	$110	€75
DS	£45	$80	€55
AP	£30	$55	€40

LL COOL J

SP	£85	$155	€105
DS	£75	$135	€95
AP	£40	$75	€50

LONDON, JULIE

SP	£75	$135	€95
DS	£60	$110	€75
AP	£40	$75	€50

LOPEZ, JENNIFER

SP	£75	$135	€95
DS	£65	$115	€80
AP	£40	$75	€50

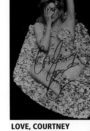

LOVE, COURTNEY

SP	£75	$135	€95
DS	£65	$115	€80
AP	£40	$75	€50

LULU

SP	£75	$135	€95
DS	£60	$110	€75
AP	£30	$55	€40

LYNGSTAD, ANNI-FRID

SP	£180	$320	€225
DS	£150	$270	€185
AP	£100	$180	€125

LYNN, VERA

SP	£50	$90	€65
DS	£40	$75	€50
AP	£30	$55	€40

LYNNE, JEFF

SP	£500	$890	€615
DS	£350	$620	€430
AP	£150	$270	€185

MADONNA

SP	£695	$1,235	€855
DS	£400	$710	€495
AP	£150	$270	€185

MAINES, NATALIE

SP	£75	$135	€95
DS	£50	$90	€65
AP	£30	$55	€40

MANILOW, BARRY

SP	£50	$90	€65
DS	£40	$75	€50
AP	£30	$55	€40

MANN, MANFRED

SP	£75	$135	€95
DS	£65	$115	€80
AP	£50	$90	€65

MANSON, MARILYN

SP	£80	$145	€100
DS	£70	$125	€90
AP	£40	$75	€50

MANSON, SHIRLEY

SP	£75	$135	€95
DS	£65	$115	€80
AP	£40	$75	€50

MANZAREK, RAY

SP	£90	$160	€115
DS	£75	$135	€95
AP	£40	$75	€50

MARLEY, BOB

SP	£4,000	$7,090	€4,915
DS	£3,500	$6,200	€4,300
AP	£2,500	$4,430	€3,075

MARTIN, CHRIS

SP	£100	$180	€125
DS	£85	$155	€105
AP	£60	$110	€75

MARTIN, MARY

SP	£80	$145	€100
DS	£60	$110	€75
AP	£30	$55	€40

MAY, BRIAN

SP	£75	$135	€95
DS	£65	$115	€80
AP	£50	$90	€65

MCBRIDE, MARTINA

SP	£50	$90	€65
DS	£40	$75	€50
AP	£30	$55	€40

MCCARTNEY, LINDA

SP	£200	$355	€250
DS	£175	$310	€215
AP	£150	$270	€185

MCCARTNEY, PAUL

SP	£2,000	$3,545	€2,460
DS	£1,500	$2,660	€1,845
AP	£975	$1,730	€1,200

MCCUTCHEON, MARTINE

SP	£150	$270	€185
DS	£120	$215	€150
AP	£85	$155	€105

MCFADDEN, KERRY

SP	£75	$135	€95
DS	£60	$110	€75
AP	£40	$75	€50

MCGUINN, ROGER

SP	£70	$125	€90
DS	£50	$90	€65
AP	£30	$55	€40

MCKENZIE, SCOTT

SP	£75	$135	€95
DS	£65	$115	€80
AP	£40	$75	€50

MCPHEE, KATHARINE

SP	£50	$90	€65
DS	£40	$75	€50
AP	£30	$55	€40

MEATLOAF

SP	£90	$160	€115
DS	£75	$135	€95
AP	£40	$75	€50

MELLENCAMP, JOHN COUGAR

SP	£30	$55	€40
DS	£20	$35	€25
AP	£15	$30	€20

MERCURY, FREDDIE

SP	£1,500	$2,660	€1,845
DS	£1,000	$1,775	€1,230
AP	£600	$1,065	€740

MICHAEL, GEORGE

SP	£150	$270	€185
DS	£100	$180	€125
AP	£70	$125	€90

MILIAN, CHRISTINA

SP	£50	$90	€65
DS	£40	$75	€50
AP	£30	$55	€40

MILSAP, RONNIE

SP	£50	$90	€65
DS	£40	$75	€50
AP	£30	$55	€40

MINNELLI, LIZA

SP	£270	$480	€335
DS	£200	$355	€250
AP	£130	$230	€160

MINOGUE, DANNI

SP	£50	$90	€65
DS	£40	$75	€50
AP	£30	$55	€40

MINOGUE, KYLIE

SP	£175	$310	€215
DS	£130	$230	€160
AP	£90	$160	€115

Music Artists

MIRANDA, CARMEN

SP	£500	$890	€615
DS	£450	$800	€555
AP	£200	$355	€250

MISSY ELLIOTT

SP	£50	$90	€65
DS	£40	$75	€50
AP	£30	$55	€40

MOORE, MANDY

SP	£75	$135	€95
DS	£60	$110	€75
AP	£40	$75	€50

MORISSETTE, ALANIS

SP	£75	$135	€95
DS	£60	$110	€75
AP	£40	$75	€50

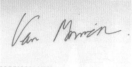

MORRISON, VAN

SP	£75	$135	€95
DS	£60	$110	€75
AP	£45	$80	€55

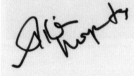

MOYET, ALISON

SP	£50	$90	€65
DS	£40	$75	€50
AP	£30	$55	€40

MS DYNAMITE

SP	£50	$90	€65
DS	£40	$75	€50
AP	£30	$55	€40

MUNGO JERRY

SP	£50	$90	€65
DS	£40	$75	€50
AP	£30	$55	€40

MURPHY, ROSE

SP	£50	$90	€65
DS	£40	$75	€50
AP	£30	$55	€40

MYA

SP	£50	$90	€65
DS	£40	$75	€50
AP	£30	$55	€40

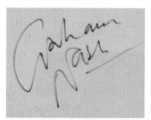

NASH, GRAHAM

SP	£70	$125	€90
DS	£60	$110	€75
AP	£40	$75	€50

NAVARRO, DAVE

SP	£75	$135	€95
DS	£65	$120	€80
AP	£50	$90	€65

NELLY

SP	£75	$135	€95
DS	£60	$110	€75
AP	£40	$75	€50

NELSON, WILLIE

SP	£75	$135	€95
DS	£60	$110	€75
AP	£40	$75	€50

NESMITH, MIKE

SP	£80	$145	€100
DS	£75	$135	€95
AP	£40	$75	€50

NEWTON JOHN, OLIVIA

SP	£175	$310	€215
DS	£100	$180	€125
AP	£65	$115	€80

NICKS, STEVIE

SP	£150	$270	€185
DS	£125	$225	€155
AP	£90	$160	€115

NURDING, LOUISE

SP	£80	$145	€100
DS	£60	$110	€75
AP	£30	$55	€40

NUTINI, PAOLO

SP	£75	$135	€95
DS	£60	$110	€75
AP	£40	$75	€50

O'CONNOR, HAZEL

SP	£60	$110	€75
DS	£45	$80	€55
AP	£35	$65	€45

OCEAN, BILLY

SP	£95	$170	€120
DS	£70	$125	€90
AP	£50	$90	€65

MIKE OLDFIELD

OLDFIELD, MIKE

SP	£75	$135	€95
DS	£65	$115	€80
AP	£50	$90	€65

ONO, YOKO

SP	£125	$225	€155
DS	£85	$155	€105
AP	£50	$90	€65

ORBISON, ROY

SP	£600	$1,065	€740
DS	£450	$800	€555
AP	£350	$620	€430

OSBOURNE, KELLY

SP	£75	$135	€95
DS	£65	$115	€80
AP	£50	$90	€65

OSBOURNE, OZZY

SP	£100	$180	€125
DS	£65	$115	€80
AP	£50	$90	€65

PARADIS, VANESSA

SP	£75	$135	€95
DS	£65	$115	€80
AP	£40	$75	€50

PARTON, DOLLY

SP	£80	$145	€100
DS	£70	$125	€90
AP	£45	$80	€55

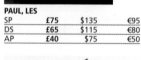

PAUL, LES

SP	£75	$135	€95
DS	£65	$115	€80
AP	£40	$75	€50

PETTY, TOM

SP	£150	$270	€185
DS	£120	$215	€150
AP	£75	$135	€95

PHAIR, LIZ

SP	£50	$90	€65
DS	£40	$75	€50
AP	£30	$55	€40

PIAF, EDITH

SP	£850	$1,510	€1,045
DS	£700	$1,240	€865
AP	£350	$620	€430

PAGE, JIMMY

SP	£450	$800	€555
DS	£350	$620	€435
AP	£275	$490	€340

PAIGE, ELAINE

SP	£75	$135	€95
DS	£65	$115	€80
AP	£40	$75	€50

PALMER, ROBERT

SP	£50	$90	€65
DS	£40	$75	€50
AP	£30	$55	€40

PERKINS, CARL

SP	£300	$535	€370
DS	£250	$445	€310
AP	£175	$310	€215

PICKETT, WILSON

SP	£75	$135	€95
DS	£60	$110	€75
AP	£40	$75	€50

PINK

SP	£75	$135	€95
DS	£40	$75	€50
AP	£30	$55	€40

PRESLEY, ELVIS

SP	£3,750	$6,645	€4,610
DS	£4,500	$7,975	€5,530
AP	£1,750	$3,100	€2,150

RAMONE, DEE DEE

SP	£200	$355	€250
DS	£150	$270	€185
AP	£90	$160	€115

PITNEY, GENE

SP	£75	$135	€95
DS	£65	$115	€80
AP	£40	$75	€50

PUCKETT, GARY

SP	£75	$135	€95
DS	£65	$115	€80
AP	£50	$90	€65

REDDING, OTIS

SP	£2,000	$3,545	€2,460
DS	£1,500	$2,660	€1,845
AP	£850	$1,510	€1,045

PLANT, ROBERT

SP	£275	$490	€340
DS	£240	$425	€295
AP	£150	$270	€185

POP, IGGY

SP	£50	$90	€65
DS	£40	$75	€50
AP	£30	$55	€40

PUFF DADDY

SP	£75	$135	€95
DS	£50	$90	€65
AP	£40	$75	€50

QUAYE, FINLEY

SP	£30	$55	€40
DS	£20	$35	€25
AP	£15	$30	€20

REED, LOU

SP	£75	$135	€95
DS	£65	$115	€80
AP	£40	$75	€50

REEVES, JIM

SP	£1,250	$2,215	€1,540
DS	£800	$1,420	€985
AP	£375	$665	€465

REEVES, MARTHA
SP	**£30**	$55	€40
DS	**£20**	$35	€25
AP	**£15**	$30	€20

REID, JAMIE
SP	**£135**	$240	€170
DS	**£100**	$180	€125
AP	**£60**	$110	€75

RENAUD, LINE
SP	**£75**	$135	€95
DS	**£65**	$115	€80
AP	**£50**	$90	€65

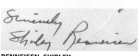

RENNEISEN, SHIRLEY
SP	**£40**	$75	€50
DS	**£30**	$55	€40
AP	**£20**	$40	€25

CLIFF RICHARD

RICHARD, CLIFF
SP	**£50**	$90	€65
DS	**£75**	$135	€95
AP	**£30**	$55	€40

RICHARDS, KEITH
SP	**£275**	$490	€340
DS	**£180**	$320	€225
AP	**£120**	$215	€150

RIMES, LEANN
SP	**£50**	$90	€65
DS	**£40**	$75	€50
AP	**£30**	$55	€40

ROBINSON, SUGAR CHILE
SP	**£75**	$135	€95
DS	**£65**	$115	€80
AP	**£50**	$90	€65

ROCK, KID
SP	**£75**	$135	€95
DS	**£60**	$110	€75
AP	**£30**	$55	€40

ROSE, AXL
SP	**£150**	$270	€185
DS	**£100**	$180	€125
AP	**£65**	$120	€80

ROSS, DIANA
SP	**£395**	$700	€485
DS	**£250**	$445	€310
AP	**£100**	$180	€125

ROTTEN, JOHNNY
SP	**£250**	$445	€310
DS	**£200**	$355	€250
AP	**£150**	$270	€185

ROZA, LITA

SP	£55	$100	€70
DS	£40	$75	€50
AP	£30	$55	€40

RYDELL, BOBBY

SP	£50	$90	€65
DS	£35	$65	€45
AP	£25	$45	€35

SANTANA, CARLOS

SP	£150	$270	€185
DS	£100	$180	€125
AP	£75	$135	€95

SEDAKA, NEIL

SP	£50	$90	€65
DS	£40	$75	€50
AP	£30	$55	€40

SHAKIRA

SP	£85	$155	€105
DS	£70	$125	€90
AP	£50	$90	€65

SHAPIRO, HELEN

SP	£75	$135	€95
DS	£60	$110	€75
AP	£45	$80	€60

SHAW, SANDIE

SP	£50	$90	€65
DS	£40	$75	€50
AP	£30	$55	€40

SIMMONS, GENE

SP	£135	$240	€170
DS	£100	$180	€125
AP	£50	$90	€65

SIMON & GARFUNKEL

SP	£375	$665	€465
DS	£250	$445	€310
AP	£150	$270	€185

SIMON, CARLY

SP	£50	$90	€65
DS	£40	$75	€50
AP	£30	$55	€40

SIMON, PAUL

SP	£75	$135	€95
DS	£65	$115	€80
AP	£50	$90	€65

SIMPSON, ASHLEE

SP	£75	$135	€95
DS	£50	$90	€65
AP	£35	$65	€45

SIMPSON, JESSICA

SP	£100	$180	€125
DS	£65	$115	€80
AP	£40	$75	€50

SINATRA, FRANK

SP	£1,500	$2,660	€1,845
DS	£1,250	$2,215	€1,540
AP	£975	$1,730	€1,200

SINGLETON, ZUTTY

SP	£300	$535	€370
DS	£280	$500	€345
AP	£160	$285	€200

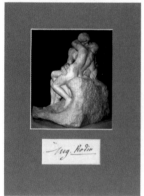

SNOOP DOGG

SP	£85	$155	€105
DS	£75	$135	€95
AP	£40	$75	€50

SPEARS, BRITNEY

SP	£150	$270	€185
DS	£95	$170	€120
AP	£60	$110	€75

SPECTOR, RONNIE

SP	£90	$160	€115
DS	£75	$135	€95
AP	£50	$90	€65

SPRINGSTEEN, BRUCE

SP	£175	$310	€220
DS	£125	$225	€155
AP	£80	$145	€100

SQUIRES, ROSEMARY

SP	£80	$145	€100
DS	£70	$125	€90
AP	£50	$90	€65

STARR, RINGO

SP	£750	$1,330	€925
DS		*	
AP	£500	$890	€615

STEFANI, GWEN

SP	£165	$295	€205
DS	£150	$270	€185
AP	£60	$110	€75

STEVENS, CAT

SP	£150	$270	€185
DS	£130	$230	€160
AP	£70	$125	€90

STEVENS, RACHEL

SP	£75	$135	€95
DS	£65	$115	€80
AP	£40	$75	€50

STEWART, ROD

SP	£150	$270	€185
DS	£85	$155	€105
AP	£60	$110	€75

STILLS, STEPHEN

SP	£100	$180	€125
DS	£85	$155	€105
AP	£75	$135	€95

STING

SP	£150	$270	€185
DS	£150	$270	€185
AP	£80	$145	€100

STIPE, MICHAEL

SP	£295	$525	€365
DS	£250	$445	€310
AP	£150	$270	€185

STONE, JOSS

SP	£150	$270	€185
DS	£85	$155	€105
AP	£60	$110	€75

STREISAND, BARBRA

SP	£600	$1,065	€740
DS	£500	$890	€615
AP	£375	$665	€465

SUTCLIFFE, STUART

SP	£800	$1,420	€985
DS	£975	$1,730	€1,200
AP	£350	$620	€435

TAUPIN, BERNIE

SP	£90	$160	€115
DS	£75	$135	€95
AP	£50	$90	€65

TAYLOR, JAMES

SP	£375	$665	€465
DS	£350	$620	€430
AP	£300	$535	€370

TAYLOR, ROGER

SP	£75	$135	€95
DS	£65	$115	€80
AP	£50	$90	€65

TIMBERLAKE, JUSTIN

SP	£50	$90	€65
DS	£150	$270	€185
AP	£40	$75	€50

TOWNSHEND, PETE

SP	£50	$90	€65
DS	£45	$80	€55
AP	£40	$75	€50

BASIA

TRZETRZELEWSKA, BASIA

SP	£100	$180	€125
DS	£85	$155	€105
AP	£60	$110	€75

TUNSTALL, K.T.

SP	£75	$135	€95
DS	£50	$90	€65
AP	£30	$55	€40

IKE & TINA TURNER

TURNER, IKE

SP	£50	$90	€65
DS	£40	$75	€50
AP	£30	$55	€40

TURNER, TINA

SP	£150	$270	€185
DS	£130	$230	€160
AP	£70	$125	€90

TYLER, STEVE

SP	**£125**	$225	€155
DS	**£80**	$145	€100
AP	**£70**	$125	€90

TWAIN, SHANIA

SP	**£75**	$135	€95
DS	**£65**	$115	€80
AP	**£50**	$90	€65

VALANCE, HOLLY

SP	**£150**	$270	€185
DS	**£125**	$225	€155
AP	**£70**	$125	€90

VALLI, FRANKIE

SP	**£75**	$135	€95
DS	**£65**	$115	€80
AP	**£50**	$90	€65

VAN HALEN, EDDIE

SP	**£50**	$90	€65
DS	**£40**	$75	€50
AP	**£30**	$55	€40

VANILLA, CHERRY

SP	**£65**	$115	€80
DS	**£50**	$90	€65
AP	**£35**	$65	€45

VAUGHAN, STEVIE RAY

SP	**£1,000**	$1,775	€1,230
DS	**£700**	$1,240	€865
AP	**£500**	$890	€615

VICIOUS, SID

SP	**£1,000**	$1,775	€1,230
DS	**£800**	$1,420	€985
AP	**£450**	$800	€555

WAHLBERG, DONNIE

SP	**£80**	$145	€100
DS	**£60**	$110	€75
AP	**£40**	$75	€50

WAITES, TOM

SP	**£50**	$90	€65
DS	**£40**	$75	€50
AP	**£30**	$55	€40

WALSH, KIMBERLEY

SP	**£75**	$135	€95
DS	**£60**	$110	€75
AP	**£50**	$90	€65

WARWICK, DIONNE

SP	**£75**	$135	€95
DS	**£65**	$115	€80
AP	**£40**	$75	€50

PETE WATERMAN

WATERMAN, PETE

SP	**£50**	$90	€65
DS	**£40**	$75	€50
AP	**£30**	$55	€40

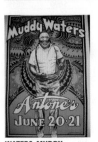

WATERS, MUDDY

SP	**£400**	$710	€495
DS	**£250**	$445	€310
AP	**£150**	$270	€185

WATERS, ROGER

SP	£200	$355	€250
DS	£175	$310	€215
AP	£125	$225	€155

WATTS, CHARLIE

SP	£50	$90	€65
DS	£40	$75	€50
AP	£30	$55	€40

WEBBER, JULIAN LLOYD

SP	£60	$110	€75
DS	£50	$90	€65
AP	£30	$55	€40

WELLER, PAUL

SP	£90	$160	€115
DS	£70	$125	€90
AP	£40	$75	€50

WILLIAMS, ROBBIE

SP	£175	$310	€220
DS	£160	$285	€200
AP	£90	$160	€115

WILSON, BRIAN

SP	£250	$445	€310
DS	£220	$390	€270
AP	£130	$230	€160

WILSON, CARL

SP	£80	$145	€100
DS	£60	$110	€75
AP	£40	$75	€50

WILSON, NANCY

SP	£75	$135	€95
DS	£65	$115	€80
AP	£40	$75	€50

WILSON, RICKY

SP	£75	$135	€95
DS	£50	$90	€65
AP	£30	$55	€40

WYMAN, BILL

SP	£90	$160	€115
DS	£60	$110	€75
AP	£40	$75	€50

WYNETTE, TAMMY

SP	£100	$180	€125
DS	£85	$155	€105
AP	£60	$110	€75

WYNTER, MARK

SP	£75	$135	€95
DS	£65	$120	€80
AP	£50	$90	€65

YOUNG, NEIL

SP	£75	$135	€95
DS	£65	$115	€80
AP	£50	$90	€65

ZAPPA, FRANK

SP	£950	$1,685	€1,170
DS	£850	$1,510	€1,045
AP	£450	$800	€555

CLASSICAL

ADLER, LARRY

SP	£100	$180	€125
DS	£75	$135	€95
AP	£40	$75	€50

ALMEIDA, MARIA

SP	£30	$55	€40
DS	£20	$40	€25
AP	£10	$20	€15

ALPERT, HERB

SP	£50	$90	€65
DS	£25	$45	€35
AP	£15	$30	€20

ANANIASHVILI, NINA

SP	£30	$55	€40
DS	£20	$40	€25
AP	£10	$20	€15

ANDERSON, MARIAN

SP	£75	$135	€95
DS	£50	$90	€65
AP	£50	$90	€65

ARKWRIGHT, ROBERT

SP	£50	$90	€65
DS	£40	$75	€50
AP	£30	$55	€40

BACKHAUS, WILHELM

SP	£100	$180	€125
DS	£75	$135	€95
AP	£60	$110	€75

BARBIERI, MARGARET

SP	£30	$55	€40
DS	£20	$40	€25
AP	£10	$20	€15

BARBIROLLI, JOHN

SP	£100	$180	€125
DS	£75	$135	€95
AP	£60	$110	€75

BARTOK, BELA

SP	£4,950	$8,770	€6,085
DS	£3,750	$6,645	€4,610
AP	£2,500	$4,430	€3,075

BEDELLS, PHYLLIS

SP	£75	$135	€95
DS	£50	$90	€65
AP	£45	$80	€60

BEETHOVEN, LUDWIG VAN

SP	*		
DS	£75,000	$132,860	€92,150
AP	£45,000	$79,720	€55,290

BENNETT, TONY

SP	£50	$90	€65
DS	£40	$75	€50
AP	£30	$55	€40

BERLIOZ, HECTOR

SP	£1,950	$3,455	€2,400
DS	£1,500	$2,660	€1,845
AP	£650	$1,155	€800

BERLIN, IRVING

SP	£295	$525	€365
DS	£225	$400	€280
AP	£150	$270	€185

BERNSTEIN, LEONARD

SP	£350	$625	€435
DS	£175	$315	€220
AP	£125	$225	€155

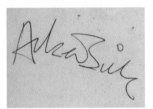

BILK, ACKER

SP	£50	$90	€65
DS	£40	$75	€50
AP	£30	$55	€40

Jacques BLUMENTHAL (1829-1905).

BLUMENTHAL, JACQUES

SP	£65	$120	€80
DS	£45	$80	€60
AP	£30	$55	€40

BOCELLI, ANDREA

SP	£100	$180	€125
DS	£85	$155	€105
AP	£40	$75	€50

BOULT, ADRIAN

SP	£50	$90	€65
DS	£40	$75	€50
AP	£30	$55	€40

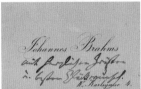

BRAHMS, JOHANNES

SP	£2,950	$5,230	€3,625
DS	£2,500	$4,430	€3,075
AP	£1,750	$3,105	€2,155

Sarah Brightman

BRIGHTMAN, SARAH

SP	£75	$135	€95
DS	£60	$110	€75
AP	£50	$90	€65

BRITTEN, BENJAMIN

SP	£850	$1,510	€1,045
DS	£550	$975	€680
AP	£295	$525	€365

BRODSKY, NICHOLAS

SP	£50	$90	€65
DS	£40	$75	€50
AP	£30	$55	€40

Ludwig Van Beethoven

Ludwig Van Beethoven was born 16 December 1770, in Bonn.

Beethoven's first music teacher was his father, a harsh instructor to the young boy. However Beethoven's talent was recognised at an early age and in 1778 Beethoven gave his first performance at Cologne. In 1782, Beethoven published his first work and before too long was hailed *"the new Mozart"*.

In 1787 Beethoven was sent to Vienna to meet Mozart and further his musical career. However he moved back home after learning his mother was suffering with tuberculosis. She passed away later that year.

In 1792 he moved back to Vienna and quickly earned the reputation of virtuoso performer, gaining much respect and admiration from fellow musicians.

In his twenties, Beethoven's hearing started to deteriorate due to tinnitus. However this did not hold him back and in the 1800's he was writing some of his best work; *The First*, *Second* and *Third Symphonies*, *The Eroica* and many more.

By 1814 Beethoven's hearing was nearly completely gone and on March 26th 1827, one of the world's most talented composers died after suffering a series of illnesses, with his close friends circled around his bed.

BROOKS, TYRONE

SP	£30	$55	€40
DS	£20	$40	€25
AP	£10	$20	€15

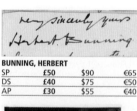

BRUSON, RENATO

SP	£30	$55	€40
DS	£20	$40	€25
AP	£10	$20	€15

BUNNING, HERBERT

SP	£50	$90	€65
DS	£40	$75	€50
AP	£30	$55	€40

BUTT, CLARA

SP	£50	$90	€65
DS	£40	$75	€50
AP	£30	$55	€40

MARIA CALLAS

2.12.1923 - 16.9.1977

CALLAS, MARIA

SP	£1,250	$2,215	€1,540
DS	£895	$1,590	€1,100
AP	£700	$1,245	€865

CARMICHAEL, HOAGY

SP	£550	$975	€680
DS	£350	$625	€435
AP	£100	$180	€125

CARRERAS, JOSE

SP	£75	$135	€95
DS	£50	$90	€65
AP	£40	$75	€50

CARUSO, ENRICO

SP	£1,250	$2,215	€1,540
DS	£950	$1,685	€1,170
AP	£750	$1,330	€925

CHALIAPIN, FEODOR IVANOVICH

SP	£550	$975	€680
DS	£375	$665	€465
AP	£325	$580	€400

COATES, EDITH

SP	£30	$55	€40
DS	£20	$40	€25
AP	£10	$20	€15

COLE, MARIA

SP	£75	$135	€95
DS	£60	$110	€75
AP	£45	$80	€60

COLE, NAT 'KING'

SP	£395	$700	€490
DS	£350	$625	€435
AP	£295	$525	€365

COLTRANE, JOHN

SP	£3,500	$6,205	€4,305
DS	£2,750	$4,875	€3,380
AP	£1,500	$2,660	€1,845

COTTON, BILLY

SP	£50	$90	€65
DS	£40	$75	€50
AP	£30	$55	€40

COUNT BASIE

SP	£100	$180	€125
DS	£75	$135	€95
AP	£50	$90	€65

DAVIES, BEN

SP	£50	$90	€65
DS	£40	$75	€50
AP	£40	$75	€50

DAVIES, CARL

SP	£75	$135	€95
DS	£60	$110	€75
AP	£50	$90	€65

DEBUSSY, CLAUDE

SP	£2,500	$4,430	€3,075
DS	£1,750	$3,105	€2,155
AP	£1,250	$2,215	€1,540

DEL RIEGO, TERESA

SP	£75	$135	€95
DS	£50	$90	€65
AP	£30	$55	€40

DENZA, LUIGI

SP	£75	$135	€95
DS	£60	$110	€75
AP	£50	$90	€65

DOLIN, ANTON

SP	£75	$135	€95
DS	£50	$90	€65
AP	£50	$90	€65

DOMINGO, PLACIDO

SP	£175	$315	€220
DS	£100	$180	€125
AP	£45	$80	€60

DUNCAN, ISADORA

SP	£1,750	$3,105	€2,155
DS	£1,450	$2,570	€1,785
AP	£1,000	$1,775	€1,230

DUNCAN, TREVOR

SP	£50	$90	€65
DS	£30	$55	€40
AP	£20	$40	€25

DVORAK, ANTONIN

SP	£2,250	$3,990	€2,765
DS	£1,250	$2,215	€1,540
AP	£850	$1,510	€1,045

ECKSTINE, BILLY

SP	£50	$90	€65
DS	£40	$75	€50
AP	£30	$55	€40

ELGAR, EDWARD

SP	£1,500	$2,660	€1,845
DS	£1,200	$2,130	€1,475
AP	£850	$1,510	€1,045

ELLINGTON, DUKE

SP	£495	$880	€610
DS	£400	$710	€495
AP	£300	$535	€370

EPSTEIN, BRIAN

SP	£1,500	$2,660	€1,845
DS	£1,200	$2,130	€1,475
AP	£800	$1,420	€985

FARMER, ART

SP	£50	$90	€65
DS	£40	$75	€50
AP	£30	$55	€40

FITZGERALD, ELLA

SP	£495	$880	€610
DS	£350	$625	€435
AP	£200	$355	€250

FLATLEY, MICHAEL

SP	£45	$80	€60
DS	£30	$55	€40
AP	£15	$30	€20

FONTEYN, MARGOT

SP	£225	$400	€280
DS	£125	$225	€155
AP	£100	$180	€125

DR. WILHELM
FURTWÄNGLER

FURTWANGLER, WILHELM

SP	£695	$1,235	€855
DS	£575	$1,020	€710
AP	£475	$845	€585

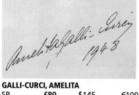

GALLI-CURCI, AMELITA

SP	£80	$145	€100
DS	£70	$125	€90
AP	£60	$110	€75

The Association of
Operatic Dancing
of Great Britain
CERTIFICATE OF MEMBERSHIP

GENEE, DAME ADELINE

SP	£50	$90	€65
DS	£40	$75	€50
AP	£30	$55	€40

GERSHWIN, GEORGE

SP		*	
DS	£1,950	$3,455	€2,400
AP	£1,000	$1,775	€1,230

GIGLI, BENIAMINO

SP	£150	$270	€185
DS	£125	$225	€155
AP	£80	$145	€100

GILBERT, WILLIAM SCHWENK

SP	£150	$270	€185
DS	£100	$180	€125
AP	£75	$135	€95

GILLESPIE, DIZZY

SP	£295	$525	€365
DS	£200	$355	€250
AP	£150	$270	€185

GILPIN, JOHN
SP	£30	$55	€40
DS	£20	$40	€25
AP	£15	$30	€20

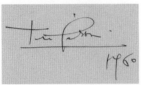

GOBBI, TITO
SP	£85	$155	€105
DS	£60	$110	€75
AP	£45	$80	€60

GODFREY, CHARLES
SP	£60	$110	€75
DS	£40	$75	€50
AP	£30	$55	€40

GRANOWSKA, KRYSTYNA
SP	£45	$80	€60
DS	£30	$55	€40
AP	£20	$40	€25

GRAPPELLI, STEPHANE
SP	£475	$845	€585
DS	£300	$535	€370
AP	£150	$270	€185

GRIEG, EDVARD
SP	£1,750	$3,105	€2,155
DP	£1,250	$2,215	€1,540
AP	£950	$1,685	€1,170

GOUNOD, CHARLES
SP	£750	$1,330	€925
DP	£350	$625	€435
AP	£150	$270	€185

HAGUE, ALBERT
SP	£75	$135	€95
DS	£50	$90	€65
AP	£40	$75	€50

HAMBOURG, MARK
SP	£50	$90	€65
DS	£40	$75	€50
AP	£30	$55	€40

HOLIDAY, BILLIE
SP	£3,500	$6,205	€4,305
DP	£2,950	$5,230	€3,625
AP	£1,950	$3,455	€2,400

HOLLOWAY, STANLEY
SP	£75	$135	€95
DS	£50	$90	€65
AP	£40	$75	€50

HOLST, GUSTAV
SP	£600	$1,065	€740
DS	£495	$880	€610
AP	£395	$700	€490

HUMPERDINCK, ENGELBERT
SP	£795	$1,410	€980
DS	£650	$1,155	€800
AP	£395	$700	€490

INFANTINO, LUIGI
SP	£100	$180	€125
DS	£50	$90	€65
AP	£30	$55	€40

ITURBI, JOSE
SP	£100	$180	€125
DS	£50	$90	€65
AP	£50	$90	€65

JOACHIM, JOSEPH

SP	£595	$1,055	€735
DS	£495	$880	€610
AP	£295	$525	€365

KENNEDY, NIGEL

SP	£50	$90	€65
DS	£40	$75	€50
AP	£30	$55	€40

KRUPA, GENE

SP	£325	$580	€400
DS	£225	$400	€280
AP	£125	$225	€155

KUBELIK, JAN

SP	£90	$160	€115
DS	£50	$90	€65
AP	£30	$55	€40

KUNZ, CHARLIE

SP	£50	$90	€65
DS	£40	$75	€50
AP	£30	$55	€40

LANZA, MARIO

SP	£450	$800	€555
DS	£350	$625	€435
AP	£295	$525	€365

LAWRENCE, MARJORIE

SP	£90	$160	€115
DS	£75	$135	€95
AP	£50	$90	€65

LEHAR, FRANZ

SP	£595	$1,055	€735
DS	£350	$625	€435
AP	£295	$525	€365

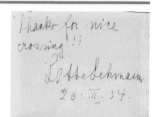

LEHMANN, LOTTE

SP	£150	$270	€185
DS	£125	$225	€155
AP	£100	$180	€125

Leoncavallo

LEONCAVALLO, RUGGIERO

SP	£995	$1,765	€1,225
DS	£750	$1,330	€925
AP	£495	$880	€610

LIEBERMANN, ROLF

SP	£50	$90	€65
DS	£40	$75	€50
AP	£30	$55	€40

LISZT, FRANZ

SP	£1,250	$2,215	€1,540
DS	£1,100	$1,950	€1,355
AP	£950	$1,685	€1,170

LLOYD WEBBER, ANDREW

SP	£150	$270	€185
DS	£75	$135	€95
AP	£50	$90	€65

LLOYD WEBBER, JULIAN

SP	£50	$90	€65
DS	£30	$55	€40
AP	£20	$40	€25

MADEIRA, JEAN

SP	£40	$75	€50
DS	£30	$55	€40
AP	£30	$55	€40

MAE, VANESSA

SP	£50	$90	€65
DS	£40	$75	€50
AP	£30	$55	€40

MALAKHOV, VLADIMIR

SP	£30	$55	€40
DS	£20	$40	€25
AP	£10	$20	€15

MANCINI, HENRY

SP	£100	$180	€125
DS	£75	$135	€95
AP	£60	$110	€75

MARKOVA, ALICIA

SP	£50	$90	€65
DS	£40	$75	€50
AP	£30	$55	€40

MARTINS, PETER

SP	£50	$90	€65
DS	£40	$75	€50
AP	£30	$55	€40

MARTZY, JOHANNA

SP	£50	$90	€65
DS	£40	$75	€50
AP	£30	$55	€40

MATTEI, TITO

SP	£50	$90	€65
DS	£40	$75	€50
AP	£30	$55	€40

MAY, PAMELA

SP	£50	$90	€65
DS	£40	$75	€50
AP	£30	$55	€40

MCCORMACK, JOHN

SP	£125	$225	€155
DS	£90	$160	€115
AP	£75	$135	€95

MCRAE, CARMEN

SP	£50	$90	€65
DS	£40	$75	€50
AP	£30	$55	€40

MELBA, NELLIE

SP	£300	$535	€370
DS	£250	$445	€310
AP	£195	$350	€240

MENDELSSOHN, FELIX

SP		*	
DS	£7,000	$12,405	€8,605
AP	£4,500	$7,975	€5,530

MENUHIN, YEHUDI

SP	£225	$400	€280
DS	£150	$270	€185
AP	£100	$180	€125

MILKINA, NINA

SP	£50	$90	€65
DS	£40	$75	€50
AP	£30	$55	€40

MILLER, GLENN

SP	£1,250	$2,215	€1,540
DS	£775	$1,375	€955
AP	£550	$975	€680

Benno Moiseiwitsch.

MOISEIWITSCH, BENNO

SP	£100	$180	€125
DS	£75	$135	€95
AP	£50	$90	€65

MOORE, GRACE

SP	£75	$135	€95
DS	£50	$90	€65
AP	£40	$75	€50

Oscar Natzka.

NATZKA, OSCAR

SP	£50	$90	€65
DS	£40	$75	€50
AP	£30	$55	€40

NERINA, NADIA

SP	£50	$90	€65
DS	£40	$75	€50
AP	£30	$55	€40

NEWMAN, YVONNE

SP	£50	$90	€65
DS	£40	$75	€50
AP	£30	$55	€40

NICOLAEVA-LEGAT, NADINE

SP	£50	$90	€65
DS	£35	$65	€45
AP	£25	$45	€35

NIKISCH, ARTHUR

SP	£50	$90	€65
DS	£40	$75	€50
AP	£30	$55	€40

NOVELLO, IVOR

SP	£65	$120	€80
DS	£55	$100	€70
AP	£45	$80	€60

NUREYEV, RUDOLF

SP	£275	$490	€340
DS	£225	$400	€280
AP	£175	$315	€220

OFFENBACH, JACQUES

SP	£995	$1,765	€1,225
DS	£750	$1,330	€925
AP	£450	$800	€555

PARAMOR, NORRIE

SP	£50	$90	€65
DS	£40	$75	€50
AP	£50	$90	€65

PARRY, CHARLES HUBERT HASTINGS

SP	£175	$315	€220
DS	£140	$250	€175
AP	£100	$180	€125

luciano pavarotti

PAVAROTTI, LUCIANO

SP	£350	$625	€435
DS	£150	$270	€185
AP	£100	$180	€125

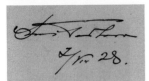

PAVLOVA, ANNA

SP	£600	$1,065	€740
DS	£500	$890	€615
AP	£400	$710	€495

PERLMAN, ITZHAK

SP	£50	$90	€65
DS	£30	$55	€40
AP	£20	$40	€25

PERRYMAN, RUFUS

SP	£30	$55	€40
DS	£25	$45	€35
AP	£15	$30	€20

PETIT, ROLAND

SP	£30	$55	€40
DS	£20	$40	€25
AP	£20	$40	€25

PETROSSIAN, RAFFI

SP	£50	$90	€65
DS	£40	$75	€50
AP	£30	$55	€40

PILARCZYK, HELGA

SP	£50	$90	€65
DS	£40	$75	€50
AP	£30	$55	€40

PORTER, COLE

SP	£750	$1,330	€925
DS	£695	$1,235	€855
AP	£550	$975	€680

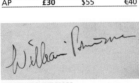

PREVIN, ANDRE

SP	£50	$90	€65
DS	£40	$75	€50
AP	£30	$55	€40

PRIMROSE, WILLIAM

SP	£50	$90	€65
DS	£40	$75	€50
AP	£30	$55	€40

PRING, KATHERINE

SP	£45	$80	€60
DS	£40	$75	€50
AP	£30	$55	€40

PUCCINI, GIACOMO

SP	£1,750	$3,105	€2,155
DS	£750	$1,330	€925
AP	£550	$975	€680

RACHMANINOFF, SERGEY

SP	£2,500	$4,430	€3,075
DS	£1,750	$3,105	€2,155
AP	£1,250	$2,215	€1,540

RAIKIN, BRUNO

SP	£50	$90	€65
DS	£40	$75	€50
AP	£30	$55	€40

RATTLE, SIMON

SP	£50	$90	€65
DS	£40	$75	€50
AP	£30	$55	€40

RAVEL, MAURICE

SP	£2,250	$3,990	€2,765
DS	£1,250	$2,215	€1,540
AP	£850	$1,510	€1,045

REEVES, (JOHN) SIMS

SP	£40	$75	€50
DS	£30	$55	€40
AP	£20	$40	€25

REYS, RITA

SP	£50	$90	€65
DS	£40	$75	€50
AP	£30	$55	€40

ROBESON, PAUL

SP	£300	$535	€370
DS	£225	$400	€280
AP	£175	$315	€220

ROSE, DAVID

SP	£50	$90	€65
DS	£40	$75	€50
AP	£30	$55	€40

ROSSINI, GIOACHINO

SP	£4,950	$8,770	€6,085
DS	£3,950	$7,000	€4,855
AP	£3,250	$5,760	€3,995

ROSTROPOWICZ, MSCISLAW

SP	£175	$315	€220
DS	£150	$270	€185
AP	£125	$225	€155

SAINT-SAENS, CAMILLE

SP	£750	$1,330	€925
DS	£395	$700	€490
AP	£250	$445	€310

SANDLER, ALBERT

SP	£50	$90	€65
DS	£40	$75	€50
AP	£30	$55	€40

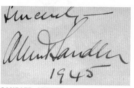

SANDLER, ARTHUR

SP	£50	$90	€65
DS	£40	$75	€50
AP	£30	$55	€40

SARGENT, MALCOLM

SP	£125	$225	€155
DS	£80	$145	€100
AP	£60	$110	€75

SCHUMANN, ROBERT

SP	*		
DS	£4,950	$8,770	€6,085
AP	£2,950	$5,230	€3,625

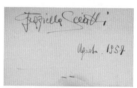

SCIUTTI, GRAZIELLA

SP	£95	$170	€120
DS	£70	$125	€90
AP	£50	$90	€65

SCOTT, HAZEL

SP	£50	$90	€65
DS	£40	$75	€50
AP	£30	$55	€40

SELLICK, PHYLLIS

SP	£50	$90	€65
DS	£40	$75	€50
AP	£30	$55	€40

SEMENOVA, MARINA

SP	£30	$55	€40
DS	£20	$40	€25
AP	£10	$20	€15

SEYMOUR, LYNN

SP	£50	$90	€65
DS	£40	$75	€50
AP	£30	$55	€40

SHABELEVSKI, YUREK

SP	£30	$55	€40
DS	£20	$40	€25
AP	£10	$20	€15

SHAND, ERNEST

SP	£100	$180	€125
DS	£75	$135	€95
AP	£60	$110	€75

SHAW, BRIAN

SP	£30	$55	€40
DS	£20	$40	€25
AP	£20	$40	€25

SHEARER, MOIRA

SP	£85	$155	€105
DS	£60	$110	€75
AP	£45	$80	€60

SHOSTAKOVICH, DIMITRI

SP	£1,250	$2,215	€1,540
DS	£950	$1,685	€1,170
AP	£550	$975	€680

SHUARD, AMY

SP	£50	$90	€65
DS	£40	$75	€50
AP	£30	$55	€40

SHUMAN, MORT

SP	£85	$155	€105
DS	£60	$110	€75
AP	£45	$80	€60

SIBELIUS, JEAN

SP	£995	$1,765	€1,225
DS	£750	$1,330	€925
AP	£650	$1,155	€800

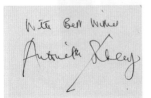

SIBLEY, ANTOINETTE

SP	£50	$90	€65
DS	£35	$65	€45
AP	£25	$45	€35

SONDHEIM, STEPHEN

SP	£100	$180	€125
DS	£75	$135	€95
AP	£50	$90	€65

SOUSA, JOHN PHILIP

SP	£1,500	$2,660	€1,845
DS	£750	$1,330	€925
AP	£450	$800	€555

SPOORENBERG, EMA

SP	£50	$90	€65
DS	£40	$75	€50
AP	£30	$55	€40

STAFFORD, JO

SP	£45	$80	€60
DS	£35	$65	€45
AP	£30	$55	€40

STARR, KAY

SP	£50	$90	€65
DS	£35	$65	€45
AP	£25	$45	€35

STITT, SONNY

SP	£150	$270	€185
DS	£100	$180	€125
AP	£75	$135	€95

STRAUSS, JOHANN (II)

SP	£1,950	$3,455	€2,400
DS	£1,500	$2,660	€1,845
AP	£995	$1,765	€1,225

STRAUSS, RICHARD

SP	£1,950	$3,455	€2,400
DS	£800	$1,420	€985
AP	£600	$1,065	€740

STRAVINSKI, IGOR

SP	£1,350	$2,395	€1,660
DS	£650	$1,155	€800
AP	£400	$710	€495

SUTHERLAND, JOAN

SP	£75	$135	€95
DS	£45	$80	€60
AP	£30	$55	€40

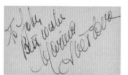

SVETLOVA, MARINA

SP	£50	$90	€65
DS	£40	$75	€50
AP	£30	$55	€40

TADDEI, GUISEPPE

SP	£50	$90	€65
DS	£40	$75	€50
AP	£30	$55	€40

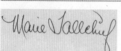

TALLCHIEF, MARIA

SP	£40	$75	€50
DS	£30	$55	€40
AP	£20	$40	€25

TARAKONOVA, NINA

SP	£30	$55	€40
DS	£20	$40	€25
AP	£10	$20	€15

TAUBER, RICHARD

SP	£50	$90	€65
DS	£40	$75	€50
AP	£30	$55	€40

TAYLOR, KOKO

SP	£75	$135	€95
DS	£60	$110	€75
AP	£45	$80	€60

TAYLOR, PAUL

SP	£30	$55	€40
DS	£20	$40	€25
AP	£10	$20	€15

TCHAIKOVSKY, PIOTR ILYICH

SP	£12,500	$22,145	€15,360
DS	£9,500	$16,830	€11,675
AP	£6,500	$11,515	€7,990

TESTORY, FRANCOIS

SP	£30	$55	€40
DS	£20	$40	€25
AP	£10	$20	€15

THEBOM, BLANCHE

SP	£50	$90	€65
DS	£40	$75	€50
AP	£30	$55	€40

THREE TENORS, THE

SP	£995	$1,765	€1,225
DS	£695	$1,235	€855
AP	£495	$880	€610

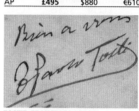

TOSTIE, FRANCESCO PAOLO

SP	£60	$110	€75
DS	£50	$90	€65
AP	£40	$75	€50

TOUMANOVA, TAMARA

SP	£50	$90	€65
DS	£40	$75	€50
AP	£30	$55	€40

PIRMIN TRECU

TRECU, PIRMIN

SP	£30	$55	€40
DS	£20	$40	€25
AP	£10	$20	€15

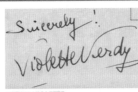

TRYON, VALERIE

SP	£50	$90	€65
DS	£40	$75	€50
AP	£30	$55	€40

TUCKER, RAVENNA

SP	£30	$55	€40
DS	£20	$40	€25
AP	£10	$20	€15

VERDY, VIOLETTE

SP	£30	$55	€40
DS	£20	$40	€25
AP	£10	$20	€15

WALL, DAVID

SP	£30	$55	€40
DS	£20	$40	€25
AP	£10	$20	€15

WEST, ELIZABETH AND CO.

SP	£75	$135	€95
DS	£60	$110	€75
AP	£45	$80	€60

VAN CAUWENBERGH, BEN

SP	£30	$55	€40
DS	£20	$40	€25
AP	£10	$20	€15

VETROV, ALEXANDER

SP	£30	$55	€40
DS	£20	$40	€25
AP	£10	$20	€15

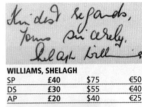

WILLIAMS, SHELAGH

SP	£40	$75	€50
DS	£30	$55	€40
AP	£20	$40	€25

VAUGHAN, SARAH

SP	£95	$170	€120
DS	£60	$110	€75
AP	£40	$75	€50

VIKHAREV, SERGI

SP	£30	$55	€40
DS	£20	$40	€25
AP	£10	$20	€15

WOICIKOWSKY, LEON

SP	£30	$55	€40
DS	£20	$40	€25
AP	£10	$20	€15

VERDI, GIUSEPPE

SP	£9,750	$17,275	€11,980
DS	£7,500	$13,290	€9,215
AP	£5,500	$9,745	€6,760

WAGNER, RICHARD

SP	*		
DS	£5,950	$10,545	€7,315
AP	£2,950	$5,230	€3,625

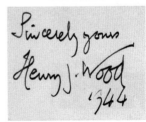

WOOD, HENRY J

SP	£60	$110	€75
DS	£50	$90	€65
AP	£40	$75	€50

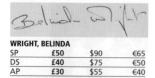

WRIGHT, BELINDA

SP	£50	$90	€65
DS	£40	$75	€50
AP	£30	$55	€40

ALLSTARS

SP	£50	$90	€65
DS	£40	$75	€50
AP	£30	$55	€40

BACKSTREET BOYS

SP	£50	$90	€65
DS	£40	$75	€50
AP	£30	$55	€40

ANIMALS, THE

SP	£125	$225	€155
DS	£100	$180	€125
AP	£75	$135	€95

YOW, DAVID

SP	£30	$55	€40
DS	£20	$40	€25
AP	£10	$20	€15

APPLETON

APPLETON

SP	£50	$90	€65
DS	£40	$75	€50
AP	£30	$55	€40

BANANARAMA

SP	£50	$90	€65
DS	£40	$75	€50
AP	£30	$55	€40

GROUPS

ABBA

SP	£895	$1,585	€1,100
DS	£850	$1,510	€1,045
AP	£575	$1,020	€710

ATOMIC KITTEN

SP	£125	$225	€155
DS	£100	$180	€125
AP	£75	$135	€95

BEACH BOYS, THE

SP	£950	$1,685	€1,170
DS	£950	$1,685	€1,170
AP	£750	$1,330	€925

AEROSMITH

SP	£160	$285	€200
DS	£200	$355	€250
AP	£100	$180	€125

AZTEC CAMERA

SP	£50	$90	€65
DS	£40	$75	€50
AP	£30	$55	€40

ALL SAINTS

SP	£250	$445	€310
DS	£200	$355	€250
AP	£125	$225	€155

BEATLES, THE

SP	£21,000	$37,200	€25,805
DS	*		
AP	£8,500	$15,060	€10,445

BEE GEES

SP	£225	$400	€280
DS	£195	$345	€240
AP	£175	$315	€220

BERRY, JAN & DEAN TORRENCE

SP	£150	$270	€185
DS	£125	$225	€155
AP	£100	$180	€125

BLACK EYED PEAS

SP	£185	$330	€230
DS	£200	$355	€250
AP	£90	$160	€115

BLINK 182

SP	£100	$180	€125
DS	£75	$135	€95
AP	£50	$90	€65

BLUE

SP	£150	$270	€185
DS	£130	$230	€160
AP	£75	$135	€95

BLUE MERCEDES

SP	£70	$125	€90
DS	£60	$110	€75
AP	£40	$75	€50

BLUR

SP	£75	$135	€95
DS	£60	$110	€75
AP	£40	$75	€50

BON JOVI

SP	£350	$620	€430
DS	£195	$345	€240
AP	£150	$270	€185

BOOMTOWN RATS, THE

SP	£75	$135	€95
DS	£50	$90	€65
AP	£30	$55	€40

BOYZONE

SP	£50	$90	€65
DS	£35	$65	€45
AP	£30	$55	€40

BRAND NEW HEAVIES

SP	£50	$90	€65
DS	£35	$65	€45
AP	£30	$55	€40

BROTHER BEYOND

SP	£50	$90	€65
DS	£45	$80	€55
AP	£35	$65	€45

BUZZCOCKS

SP	£50	$90	€65
DS	£40	$75	€50
AP	£30	$55	€40

THE CARDIGANS

CARDIGANS, THE

SP	£100	$180	€125
DS	£65	$115	€80
AP	£40	$75	€50

CARPENTERS, THE

SP	£1,800	$3,190	€2,215
DS	£1,800	$3,190	€2,215
AP	£1,400	$2,485	€1,725

CHAS AND DAVE

SP	£70	$125	€90
DS	£65	$115	€80
AP	£50	$90	€65

CHEMICAL BROTHERS, THE

SP	£70	$125	€90
DS	£60	$110	€75
AP	£30	$55	€40

CHINA CRISIS

SP	£50	$90	€65
DS	£40	$75	€50
AP	£30	$55	€40

COLDPLAY

SP	£200	$355	€250
DS	£150	$270	€185
AP	£90	$160	€115

CORRS, THE

SP	£175	$310	€215
DS	£150	$270	€185
AP	£70	$125	€90

CRANBERRIES, THE

SP	£50	$90	€65
DS	£40	$75	€50
AP	£30	$55	€40

CREAM

SP	£950	$1,685	€1,170
DS	£600	$1,065	€740
AP	£475	$845	€585

CREEDENCE CLEARWATER REVIVAL

SP	£475	$845	€585
DS	£180	$320	€225
AP	£125	$225	€155

CURE, THE

SP	£270	$480	€335
DS	£295	$525	€365
AP	£120	$215	€150

CURIOSITY KILLED THE CAT

SP	£50	$90	€65
DS	£40	$75	€50
AP	£30	$55	€40

DARKNESS, THE

SP	£150	$270	€185
DS	£140	$250	€175
AP	£80	$145	€100

DEATH

SP	£80	$145	€100
DS	£75	$135	€95
AP	£40	$75	€50

DEL AMITRI

SP	£75	$135	€95
DS	£70	$125	€90
AP	£35	$65	€45

DIXIE CHICKS, THE

SP	£125	$225	€155
DS	£125	$225	€155
AP	£75	$135	€95

DUBSTAR

SP	£50	$90	€65
DS	£40	$75	€50
AP	£30	$55	€40

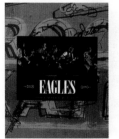

DURAN DURAN

SP	£195	$345	€240
DS	£125	$225	€155
AP	£90	$160	€115

EAGLES, THE

SP	£675	$1,200	€830
DS	£500	$890	€615
AP	£350	$625	€435

EMERSON, LAKE & PALMER

SP	£90	$160	€115
DS	£80	$145	€100
AP	£40	$75	€50

EMF

SP	£50	$90	€65
DS	£40	$75	€50
AP	£30	$55	€40

ERASURE

SP	£60	$110	€75
DS	£50	$90	€65
AP	£45	$80	€60

EURYTHMICS

SP	£130	$230	€160
DS	£125	$225	€155
AP	£60	$110	€75

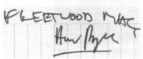

FLEETWOOD MAC

SP	*		
DS	£2,750	$4,875	€3,380
AP	£1,500	$2,660	€1,845

FOO FIGHTERS

SP	£175	$310	€215
DS	£160	$285	€200
AP	£80	$145	€100

FOUR PENNIES, THE

SP	£75	$135	€95
DS	£60	$110	€75
AP	£40	$75	€50

FREDDIE AND THE DREAMERS

SP	£75	$135	€95
DS	£65	$115	€80
AP	£35	$65	€45

GENESIS

SP	£350	$620	€430
DS	£295	$525	€365
AP	£250	$445	€310

Music Groups

GIRLS ALOUD

SP	**£225**	$400	€280
DS	**£175**	$310	€215
AP	**£100**	$180	€125

GUN

SP	**£75**	$135	€95
DS	**£65**	$115	€80
AP	**£40**	$75	€50

HAWKWIND

SP	**£200**	$355	€250
DS	**£175**	$310	€215
AP	**£125**	$225	€155

GO GO'S, THE

SP	**£50**	$90	€65
DS	**£50**	$90	€65
AP	**£40**	$75	€50

GUNS N' ROSES

SP	**£275**	$490	€340
DS	**£250**	$445	€310
AP	**£125**	$225	€155

HEAR'SAY

SP	**£75**	$135	€95
DS	**£65**	$115	€80
AP	**£50**	$90	€65

GRATEFUL DEAD, THE

SP	**£1,500**	$2,660	€1,845
DS	**£1,000**	$1,775	€1,230
AP	**£800**	$1,420	€985

HALEY, BILL & THE COMETS

SP	**£775**	$1,375	€955
DS	**£700**	$1,240	€860
AP	**£350**	$625	€435

HERMAN'S HERMITS

SP	**£75**	$135	€95
DS	**£65**	$115	€80
AP	**£40**	$75	€50

GRYPHON

SP	**£75**	$135	€95
DS	**£65**	$115	€80
AP	**£40**	$75	€50

HANSON

SP	**£40**	$75	€50
DS	**£30**	$55	€40
AP	**£25**	$45	€35

HOLLIES, THE

SP	**£50**	$90	€65
DS	**£40**	$75	€50
AP	**£30**	$55	€40

Music Groups

HOTHOUSE FLOWERS
SP	£75	$135	€95
DS	£40	$75	€50
AP	£30	$55	€40

JIMI HENDRIX EXPERIENCE
SP		*	
DS	£4,500	$7,975	€5,530
AP	£3,500	$6,205	€4,305

LIBERTY X
SP	£100	$180	€125
DS	£90	$160	€115
AP	£60	$110	€75

MAGUIRE SISTERS, THE
SP	£75	$135	€95
DS	£60	$110	€75
AP	£40	$75	€50

HUEY LEWIS AND THE NEWS
SP	£60	$110	€75
DS	£40	$75	€50
AP	£30	$55	€40

KEANE
SP	£150	$270	€185
DS	£130	$230	€160
AP	£75	$135	€95

MANFRED MANN
SP	£75	$135	€95
DS	£50	$90	€65
AP	£35	$65	€45

INDIGO GIRLS
SP	£50	$90	€65
DS	£40	$75	€50
AP	£30	$55	€40

KINKS, THE
SP	£50	$90	€65
DS	£40	$70	€50
AP	£30	$55	€40

IRON MAIDEN
SP	£100	$180	€125
DS	£100	$180	€125
AP	£50	$90	€65

KISS
SP	£600	$1,065	€740
DS	£600	$1,065	€740
AP	£375	$665	€465

MANIC STREET PREACHERS
SP	£250	$445	€310
DS	£250	$445	€310
AP	£100	$180	€125

JAM, THE
SP	£350	$620	€430
DS	£250	$445	€310
AP	£150	$270	€185

LED ZEPPELIN
SP	£5,950	$10,540	€7,315
DS	£5,500	$9,745	€6,760
AP	£3,950	$7,000	€4,855

MERSEYBEATS, THE
SP	£60	$110	€75
DS	£55	$100	€70
AP	£30	$55	€40

MISTEEQ

SP	£50	$90	€65
DS	£75	$135	€95
AP	£30	$55	€40

N.E.R.D.

SP	£75	$135	€95
DS	£40	$75	€50
AP	£30	$55	€40

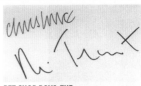

PET SHOP BOYS, THE

SP	£95	$170	€120
DS	£75	$135	€95
AP	£50	$90	€65

MONKEES, THE

SP	£650	$1,155	€800
DS	£250	$445	€310
AP	£200	$355	€250

NSYNC

SP	£125	$225	€155
DS	£110	$195	€135
AP	£50	$90	€65

PINK FLOYD

SP	£1,950	$3,455	€2,400
DS	£1,750	$3,100	€2,150
AP	£1,250	$2,215	€1,540

MOVE, THE

SP	£75	$135	€95
DS	£60	$110	€75
AP	£50	$90	€65

OASIS

SP	£295	$525	€365
DS	£275	$490	€340
AP	£150	$270	€185

POLICE, THE

SP	£995	$1,765	€1,225
DS	£1,500	$2,660	€1,845
AP	£495	$880	€610

NASHVILLE TEENS

SP	£75	$135	€95
DS	£40	$75	€50
AP	£30	$55	€40

OCEAN COLOUR SCENE

SP	£75	$135	€95
DS	£60	$110	€75
AP	£30	$55	€40

QUEEN

SP	£1,750	$3,100	€2,150
DS	£1,500	$2,660	€1,845
AP	£1,250	$2,215	€1,540

R.E.M.

SP	£375	$665	€465
DS	£300	$535	€370
AP	£150	$270	€185

RADIOHEAD

RADIOHEAD

SP	£225	$400	€280
DS	£200	$355	€250
AP	£100	$180	€125

THE RAMONES

RAMONES, THE

SP	£125	$225	€155
DS	£100	$180	€125
AP	£60	$110	€75

RED HOT CHILI PEPPERS, THE

SP	£275	$490	€340
DS	£250	$445	€310
AP	£130	$235	€160

ROLLING STONES, THE

SP	£5,000	$8,860	€6,145
DS	£4,950	$8,770	€6,085
AP	£1,750	$3,105	€2,155

S CLUB 7

SP	£200	$355	€250
DS	£150	$270	€185
AP	£150	$270	€185

SADE

SP	£85	$155	€105
DS	£75	$135	€95
AP	£40	$75	€50

SEARCHERS, THE

SP	£75	$135	€95
DS	£75	$135	€95
AP	£35	$65	€45

SEX PISTOLS, THE

SP	£2,950	$5,230	€3,625
DS	£3,000	$5,315	€3,690
AP	£2,000	$3,545	€2,460

SHADOWS

SP	£200	$355	€250
DS	£175	$310	€215
AP	£125	$225	€155

SIMON & GARFUNKEL

SP	£595	$1,055	€735
DS	£350	$620	€430
AP	£275	$490	€340

SLASH

SP	£100	$180	€125
DS	£80	$145	€100
AP	£50	$90	€65

SONNY & CHER

SP	£150	$270	€185
DS	£150	$270	€185
AP	£125	$225	€155

SPARKS

SP	£75	$135	€95
DS	£75	$135	€95
AP	£40	$75	€50

SPICE GIRLS, THE

SP	£350	$620	€430
DS	£300	$535	€370
AP	£200	$355	€250

SPRINGFIELDS, THE

SP	£80	$145	€100
DS	£75	$135	€95
AP	£40	$75	€50

SPRINGSTEEN, BRUCE & E STREET BAND

SP	£2,950	$5,230	€3,625
DS	£2,500	$4,430	€3,075
AP	£1,950	$3,455	€2,400

STATUS QUO

SP	£75	$135	€95
DS	£65	$115	€80
AP	£40	$75	€50

STEELY DAN

SP	£75	$135	€95
DS	£60	$110	€75
AP	£50	$90	€65

STEREOPHONICS

SP	£75	$135	€95
DS	£70	$125	€90
AP	£30	$55	€40

STRANGLERS, THE

SP	£50	$90	€65
DS	£40	$75	€50
AP	£30	$55	€40

STROKES, THE

SP	£150	$270	€185
DS	£150	$270	€185
AP	£75	$135	€95

SUGABABES

SP	£100	$180	€125
DS	£85	$155	€105
AP	£35	$65	€45

SUM 41

SP	£75	$135	€95
DS	£65	$115	€80
AP	£30	$55	€40

SWINGING BLUE JEANS, THE

SP	£150	$270	€185
DS	£100	$180	€125
AP	£40	$75	€50

T.REX

SP	£1,950	$3,455	€2,400
DS	£1,750	$3,100	€2,150
AP	£1,000	$1,775	€1,230

TAKE THAT

SP	£295	$525	€365
DS	£275	$490	€340
AP	£125	$225	€155

TEN CC

SP	£100	$180	€125
DS	£100	$180	€125
AP	£60	$110	€75

THEM

SP	£150	$270	€185
DS	£130	$230	€160
AP	£75	$135	€95

TIN MACHINE

SP	£225	$400	€280
DS	£125	$225	€155
AP	£60	$110	€75

TORRES, TICO

SP	£75	$135	€95
DS	£70	$125	€90
AP	£35	$65	€45

TRAVIS

SP	£150	$270	€185
DS	£130	$230	€160
AP	£70	$125	€90

TROGGS, THE

SP	£75	$135	€95
DS	£60	$110	€75
AP	£40	$75	€50

U2

SP	£795	$1,410	€980
DS	£400	$710	€495
AP	£300	$535	€370

UNIT 4 PLUS 2

SP	£75	$135	€95
DS	£60	$110	€75
AP	£35	$65	€45

WAS NOT WAS

SP	£50	$90	€65
DS	£40	$75	€50
AP	£30	$55	€40

WESTLIFE

SP	£175	$310	€215
DS	£100	$180	€125
AP	£75	$135	€95

WET WET WET

SP	£50	$90	€65
DS	£35	$65	€45
AP	£30	$55	€40

WHAM

SP	£175	$310	€215
DS	£150	$270	€185
AP	£75	$135	€95

WHEATUS

SP	£50	$90	€65
DS	£40	$75	€50
AP	£30	$55	€40

WHO, THE

SP	£4,500	$7,975	€5,530
DS	£3,500	$6,200	€4,300
AP	£2,500	$4,430	€3,075

The Who

In 1961 a band was formed by Roger Daltrey and John Entwistle, originally called *The Detours*. Pete Townshend joined the band a year later and finally, in 1964, after the band changed their name to *The Who*, Keith Moon was recruited as the band's drummer. *The Who* rose to fame in the UK and became famous with their instrument destruction on stage. They had a series of top ten singles including perhaps most famously *"My Generation"* and four top selling albums. The band broke America in 1967 and 1969 saw the release of *"Tommy"*, their fifth album. The band was going from strength to strength, until tragedy struck in 1978 with the death of Keith Moon. However, the band continued producing, releasing two more albums with new drummer Kenney Jones. It was not until 1983 that the band officially split.

The Who reformed briefly for events such as Live Aid and reunion tours including their 25th anniversary tour in 1989.

John Entwistle died in 2002, leaving Roger Daltrey and Pete Townshend as the only surviving original members of *The Who*. In 2006 they finally got back together for a 6th album, *"Endless Wire"*, which was a top ten hit in the UK and US, and the band toured once more in 2007.

Politics

Politics is one of the more popular areas of collecting, particularly in the USA where there is a strong focus on collecting presidential signatures. Among British collectors there tends not to be as great a focus on prime ministers as there is on American presidents.

The value of a political personality's autograph is directly determined by the effect they have had on their country's history, whether positive or negative, if they appear in history books then you can pretty much bet that their autograph will hold some significant value. Of course autographs dated during their period of office are far more desirable than earlier or later examples. Certain types of material on which the autograph appears are common – clipped pages, index cards and signed business cards are prevalent and therefore are not as desirable as documents. Documents, such as military appointments, discharges and land grants, which offer unique political insights into the administration, are far rarer as they are generally held in state archiving and therefore command higher prices. The name that commands the most interest in the field of collecting at the moment is George Washington, his signature can command exceptionally high prices, averaging around £30,000 for a good clean example. U.S. Grant's signature is a close second and rising in value rapidly as demand increases and more examples disappear into private collections.

It is does not necessarily follow that if a name holds a high value that it is the most desirable to collectors, the market at the moment is trying to meet a high demand for J.F. Kennedy's and Margaret Thatcher's signatures. In recent years the demand for other modern names in the political field has also risen - Nelson Mandela, Fidel Castro, Che Guevara and Mahatma Gandhi, all of which are relatively hard to come by as documents are still retained by private institutes.

Collectors may be surprised at how early the autopen was utilised, both J.F. Kennedy and Winston Churchill sent out autopen letters during their terms in office. The market is flooded with Churchill's autopen thank you letters on headed paper which were sent out en masse to those who had wished him well on his birthday or perhaps sent a gift. The general rule is that if the letter in question has not been addressed or made out to anyone in particular then you may be looking at an autopen example. Nearly 90% of these letters are autopen examples and are therefore worthless copies of Churchill's authentic signature. Also be particularly wary of secretarial, facsimile and printed signatures. Forgeries are rife within this area of collecting as there is such a high demand for investment grade authenticated examples. As ever, it is always best to deal with a reputable dealer.

Politics

ADAMS, GERRY

SP	£100	$180	€125
DS	£75	$135	€95
AP	£50	$90	€65

ASQUITH, HERBERT HENRY

SP	£2,500	$4,430	€3,075
DS	£1,750	$3,100	€2,150
AP	£1,250	$2,215	€1,540

ASTOR, WALDORF. K

SP	£125	$225	€155
DS	£75	$135	€95
AP	£50	$90	€65

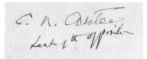

ATLEE, CLEMENT

SP	£125	$225	€155
DS	£75	$135	€95
AP	£50	$90	€65

ATTWOOD, THOMAS

SP	*		
DS	£60	$110	€75
AP	£40	$75	€50

BALDWIN, STANLEY

SP	£450	$800	€555
DS	£350	$620	€430
AP	£275	$490	€340

BALFOUR, ARTHUR JAMES

SP	£325	$580	€400
DS	£250	$445	€310
AP	£200	$355	€250

BEGIN, MENACHEM

SP	£125	$225	€155
DS	£100	$180	€125
AP	£75	$135	€95

BEVAN, ANEURIN

SP	£45	$80	€55
DS	£35	$65	€45
AP	£20	$35	€25

BEVIN, ERNEST

SP	£50	$90	€65
DS	£45	$80	€55
AP	£30	$55	€40

BLAIR, TONY

SP	£350	$620	€430
DS	£250	$445	€310
AP	£125	$225	€155

BOTHA, LOUIS

SP	£150	$270	€185
DS	£100	$180	€125
AP	£80	$145	€100

BUTLER, RAB

SP	£90	$160	€115
DS	£70	$125	€90
AP	£50	$90	€65

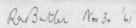

BUTLER, RICHARD AUSTIN

SP	£100	$180	€125
DS	£85	$155	€105
AP	£45	$80	€55

CALLAGHAN, JAMES

SP	£150	$270	€185
DS	£100	$180	€125
AP	£75	$135	€95

CANNING, GEORGE

SP	£250	$445	€310
DS	£180	$320	€225
AP	£125	$225	€155

CARDIGAN, JAMES THOMAS BRUDENELL

SP	£650	$1,155	€800
DS	£495	$880	€610
AP	£350	$620	€435

CASTLE, BARBARA

SP	£65	$115	€80
DS	£45	$80	€55
AP	£30	$55	€40

CASTRO, FIDEL

SP	£3,950	$7,000	€4,855
DS	£2,500	$4,430	€3,075
AP	£1,750	$3,100	€2,150

CHAMBERLAIN, AUSTEN

SP	£150	$270	€185
DS	£100	$180	€125
AP	£75	$135	€95

CHAMBERLAIN, JOSEPH

SP	£300	$535	€370
DS	£250	$445	€310
AP	£195	$345	€240

Mahatma Gandhi

Born Mohandas Karamchand Gandhi on October 2nd 1869, he is better known by the name of Mahatma, meaning *"great soul"*. Aged 19 he travelled to England to study law. After returning to India in 1891, he then travelled on to South Africa - as the country's first *"non-white"* lawyer - where he was to remain for 20 years.

Returning to India in 1914, it is here where he is now best remembered for his campaign for home rule and for India to gain her independence from Great Britain. Mahatma always insisted on his campaign through non-violence. Although imprisoned on many occasions, this never weakened his resolve on anything other than peaceful means.

In 1947 India finally won her independence from Britain, though unfortunately the partitioning of the country to form two nations, India and Pakistan, dampened enthusiasm for the change. Just one year later in 1948, Mahatma was assassinated by a fellow Hindu who felt he had betrayed the Hindu cause.

CHURCHILL, WINSTON

SP	£5,500	$9,745	€6,760
DS	£4,750	$8,415	€5,840
AP	£2,250	$3,990	€2,765

CLINTON, BILL

SP	£995	$1,765	€1,225
DS	£450	$800	€555
AP	£250	$445	€310

with best wishes, Hillary Rodham Clinton

CLINTON, HILLARY

SP	£85	$155	€105
DS	£75	$135	€95
AP	£50	$90	€65

COSGROVE, W T

SP	£100	$180	€125
DS	£80	$145	€100
AP	£60	$110	€75

COTTENHAM, CHARLES PEPYS - EARL OF

SP	£85	$155	€105
DS	£60	$110	€75
AP	£45	$80	€55

Frank Cousins

COUSINS, FRANK

SP	£75	$135	€95
DS	£50	$90	€65
AP	£30	$55	€40

DAYAN, MOSHE

SP	£550	$975	€680
DS	£450	$800	€555
AP	£300	$535	€370

DE GAULLE, CHARLES

SP	£1,750	$3,100	€2,150
DS	£995	$1,765	€1,225
AP	£750	$1,330	€925

DERBY, LORD

SP	£150	$270	€185
DS	£100	$180	€125
AP	£80	$145	€100

DEWET, N.J

SP	£90	$160	€115
DS	£75	$135	€95
AP	£45	$80	€55

DISRAELI, BENJAMIN

SP	£950	$1,685	€1,170
DS	£775	$1,375	€955
AP	£395	$700	€490

EISENHOWER, DWIGHT D

SP	£750	$1,330	€925
DS	£450	$800	€555
AP	£250	$445	€310

Politics

FORD, GERALD

SP	£750	$1,330	€925
DS	£775	$1,375	€955
AP	£125	$225	€155

FOX, CHARLES JAMES

SP	*		
DS	£295	$525	€365
AP	£200	$355	€250

FRANCO, FRANCISCO

SP	£995	$1,765	€1,225
DS	£750	$1,330	€925
AP	£350	$620	€430

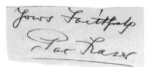

FRASER, PAT

SP	£75	$135	€95
DS	£65	$115	€80
AP	£45	$80	€55

GADDAFI, COLONEL MUAMMAR

SP	£450	$800	€555
DS	£350	$620	€430
AP	£295	$525	€365

GANDHI, INDIRA

SP	£375	$665	€465
DS	£300	$535	€370
AP	£225	$400	€280

GANDHI, MAHATMA

SP	£4,500	$7,975	€5,530
DS	£1,250	$2,215	€1,540
AP	£950	$1,685	€1,170

GLADSTONE, JOHN

SP	*		
DS	£45	$80	€55
AP	£30	$55	€40

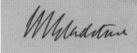

GLADSTONE, WILLIAM E

SP	£750	$1,330	€925
DS	£350	$620	€430
AP	£200	$355	€250

GORBACHEV, MIKHAIL

SP	£495	$880	€610
DS	£300	$535	€370
AP	£250	$445	€310

GORE, AL

SP	£350	$620	€430
DS	£250	$445	€310
AP	£125	$225	€155

GRANT, ULYSSES S.

SP	£4,950	$8,770	€6,085
DS	£1,750	$3,100	€2,150
AP	£1,250	$2,215	€1,540

GRANVILLE, GEORGE - EARL GRANVILLE

SP	£100	$180	€125
DS	£75	$135	€95
AP	£45	$80	€55

GREY, CHARLES

SP	*		
DS	£95	$170	€120
AP	£75	$135	€95

GUEVARA, CHE

SP	£6,500	$11,515	€7,990
DS	£4,950	$8,770	€6,085
AP	£3,000	$5,315	€3,690

HEATH, EDWARD

SP	£100	$180	€125
DS	£85	$155	€105
AP	£75	$135	€95

Adolf Hitler

Born on April 20th 1889 in Braunau am Inn, Austria. One of six children, Adolf was said to have had a troubled childhood. Indeed he is said to have told his secretary in later years that *"I then resolved never again to cry when my father whipped me"*. Whether this troubled childhood was the catalyst for his later years has always been the subject of great debate.

It was often said that Adolf's father wanted him to follow in his footsteps and become a customs official. Adolf himself wanted to become a painter, and in addition to his painting he was also a writer and a politician. In 1932 he gave up his Austrian citizenship and became a native German.

For all the evil history behind the man, Hitler memorabilia is nonetheless extremely collectable. Among the two top selling forms of Hitler memorabilia are signed autographs and his water colours. By taking a look through this guide, you will see that to own a Hitler autograph will be an investment along the lines of Churchill and Che Guevara.

HESELTINE, MICHAEL

SP	£50	$90	€65
DS	£40	$75	€50
AP	£30	$55	€40

HESS, RUDOLPH

SP	£1,500	$2,660	€1,845
DS	£750	$1,330	€925
AP	£450	$800	€555

HINDENBURG, PAUL VON

SP	£2,950	$5,230	€3,625
DS	£2,000	$3,545	€2,460
AP	£1,500	$2,660	€1,845

HIROHITO - EMPEROR OF JAPAN

SP	*		
DS	£6,750	$11,960	€8,295
AP	£3,500	$6,200	€4,300

HITLER, ADOLF

SP	£4,950	$8,770	€6,085
DS	£4,250	$7,530	€5,225
AP	£2,500	$4,430	€3,075

P. C.   G. C. B.   C. H.
Prime Minister of New Zealand 1949 - 1957.

HOLLAND, SIDNEY

SP	£60	$110	€75
DS	£45	$80	€55
AP	£30	$55	€40

HOME, LORD

SP	£500	$890	€615
DS	£350	$620	€430
AP	£250	$445	€310

HOOVER, J. EDGAR

SP	£275	$490	€340
DS	£195	$345	€240
AP	£150	$270	€185

HUME, JOSEPH

SP	£100	$180	€125
DS	£75	$135	€95
AP	£30	$55	€40

HUSKISSON, WILLIAM

SP	£225	$400	€280
DS	£150	$270	€185
AP	£100	$180	€125

HUSSEIN, SADDAM

SP	£1,750	$3,100	€2,150
DS	£1,250	$2,215	€1,540
AP	£250	$445	€310

INGLES, ROBERT

SP	£65	$115	€80
DS	£45	$80	€55
AP	£30	$55	€40

JEFFREYS, GEORGE

SP	*		
DS	£3,950	$7,000	€4,855
AP	£3,000	$5,315	€3,690

KAISER, WILHELM I

SP	£1,750	$3,100	€2,150
DS	£1,250	$2,215	€1,540
AP	£850	$1,510	€1,045

Politics

KAISER, WILHELM II

SP	£450	$800	€555
DS	£250	$445	€310
AP	£180	$320	€225

KAI-SHEK, CHANG

SP	£950	$1,685	€1,170
DS	£750	$1,330	€925
AP	£450	$800	€555

KENNEDY, JACQUELINE

SP	£2,250	$3,990	€2,765
DS	£1,450	$2,570	€1,785
AP	£850	$1,510	€1,045

KENNEDY, JOHN & ROBERT & TED

SP	£6,950	$12,315	€8,540
DS		*	
AP	£2,950	$5,230	€3,625

KENNEDY, JOHN F

SP	£4,500	$7,975	€5,530
DS	£2,550	$4,520	€3,135
AP	£2,000	$3,545	€2,460

KENNEDY, ROBERT F.

SP	£1,500	$2,660	€1,845
DS	£875	$1,550	€1,075
AP	£550	$975	€680

KENNEDY, TED

SP	£450	$800	€555
DS	£295	$525	€365
AP	£150	$270	€185

Martin Luther King

Born January 15th 1929, much has been written, discussed and said about the son of a pastor from a Baptist Church in Atlanta, Georgia, USA. Born Michael Luther King Jnr., he later changed his name to Martin and attended segregated public schools in Georgia before graduating from high school aged 15.

Between 1957 and 1968, Martin Luther King travelled over 6 million miles, spoke over 2,500 times, met with President John F. Kennedy, campaigned for Lyndon Johnson, was arrested around 25 times and wrote five books. In 1964 aged just 35, he was awarded the Nobel Peace Prize.

In August 1963 he delivered his *"I have a dream"* speech in which he envisioned that one day there would be equality and freedom for all in America. He even predicted that he may not live to see this dream. It was on a visit to Memphis, Tennessee in April 1968, aged just 39, when he was assassinated by a lone gunman.

KHOMEINI, AYATOLLAH

SP	£1,500	$2,660	€1,845
DS	£1,000	$1,775	€1,230
AP	£875	$1,550	€1,075

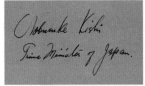

KHRUSCHEV, NIKITA

SP	£1,950	$3,455	€2,400
DS	£1,500	$2,660	€1,845
AP	£1,000	$1,775	€1,230

KING, MARTIN LUTHER

SP	£7,500	$13,290	€9,215
DS	£4,500	$7,975	€5,530
AP	£2,950	$5,230	€3,625

KISHI, NOBUSUKE

SP	£85	$155	€105
DS	£65	$115	€80
AP	£45	$80	€55

LANDSDOWN, HENRY - MARQUIS OF

SP	£75	$135	€95
DS	£50	$90	€65
AP	£30	$55	€40

LINCOLN, ABRAHAM

SP	*		
DS	£15,000	$26,575	€18,430
AP	£1,950	$3,455	€2,400

MACMILLAN, HAROLD

SP	£300	$535	€370
DS	£225	$400	€280
AP	£125	$225	€155

MAJOR, JOHN

SP	£150	$270	€185
DS	£100	$180	€125
AP	£75	$135	€95

MANDELA, NELSON

SP	£1,250	$2,215	€1,540
DS	£1,000	$1,775	€1,230
AP	£750	$1,330	€925

McCARTHYISM
THE FIGHT FOR AMERICA

MCCARTHY, JOE

SP	£750	$1,330	€925
DS	£595	$1,055	€735
AP	£350	$620	€430

MELBOURNE, WILLIAM LAMB - 2ND VISCOUNT

SP	*		
DS	£395	$700	€485
AP	£275	$490	€340

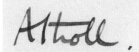

MURRAY, KATHERINE - DUCHESS OF ATHOLL

SP	£75	$135	€95
DS	£50	$90	€65
AP	£30	$55	€40

MUSSOLINI, BENITO & VICTOR EMMANUEL III

SP	£2,750	$4,875	€3,380
DS	£975	$1,730	€1,200
AP	£350	$620	€430

NASH, WALTER

SP	£65	$115	€80
DS	£45	$80	€55
AP	£30	$55	€40

"I made my mistakes, but in all of my years of public life, I have never profited, never profited from public service-I have earned every cent. And in all of my years of public life, I have never obstructed justice. And I think, too, that I could say that in my years of public life, that I welcome that kind of examination, because people have got to know whether or not their President is a crook. Well, I am not a crook. I have earned everything I have got."

President Richard Nixon, November 17, 1973

NIXON, RICHARD

SP	£1,500	$2,660	€1,845
DS	£1,250	$2,215	€1,540
AP	£950	$1,685	€1,170

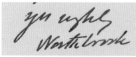

NORIEGA, MANUEL

SP	£75	$135	€95
DS	£50	$90	€65
AP	£30	$55	€40

NORTHBROOK, THOMAS BARING - EARL

SP	£75	$135	€95
DS	£45	$80	€55
AP	£30	$55	€40

OWEN, DAVID

SP	£65	$115	€80
DS	£45	$80	€55
AP	£30	$55	€40

PALMERSTON, HENRY - 3RD VISCOUNT

SP	*		
DS	£450	$800	€555
AP	£100	$180	€125

PEEL, ROBERT

SP	*		
DS	£400	$710	€495
AP	£225	$400	€280

PEPYS, SAMUEL

SP	*		
DS	£4,500	$7,975	€5,530
AP	£3,500	$6,200	€4,300

PERCEVAL, SPENCER

SP	*		
DS	£275	$490	€340
AP	£200	$355	€250

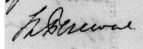

PERON, EVA

SP	£995	$1,765	€1,225
DS	£950	$1,685	€1,170
AP	£850	$1,510	€1,045

PERON, JUAN

SP	£650	$1,155	€800
DS	£375	$665	€465
AP	£250	$445	€310

PINOCHET, AUGUSTO

SP	£400	$710	€495
DS	£325	$580	€400
AP	£250	$445	€310

POWELL, ENOCH

SP	£75	$135	€95
DS	£50	$90	€65
AP	£50	$90	€65

RABIN, ITZHAK

SP	£125	$225	€155
DS	£100	$180	€125
AP	£75	$135	€95

REAGAN, RONALD

SP	£1,500	$2,660	€1,845
DS	£1,250	$2,215	€1,540
AP	£650	$1,155	€800

RUSSELL, LORD JOHN EARL

SP	*		
DS	£275	$490	€340
AP	£225	$400	€280

SIDMOUTH, HENRY ADDINGTON - 1ST VISCOUNT

SP	*		
DS	£250	$445	€310
AP	£100	$180	€125

SMITH, IAN DOUGLAS -

SP	£100	$180	€125
DS	£75	$135	€95
AP	£60	$110	€75

SMUTS, JAN CHRISTIAAN

SP	£150	$270	€185
DS	£125	$225	€155
AP	£100	$180	€125

STRANG, GAVIN

SP	£65	$115	€80
DS	£45	$80	€55
AP	£30	$55	€40

TAFT, WILLIAM HOWARD

SP	£750	$1,330	€925
DS	£600	$1,065	€740
AP	£495	$880	€610

TAYLOR, ANN

SP	£75	$135	€95
DS	£45	$80	€55
AP	£30	$55	€40

THATCHER, MARGARET

SP	£395	$700	€485
DS	£250	$445	€310
AP	£120	$215	€150

THORPE, JEREMY

SP	£85	$155	€105
DS	£65	$115	€80
AP	£40	$75	€50

TROTSKY, LEON

SP	£3,950	$7,000	€4,855
DS	£2,750	$4,875	€3,380
AP	£1,500	$2,660	€1,845

WALESA, LECH

SP	£150	$270	€185
DS	£100	$180	€125
AP	£75	$135	€95

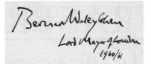

WALEY - COHEN, BERNARD

SP	£1,500	$2,660	€1,845
DS	£75	$135	€95
AP	£30	$55	€40

WALPOLE, ROBERT

SP	£550	$975	€680
DS	£525	$935	€645
AP	£350	$620	€430

WASHINGTON, GEORGE

SP	*		
DS	£19,950	$35,345	€24,515
AP	£12,000	$21,260	€14,745

WATERSON, SIDNEY

SP	£75	$135	€95
DS	£45	$80	€55
AP	£30	$55	€40

WILKINSON, ELLEN

SP	£75	$135	€95
DS	£45	$80	€55
AP	£30	$55	€40

WILSON, HAROLD

SP	£100	$180	€125
DS	£65	$115	€80
AP	£30	$55	€40

Royalty

Documents signed by monarchs and aristocrats are highly collectable as they tend to be of historic significance and if the documents are dated to a period of notoriety within the monarch's reign then this furthers the value of the signature. Documents signed by popular, early monarchs such as Elizabeth I and Henry VIII, if in fine condition, can also be very attractive display pieces as they are usually large pieces on parchment or vellum in a handwritten script, those with original seals, signed boldly and elaborately by the monarch are particularly desirable to collectors.

It is also important that a collector of royalty and aristocracy learns to recognise the signed initials and monograms of the monarchs, as often they would not sign in full. For example, Henry IV signed 'H.R.' and Richard II 'Le roy R.S.'. Luckily, due to the thorough documentation of monarch's reigns we can more easily account for changes in their style of signing. Later in his reign, when George III became blind and suffered from insanity, his signature varied considerably, becoming ill formed at times and even illegible. If such a signature appeared on the market, dated from this period in George's reign we may assume that not all would recognise the incomprehensible scribble for what it is, this is the satisfaction that comes from collecting within the field of royalty.

Even today it can be particularly difficult to find a signed photograph of a monarch, they are particularly rare due to the fact that signed photographs are usually given as commemorative gifts and so are retained privately; therefore they rarely appear on the open market. Likewise, a large majority of royal signatures are held by museums and public archives, which consequently drives up the signer's value.

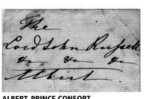

ADELAIDE, MARY - DUCHESS OF TECK

SP	*		
DS	£375	$665	€465
AP	£250	$445	€310

ALBERT, PRINCE CONSORT

SP	*		
DS	£600	$1,065	€740
AP	£295	$525	€365

monday 25 April, 1960

ALEXANDRA, PRINCESS OF WALES

SP	*		
DS	£300	$535	€370
AP	£50	$90	€65

ANNE - QUEEN OF ENGLAND, SCOTLAND & IRELAND

SP	*		
DS	£5,950	$10,545	€7,315
AP	£3,000	$5,315	€3,690

BEDFORD, DUCHESS OF

SP	*		
DS	£150	$270	€185
AP	£30	$55	€40

BEDFORD, DUKE OF

SP	*		
DS	£150	$270	€185
AP	£30	$55	€40

BLANTYRE, LORD

SP	*		
DS	£150	$270	€185
AP	£50	$90	€65

CAMBRIDGE, GEORGE - DUKE OF

SP	*		
DS	£165	$295	€205
AP	£65	$120	€80

CATHERINE THE GREAT

SP	*		
DS	£5,000	$8,860	€6,145
AP	£2,250	$3,990	€2,765

CHARLES I

SP	*		
DS	£4,500	$7,975	€5,530
AP	£2,500	$4,430	€3,075

CHARLES II

SP	*		
DS	£4,500	$7,975	€5,530
AP	£2,000	$3,545	€2,460

CHARLES & DIANA

SP	£8,000	$14,175	€9,830
DS	£4,950	$8,770	€6,085
AP	£3,500	$6,205	€4,305

DEVEREUX, ROBERT - ESSEX, 2ND EARL OF

SP	*		
DS	£5,000	$8,860	€6,145
AP	£2,500	$4,430	€3,075

DIANA, PRINCESS OF WALES

SP	£7,500	$13,290	€9,215
DS	£3,500	$6,205	€4,305
AP	£2,500	$4,430	€3,075

EDWARD SEYMOUR, DUKE OF SOMERSET

SP	*		
DS	*		
AP	£2,500	$4,430	€3,075

EDWARD IV

SP	*		
DS	£150,000	$265,720	€184,300
AP	*		

EDWARD VI

SP	*		
DS	£30,000	$53,145	€36,860
AP	£18,500	$32,775	€22,735

EDWARD VII

SP	£1,250	$2,215	€1,540
DS	£850	$1,510	€1,045
AP	£450	$800	€555

EDWARD VIII

SP	**£5,000**	$8,860	€6,145
DS	**£3,500**	$6,205	€4,305
AP	**£1,500**	$2,660	€1,845

EDWARD, DUKE OF WINDSOR

SP	**£950**	$1,685	€1,170
DS	**£750**	$1,330	€925
AP	**£400**	$710	€495

ELIZABETH I

SP	*		
DS	**£39,000**	$69,090	€47,920
AP	**£20,000**	$35,430	€24,575

ELIZABETH II

SP	**£2,000**	$3,545	€2,460
DS	**£1,500**	$2,660	€1,845
AP	**£800**	$1,420	€985

Elizabeth I

Possibly the most famous signature of all time is that of one of England's most famous monarchs. Elizabeth I is credited for one of the golden eras of English history. Born on 7th September 1533, she was declared illegitimate by her Father, Henry VIII, when her mother Anne Boleyn was executed when she was just three years old.

She was reinstated in 1558 when her sister, the Catholic, Queen Mary, died. Although Elizabeth was only 25 years old, she set out to rule by good council and surrounded herself with trusted advisors, who she depended on greatly.

This strong base would be tested several times throughout her reign, not least by Philippe of Spain, who in 1588 sent a huge armada to ferry the Spanish invasion fleet across the channel from Flanders and Holland. Disaster was averted at the last moment by the quick thinking English fleet and not a small amount of luck.

Her rule was always underlined by religion, her decision not to marry and the great works of literacy by the likes of Marlowe and Shakespeare. But the stability of her 44 years on the throne saw Britain take the first steps to a national identity and the country gradually becoming one of the foremost international powers.

ELIZABETH II & PRINCE PHILIP

SP	*		
DS	**£1,950**	$3,455	€2,400
AP	*		

ELIZABETH, THE QUEEN MOTHER

SP	**£1,500**	$2,660	€1,845
DS	**£900**	$1,595	€1,110
AP	**£500**	$890	€615

EMPRESS EUGENIE DE MONJITO

SP	*		
DS	*		
AP	**£200**	$355	€250

FAISAL, KING OF SAUDI ARABIA

SP	**£700**	$1,245	€865
DS	*		
AP	*		

FRANCIS I, KING OF SPAIN

SP	*		
DS	£5,000	$8,860	€6,145
AP	*		

GEORGE - DUKE OF KENT

SP	*		
DS	£300	$535	€370
AP	£125	$225	€155

GEORGE, EARL OF ABERDEEN

SP	*		
DS	£250	$445	€310
AP	£100	$180	€125

GEORGE II, KING OF GREAT BRITAIN

SP	*		
DS	£850	$1,510	€1,045
AP	£550	$975	€680

GEORGE III, KING OF ENGLAND

SP	£1,250	$2,215	€1,540
DS	£900	$1,595	€1,110
AP	£450	$800	€555

GEORGE IV, KING OF GREAT BRITAIN

SP	*		
DS	£495	$880	€610
AP	£395	$700	€490

GEORGE V, KING OF GREAT BRITAIN

SP	£1,400	$2,485	€1,725
DS	£1,500	$2,660	€1,845
AP	£900	$1,595	€1,110

GEORGE VI, KING OF GREAT BRITAIN

SP	£800	$1,420	€985
DS	£550	$975	€680
AP	£200	$355	€250

GEORGE, PRINCE OF CAMBRIDGE

SP	*		
DS	£50	$90	€65
AP	£30	$55	€40

GUSTAVUS V, KING OF SWEDEN

SP	*		
DS	£200	$355	€250
AP	£100	$180	€125

HADDOCK, SIR RICHARD

SP	*		
DS	£400	$710	€495
AP	£150	$270	€185

HENRY VIII

SP	*		
DS	£40,000	$70,860	€49,150
AP	£20,000	$35,430	€24,575

ISABELLA I, QUEEN OF SPAIN

SP	*		
DS	£5,000	$8,860	€6,145
AP	*		

JAMES I,
KING OF ENGLAND AND SCOTLAND

SP	*		
DS	£4,500	$7,975	€5,530
AP	*		

JAMES II, KING OF ENGLAND

SP	*		
DS	£5,000	$8,860	€6,145
AP	*		

KELLY, GRACE & PRINCE RAINIER

SP	£850	$1,510	€1,045
DS	£750	$1,330	€925
AP	£495	$880	€610

LOUIS XIV

SP	*		
DS	£5,950	$10,545	€7,315
AP	£4,995	$8,850	€6,140

LOUIS XVI, KING OF FRANCE

SP	*		
DS	£2,000	$3,545	€2,460
AP	*		

LOUIS XV, KING OF FRANCE

SP	*		
DS	£975	$1,730	€1,200
AP	£750	$1,330	€925

MARGARET, PRINCESS

SP	*		
DS	£100	$180	€125
AP	£50	$90	€65

MARIE ANTOINETTE

SP	*		
DS	£7,500	$13,290	€9,215
AP	*		

MARY, QUEEN OF GREAT BRITAIN

SP	*		
DS	£500	$890	€615
AP	£195	$350	€240

MARY I, QUEEN OF SCOTS

SP	*		
DS	£40,000	$70,860	€49,150
AP	*		

MARY HANOVER,
DUCHESS OF GLOUCESTER

SP	*		
DS	£225	$400	€280
AP	£50	$90	€65

MONMOUTH, DUKE OF

SP	*		
DS	£1,250	$2,215	€1,540
AP	£550	$975	€680

NICHOLAS I

SP	*		
DS	£1,500	$2,660	€1,845
AP	£750	$1,330	€925

NICHOLAS II

SP	*		
DS	£2,500	$4,430	€3,075
AP	£1,500	$2,660	€1,845

Royalty

PETER I OF RUSSIA

SP	*		
DS	£35,000	$62,005	€43,005
AP	*		

PRINCE PHILIP, DUKE OF EDINBURGH

SP	£675	$1,200	€830
DS	£495	$880	€610
AP	£195	$350	€240

PRINCESS LOUISE, DUCHESS OF ARGYLL

SP	*		
DS	£75	$135	€95
AP	£40	$75	€50

STEPHANIE OF MONACO

SP	£125	$225	€155
DS	£100	$180	€125
AP	£45	$80	€60

PRINCE ANDREW & SARAH, DUCHESS OF YORK

SP	*		
DS	£250	$445	€310
AP	*		

PRINCE CHARLES

SP	£1,600	$2,835	€1,970
DS	£850	$1,510	€1,045
AP	£450	$800	€555

PRINCE GEORGE, DUKE OF CAMBRIDGE

SP	*		
DS	£60	$110	€75
AP	£30	$55	€40

PRINCE RAINIER

SP	£495	$880	€610
DS	£295	$525	€365
AP	£150	$270	€185

PRINCESS ANNE & CAPTAIN MARK PHILLIPS

SP	*		
DS	£900	$1,595	€1,110
AP	*		

PRINCESS CHARLOTTE

SP	*		
DS	£75	$135	€95
AP	£40	$75	€50

VICTORIA, QUEEN OF GREAT BRITAIN

SP	£4,000	$7,090	€4,915
DS	£950	$1,685	€1,170
AP	£295	$525	€365

WALLIS, DUCHESS OF WINDSOR

SP	£600	$1,065	€740
DS	£400	$710	€495
AP	£275	$490	€340

PRINCE JOHN OF THE UNITED KINGDOM - THE LOST PRINCE

SP	£3,500	$6,205	€4,305
DS	*		
AP	*		

WILLIAM IV, KING OF THE UNITED KINGDOM

SP	*		
DS	£500	$890	€615
AP	£250	$445	€310

Sport

The most profitable area of collecting in the sport field is signed memorabilia – autographed football shirts, golf flags, boxing gloves, racing helmets – all command the highest prices, particularly those items that can be directly linked to the event, i.e. match-worn signed shirts.

At the moment it is the sporting greats that are the best selling names, those with long and successful careers in which they stood apart from their contemporaries, these include Muhammad Ali, the England 1966 World Cup team, George 'Babe' Ruth and W.G. Grace. These names have transcended the world of sport; the more iconic they become, the better the investment.

Of course the popularity of a name will largely depend on where it is being sold – in the United States of America collectors will tend to focus on baseball and golf, British collectors will more than likely be interested in football and a high demand for cricketers' names stems from India.

Sport is one of the more difficult areas of collecting; the constant fluctuation in prices and demand can lead to an autograph of some value becoming an autograph of little value within the year, so sport tends to be collected more for passion than profit. The nature of a sportsman's employment can dramatically influence their demand, footballers will be transferred from one team to another, athletes may not win gold at the Olympics and cricketers could lose the test, which all makes for an unstable area of collecting. The limited shelf life of a footballer's career and detrimental transfers can exacerbate the rate by which a sporting autograph falls in value. For example, when Michael Owen was with Liverpool F.C. the value of his signature was £125 - £150 for a signed photograph, upon moving to Real Madrid the value remained steady but it has subsequently dipped with his move to Newcastle F.C. having lost the backing of collecting fans from two major clubs.

As a result, a sporting collector must have the ability to predict the future in order to collect successfully, you should be able to understand the trends in the market and accurately identify who will be the next 'great', this means that a gamble has to be made on whether the collector believes the sportsman will go on to greatness. Recently those names that have begun to rise in the market are Lance Armstrong, Lewis Hamilton and Amir Khan. You must always stay one step ahead of the game.

ATHLETICS

BANNISTER, ROGER

SP	£250	$445	€325
DS	£200	$355	€260
AP	£150	$270	€195

BRASHER, CHRIS

SP	£50	$90	€65
DS	£40	$75	€55
AP	£25	$45	€35

FRASER, DONNA

SP	£95	$170	€125
DS	£85	$155	€115
AP	£75	$135	€100

Liz McColgan

MCCOLGAN, LIZ

SP	£50	$90	€65
DS	£40	$75	€55
AP	£30	$55	€40

METCALFE, ADRIAN

SP	£75	$135	€100
DS	£60	$110	€80
AP	£50	$90	€65

OWENS, JESSE

SP	£575	$1,020	€750
DS	£450	$800	€585
AP	£350	$625	€455

RADCLIFFE, PAULA

SP	£75	$135	€100
DS	£60	$110	€80
AP	£45	$80	€60

BOXING

ALI, MUHAMMAD

SP	£495	$880	€645
DS	£300	$535	€390
AP	£175	$310	€230

BATTALINO, CHRISTOPHER

SP	£85	$155	€115
DS	£70	$125	€95
AP	£60	$110	€80

CARNERA, PRIMO

SP	£790	$1,400	€1,030
DS	£695	$1,235	€905
AP	£550	$975	€715

CARPENTIER, GEORGES

SP	£85	$155	€115
DS	£50	$90	€65
AP	£60	$110	€80

CHRISTOFORDIS, ANTON

SP	£75	$135	€100
DS	£50	$90	€65
AP	£40	$75	€55

COOPER, HENRY

SP	£100	$180	€130
DS	£75	$135	€100
AP	£30	$55	€40

CUTHBERT, JOHNNY

SP	£50	$90	€65
DS	£25	$45	€35
AP	£25	$45	€35

HAMED, PRINCE NASEEM

SP	£75	$135	€100
DS	£50	$90	€65
AP	£30	$55	€40

LA MOTTA, JAKE

SP	£250	$445	€325
DS	£200	$355	€260
AP	£150	$270	€195

DE LA HOYA, OSCAR

SP	£85	$155	€115
DS	£75	$135	€100
AP	£50	$90	€65

HARRISON, AUDLEY

SP	£100	$180	€130
DS	£75	$135	€100
AP	£75	$135	€100

DURAN, ROBETO

SP	£250	$445	€325
DS	£200	$355	€260
AP	£125	$225	€165

HOLYFIELD, EVANDER

SP	£195	$345	€255
DS	£150	$270	€195
AP	£125	$225	€165

LEWIS, LENNOX

SP	£100	$180	€130
DS	£75	$135	€100
AP	£50	$90	€65

LEWIS, TED 'KID'

SP	£75	$135	€100
DS	£65	$115	€85
AP	£50	$90	€65

FOREMAN, GEORGE

SP	£100	$180	€130
DS	£85	$155	€115
AP	£75	$135	€100

KHAN, AMIR

SP	£100	$180	€130
DS	£75	$135	€100
AP	£50	$90	€65

LISTON, SONNY

SP	£1,250	$2,215	€1,625
DS	£1,100	$1,950	€1,430
AP	£995	$1,765	€1,295

Rocky Marciano

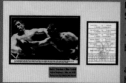

Rocky Marciano was born Rocco Francis Marchegiano, on 1 September 1923, in Brockton, Massachusetts.

There were those who didn't think much would become of the 190-pound heavyweight in the early days, having not taken up boxing until after 1943, when he was drafted into the Army.

However, in 1948, Marciano won his first ever professional fight against a fighter called Harry Bilizarian. He would go on to win his first 16 bouts all by way of knockout. Marciano won the World Heavyweight Championship in 1952 after knocking 'Jersey' Joe Walcott out in the thirteenth round, despite being knocked down by Walcott in the very first round of the fight.

Marciano held the heavyweight boxing title for four years in the 1950's, from 1952 to 1956, and remains the only heavyweight champion in boxing history to retire undefeated with an impressive record of 49 Wins (43 knockouts).

Rocky Marciano tragically lost his life at the age of 46, after the small private plane he was flying in hit a tree two miles short of a small airfield outside Iowa.

MARCIANO, ROCKY

SP	**£3,950**	$7,000	€5,135
DS	**£1,950**	$3,455	€2,535
AP	**£2,500**	$4,430	€3,250

O'BRIEN, BOB ARCHER

SP	**£50**	$90	€65
DS	**£30**	$55	€40
AP	**£20**	$35	€30

PROUD, DAVE

SP	**£30**	$55	€40
DS	**£25**	$45	€35
AP	**£10**	$20	€15

MCGUIGAN, BARRY

SP	**£50**	$90	€65
DS	**£30**	$55	€40
AP	**£20**	$35	€30

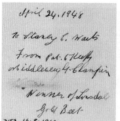

O'KEEFE, PAT

SP	**£60**	$110	€80
DS	**£40**	$75	€55
AP	**£30**	$55	€40

MULLIGAN, TOMMY

SP	**£60**	$110	€80
DS	**£35**	$65	€50
AP	**£25**	$45	€35

RICKY HATTON

SP	**£125**	$225	€165
DS	**£60**	$110	€80
AP	**£50**	$90	€65

OAKELEY, ATHOLL

SP	**£50**	$90	€65
DS	**£30**	$55	€40
AP	**£25**	$45	€35

PATTERSON, FLOYD

SP	**£275**	$490	€360
DS	**£225**	$400	€295
AP	**£150**	$270	€195

ROBINSON, SUGAR RAY

SP	£475	$845	€620
DS	£395	$700	€515
AP	£325	$580	€425

WON LONSDALE BELT FROM
TOMMY NOBLE. 1919.
BEAT - DIGGER STANLEY
JOHNNY HUGHES
BILL BEYNON
FOUGHT - EUGENE CRIQUI in FRANCE,
CHARLES LEDOUX.
ALL 20 3MINS ROUNDS.
BANTAM-WEIGHT CHAMPION
OF ENGLAND.
Kind Regards from
Walter Ross

ROSS, WALTER

SP	£50	$90	€65
DS	£30	$55	€40
AP	£20	$35	€30

SCHMELING, MAX

SP	£50	$90	€65
DS	£40	$75	€55
AP	£30	$55	€40

SOLOMONS, JACK

SP	£95	$170	€125
DS	£75	$135	€100
AP	£50	$90	€65

SPINKS, LEON

SP	£50	$90	€65
DS	£40	$75	€55
AP	£30	$55	€40

JOHN H. STRACEY
(Former Welterweight Champion of the world)

STRACEY, JOHN. H

SP	£75	$135	€100
DS	£60	$110	€80
AP	£40	$75	€55

TOGO THE GREAT

SP	£50	$90	€65
DS	£40	$75	€55
AP	£25	$45	€35

FIGHT THRILLS OF THE CENTURY

JACK DEMPSEY v. GENE TUNNEY
Chicago September 22, 1927

TUNNEY, GENE

SP	£180	$320	€235
DS	£140	$250	€185
AP	£100	$180	€130

TYSON, MIKE

SP	£150	$270	€195
DS	£100	$180	€130
AP	£75	$135	€100

22/1/02 Gary Baines (Caught) 7 wickets for 16 runs –
ABuS S.C.

BAINES, GARY

SP	£40	$75	€55
DS	£25	$45	€35
AP	£15	$30	€20

Ali Brown

SURREY
COUNTY CRICKET CLUB

BROWN, ALISTAIR

SP	£75	$135	€100
DS	£50	$90	€65
AP	£30	$55	€40

Mark Butcher

SURREY
COUNTY CRICKET CLUB

BUTCHER, MARK

SP	£50	$90	€65
DS	£40	$75	€55
AP	£25	$45	€35

8. STEPHEN FLEMING - NEW ZEALAND - Group B

FLEMING, STEPHEN

SP	£50	$90	€65
DS	£40	$75	€55
AP	£25	$45	€35

GOOCH, GRAHAM

SP	£50	$90	€65
DS	£30	$55	€40
AP	£15	$30	€20

GOUGH, DARREN

SP	£50	$90	€65
DS	£40	$75	€55
AP	£30	$55	€40

GOWER, DAVID

SP	£45	$80	€60
DS	£25	$45	€35
AP	£15	$30	€20

GRACE, EDWARD MILLS

SP	£295	$525	€385
DS	£295	$525	€385
AP	£200	$355	€260

GRACE, W.G

SP	£2,950	$5,230	€3,835
DS	£1,950	$3,455	€2,535
AP	£1,250	$2,215	€1,625

HAMMOND, WALTER

SP	£75	$135	€100
DS	£60	$110	€80
AP	£50	$90	€65

HOBBS, JACK

SP	£395	$700	€515
DS	£225	$400	€295
AP	£200	$355	€260

103. BEN HOLLIOAKE – Surrey/England

HOLLIOAKE, BEN

SP	£75	$135	€100
DS	£50	$90	€65
AP	£30	$55	€40

HUTTON, LEN

SP	£100	$180	€130
DS	£75	$135	€100
AP	£50	$90	€65

Azhar Mahmood

MAHMOOD, AZHAR

SP	£50	$90	€65
DS	£40	$75	€55
AP	£30	$55	€40

James Ormond

ORMOND, JAMES

SP	£75	$135	€100
DS	£40	$75	€55
AP	£30	$55	€40

PONTING, RICKY

SP	£75	$135	€100
DS	£40	$75	€55
AP	£30	$55	€40

Mark Ramprakash · SURREY COUNTY CRICKET CLUB

RAMPRAKASH, MARK

SP	£50	$90	€65
DS	£35	$65	€50
AP	£25	$45	€35

ROW, RAMAN SUBBA

SP	£75	$135	€100
DS	£50	$90	€65
AP	£40	$75	€55

ROYLE, REV. VERNON P.F.A.

SP	£495	$880	€645
DS	£395	$700	€515
AP	£295	$525	€385

RUSSELL, JACK

SP	£100	$180	€130
DS	£75	$135	€100
AP	£30	$55	€40

Ian Salisbury · SURREY COUNTY CRICKET CLUB

SALISBURY, IAN

SP	£50	$90	€65
DS	£40	$75	€55
AP	£30	$55	€40

Alec Stewart · SURREY COUNTY CRICKET CLUB

STEWART, ALEC

SP	£50	$90	€65
DS	£40	$75	€55
AP	£30	$55	€40

STRAUSS, ANDREW

SP	£175	$315	€230
DS	£125	$225	€165
AP	£70	$125	€95

Graham Thorpe · SURREY COUNTY CRICKET CLUB

THORPE, GRAHAM

SP	£50	$90	€65
DS	£40	$75	€55
AP	£30	$55	€40

Alex Tudor · SURREY COUNTY CRICKET CLUB

TUDOR, ALEX

SP	£50	$90	€65
DS	£40	$75	€55
AP	£30	$55	€40

TUFFNELL, PHIL

SP	£30	$55	€40
DS	£20	$35	€30
AP	£10	$20	€15

Ian Ward · SURREY COUNTY CRICKET CLUB

WARD, IAN

SP	£50	$90	€65
DS	£40	$75	€55
AP	£30	$55	€40

WARNE, SHANE

SP	£75	$135	€100
DS	£50	$90	€65
AP	£40	$75	€55

WAUGH, STEPHEN

SP	£75	$135	€100
DS	£50	$90	€65
AP	£40	$75	€55

WILSON, GEOFFREY

SP	£85	$155	€115
DS	£65	$115	€85
AP	£50	$90	€65

Sport Football

ABBIATI, CHRISTIAN

SP	£75	$135	€100
DS	£50	$90	€65
AP	£40	$75	€55

ADAMS, TONY

SP	£50	$90	€65
DS	£40	$75	€55
AP	£25	$45	€35

ADRIANO

SP	£75	$135	€100
DS	£40	$75	€55
AP	£30	$55	€40

ALBERTO GILADRINO

SP	£75	$135	€100
DS	£40	$75	€55
AP	£30	$55	€40

ALESSANDRO NESTA

SP	£75	$135	€100
DS	£40	$75	€55
AP	£30	$55	€40

ALLARDYCE, SAM

SP	£50	$90	€65
DS	£35	$65	€50
AP	£25	$45	€35

ALLEN, CLIVE

SP	£50	$90	€65
DS	£35	$65	€50
AP	£25	$45	€35

ANDREA PIRLO

SP	£75	$135	€100
DS	£40	$75	€55
AP	£30	$55	€40

ASHLEY COLE

SP	£95	$170	€125
DS	£55	$100	€75
AP	£45	$80	€60

BABAYARO, CELESTINE

SP	£50	$90	€65
DS	£35	$65	€50
AP	£25	$45	€35

BANKS, GORDON

SP	£100	$180	€130
DS	£75	$135	€100
AP	£40	$75	€55

BAROS, MILAN

SP	£75	$135	€100
DS	£50	$90	€65
AP	£30	$55	€40

BARTHEZ, FABIEN

SP	£50	$90	€65
DS	£40	$75	€55
AP	£30	$55	€40

BERGER, PATRICK

SP	£50	$90	€65
DS	£30	$55	€40
AP	£20	$35	€30

BJORKLUND, JOACHIM

SP	£40	$75	€55
DS	£30	$55	€40
AP	£20	$35	€30

BECKENBAUER, FRANZ

SP	£75	$135	€100
DS	£50	$90	€65
AP	£30	$55	€40

BERGKAMP, DENNIS

SP	£100	$180	€130
DS	£75	$135	€100
AP	£40	$75	€55

BOWYER, LEE

SP	£50	$90	€65
DS	£30	$55	€40
AP	£20	$35	€30

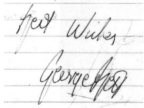

BEST, GEORGE

SP	£250	$445	€325
DS	£175	$310	€230
AP	£125	$225	€165

BREMNER, BILLY

SP	£50	$90	€65
DS	£30	$55	€40
AP	£20	$35	€30

BECKHAM, DAVID

SP	£195	$345	€255
DS	£100	$180	€130
AP	£50	$90	€65

BENNETT, DAVID

SP	£75	$135	€100
DS	£50	$90	€65
AP	£30	$55	€40

BIRTLES, GARRY

SP	£40	$75	€55
DS	£30	$55	€40
AP	£20	$35	€30

BROWN, CRAIG

SP	£50	$90	€65
DS	£40	$75	€55
AP	£30	$55	€40

BROWN, LAURIE

SP	£50	$90	€65
DS	£30	$55	€40
AP	£20	$35	€30

BRUCE, STEVE

SP	£50	$90	€65
DS	£30	$55	€40
AP	£20	$35	€30

BUCHAN, MARTIN

SP	£50	$90	€65
DS	£30	$55	€40
AP	£20	$35	€30

BUSBY, MATT

SP	£395	$700	€515
DS	£325	$580	€425
AP	£250	$445	€325

CAFU

SP	£75	$135	€100
DS	£60	$110	€80
AP	£40	$75	€55

CAMPBELL, SOL

SP	£75	$135	€100
DS	£40	$75	€55
AP	£30	$55	€40

CANTONA, ERIC

SP	£200	$355	€260
DS	£150	$270	€195
AP	£80	$145	€105

CARLOS TEVEZ

SP	£75	$135	€100
DS	£40	$75	€55
AP	£30	$55	€40

CARLOS, ROBERTO

SP	£100	$180	€130
DS	£60	$110	€80
AP	£40	$75	€55

CARRAGHER, JAMIE

SP	£75	$135	€100
DS	£40	$75	€55
AP	£30	$55	€40

CARRICK, MICHAEL

SP	£75	$135	€100
DS	£40	$75	€55
AP	£30	$55	€40

CHARLTON, BOBBY

SP	£75	$135	€100
DS	£40	$75	€55
AP	£30	$55	€40

CHARLTON, JACK

SP	£50	$90	€65
DS	£30	$55	€40
AP	£20	$35	€30

CHIVERS, MARTIN

SP	£75	$135	€100
DS	£40	$75	€55
AP	£30	$55	€40

CLEMENCE, RAY

SP	£75	$135	€100
DS	£40	$75	€55
AP	£30	$55	€40

CLEMENT, DAVE

SP	£50	$90	€65
DS	£30	$55	€40
AP	£20	$35	€30

CLOUGH, BRIAN

SP	£100	$180	€130
DS	£125	$225	€165
AP	£50	$90	€65

COHEN, GEORGE

SP	£100	$180	€130
DS	£80	$145	€105
AP	£60	$110	€80

COLE, ANDY

SP	£75	$135	€100
DS	£50	$90	€65
AP	£40	$75	€55

COLE, JOE

SP	£100	$180	€130
DS	£60	$110	€80
AP	£40	$75	€55

COPPELL, STEVE

SP	£50	$90	€65
DS	£30	$55	€40
AP	£20	$35	€30

CURBISHLEY, ALAN

SP	£50	$90	€65
DS	£30	$55	€40
AP	£20	$35	€30

CURRIE, TONY

SP	£50	$90	€65
DS	£30	$55	€40
AP	£20	$35	€30

CURTIS, ALAN

SP	£75	$135	€100
DS	£40	$75	€55
AP	£30	$55	€40

DALGLISH, KENNY

SP	£100	$180	€130
DS	£50	$90	€65
AP	£30	$55	€40

DEFOE, JERMAIN

SP	£125	$225	€165
DS	£80	$145	€105
AP	£50	$90	€65

DIMATTEO, ROBERTO

SP	£50	$90	€65
DS	£30	$55	€40
AP	£20	$35	€30

DARREN BENT

SP	£75	$135	€100
DS	£40	$75	€55
AP	£30	$55	€40

DESAILLY, MARCEL

SP	£50	$90	€65
DS	£30	$55	€40
AP	£20	$35	€30

DROGBA, DIDIER

SP	£100	$180	€130
DS	£50	$90	€65
AP	£40	$75	€55

DAVIES, SIMON

SP	£50	$90	€65
DS	£30	$55	€40
AP	£20	$35	€30

DI CANIO, PAOLO

SP	£50	$90	€65
DS	£30	$55	€40
AP	£20	$35	€30

DUDEK, JERZY

SP	£50	$90	€65
DS	£30	$55	€40
AP	£20	$35	€30

DEEHAN, JOHN

SP	£50	$90	€65
DS	£30	$55	€40
AP	£20	$35	€30

DICKINSON, JIMMY

SP	£50	$90	€65
DS	£30	$55	€40
AP	£20	$35	€30

DUXBURY, MIKE

SP	£50	$90	€65
DS	£30	$55	€40
AP	£20	$35	€30

DYER, KIERAN

SP	£75	$135	€100
DS	£40	$75	€55
AP	£30	$55	€40

EDU

SP	£75	$135	€100
DS	£50	$90	€65
AP	£30	$55	€40

ELIOTT, SHAUN

SP	£50	$90	€65
DS	£30	$55	€40
AP	£20	$35	€30

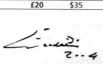

ERIKSSON, SVEN-GORAN

SP	£50	$90	€65
DS	£30	$55	€40
AP	£20	$35	€30

EUSEBIO

SP	£195	$345	€255
DS	£125	$225	€165
AP	£80	$145	€105

FABREGAS, CESC

SP	£75	$135	€100
DS	£40	$75	€55
AP	£30	$55	€40

FERDINAND, RIO

SP	£100	$180	€130
DS	£90	$160	€120
AP	£60	$110	€80

FERNANDO TORRES

SP	£100	$180	€130
DS	£50	$90	€65
AP	£40	$75	€55

FIGO, LUIS

SP	£100	$180	€130
DS	£60	$110	€80
AP	£40	$75	€55

FINNEY, TOM

SP	£50	$90	€65
DS	£40	$75	€55
AP	£30	$55	€40

FOWLER, ROBBIE

SP	£75	$135	€100
DS	£40	$75	€55
AP	£30	$55	€40

GARCIA, LUIS

SP	£75	$135	€100
DS	£75	$135	€100
AP	£50	$90	€65

GASCOIGNE, PAUL

SP	£100	$180	€130
DS	£60	$110	€80
AP	£50	$90	€65

GERRARD, STEVEN

SP	£125	$225	€165
DS	£80	$145	€105
AP	£60	$110	€80

GIGGS, RYAN

SP	£75	$135	€100
DS	£40	$75	€55
AP	£30	$55	€40

GILES, JOHN

SP	£50	$90	€65
DS	£40	$75	€55
AP	£30	$55	€40

GINOLA, DAVID

SP	£75	$135	€100
DS	£60	$110	€80
AP	£30	$55	€40

GOLAC, IVAN

SP	£50	$90	€65
DS	£30	$55	€40
AP	£20	$35	€30

GREENHOFF, JIMMY

SP	£75	$135	€100
DS	£40	$75	€55
AP	£30	$55	€40

GROBBELAAR, BRUCE

SP	£50	$90	€65
DS	£30	$55	€40
AP	£20	$35	€30

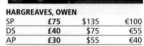

GULLIT, RUUD

SP	£75	$135	€100
DS	£50	$90	€65
AP	£40	$75	€55

HALLER, HELMUT

SP	£75	$135	€100
DS	£60	$110	€80
AP	£40	$75	€55

HARGREAVES, OWEN

SP	£75	$135	€100
DS	£40	$75	€55
AP	£30	$55	€40

HART, PAUL

SP	£75	$135	€100
DS	£40	$75	€55
AP	£30	$55	€40

HASSELBAINK, JIMMY FLOYD

SP	£75	$135	€100
DS	£40	$75	€55
AP	£30	$55	€40

HEIGHWAY, STEVE

SP	£75	$135	€100
DS	£40	$75	€55
AP	£30	$55	€40

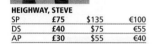

HENRY, THIERRY

SP	£125	$225	€165
DS	£100	$180	€130
AP	£60	$110	€80

HESKEY, EMILE

SP	£75	$135	€100
DS	£40	$75	€55
AP	£30	$55	€40

HESP, RUDD

SP	£50	$90	€65
DS	£30	$55	€40
AP	£20	$35	€30

HODDLE, GLENN

SP	£125	$225	€165
DS	£80	$145	€105
AP	£50	$90	€65

HUDSON, ALAN

SP	£50	$90	€65
DS	£30	$55	€40
AP	£20	$35	€30

HUGHES, MARK

SP	£65	$115	€85
DS	£40	$75	€55
AP	£30	$55	€40

HUNT, ROGER

SP	£100	$180	€130
DS	£50	$90	€65
AP	£40	$75	€55

HURST, GEOFF

SP	£175	$310	€230
DS	£125	$225	€165
AP	£60	$110	€80

INCE, PAUL

SP	£75	$135	€100
DS	£40	$75	€55
AP	£30	$55	€40

JACKSON, COLIN

SP	£75	$135	€100
DS	£40	$75	€55
AP	£30	$55	€40

JAMES, ALEX

SP	£125	$225	€165
DS	£90	$160	€120
AP	£60	$110	€80

JAMES, DAVID

SP	£75	$135	€100
DS	£40	$75	€55
AP	£30	$55	€40

JAN VENNEGOOR OF HESSELINK

SP	£75	$135	€100
DS	£40	$75	€55
AP	£30	$55	€40

JENAS, JERMAINE

SP	£60	$110	€80
DS	£40	$75	€55
AP	£30	$55	€40

JEWELL, PAUL

SP	£50	$90	€65
DS	£30	$55	€40
AP	£20	$35	€30

JONES, DAVE

SP	£50	$90	€65
DS	£30	$55	€40
AP	£20	$35	€30

JONES, JOEY

SP	£50	$90	€65
DS	£30	$55	€40
AP	£20	$35	€30

JONES, VINNIE

SP	£85	$155	€115
DS	£60	$110	€80
AP	£50	$90	€65

JORDAN, JOE

SP	£75	$135	€100
DS	£40	$75	€55
AP	£30	$55	€40

KAHN, OLIVER

SP	£50	$90	€65
DS	£30	$55	€40
AP	£20	$35	€30

KAKA

SP	£100	$180	€130
DS	£50	$90	€65
AP	£40	$75	€55

KEANE, ROBBIE

SP	£75	$135	€100
DS	£40	$75	€55
AP	£30	$55	€40

KEANE, ROY

SP	£75	$135	€100
DS	£40	$75	€55
AP	£30	$55	€40

KEEGAN KEVIN

SP	£100	$180	€130
DS	£50	$90	€65
AP	£35	$65	€50

KIDD, BRIAN

SP	£75	$135	€100
DS	£40	$75	€55
AP	£30	$55	€40

KILY GONZALEZ

SP	£75	$135	€100
DS	£40	$75	€55
AP	£30	$55	€40

KING, LEDLEY

SP	£75	$135	€100
DS	£40	$75	€55
AP	£30	$55	€40

KUYT, DIRK

SP	£75	$135	€100
DS	£40	$75	€55
AP	£30	$55	€40

LAMPARD, FRANK

SP	£125	$225	€165
DS	£75	$135	€100
AP	£40	$75	€55

LAW, DENIS

SP	£75	$135	€100
DS	£40	$75	€55
AP	£30	$55	€40

LAWRENSON, MARK

SP	£50	$90	€65
DS	£30	$55	€40
AP	£20	$35	€30

LE SAUX, GRAEME

SP	£50	$90	€65
DS	£30	$55	€40
AP	£20	$35	€30

LEE, FRANCIS

SP	£50	$90	€65
DS	£30	$55	€40
AP	£20	$35	€30

LEE, SAMMY

SP	£50	$90	€65
DS	£30	$55	€40
AP	£20	$35	€30

LENNON, AARON

SP	£75	$135	€100
DS	£40	$75	€55
AP	£30	$55	€40

LEWINGTON, RAY

SP	£50	$90	€65
DS	£30	$55	€40
AP	£20	$35	€30

MACARI, LOU

SP	£50	$90	€65
DS	£30	$55	€40
AP	£20	$35	€30

MATTHEWS, STANLEY

SP	£125	$225	€165
DS	£85	$155	€115
AP	£50	$90	€65

LJUNGBERG, FREDDIE

SP	£75	$135	€100
DS	£60	$110	€80
AP	£40	$75	€55

MALDINI, PAOLO

SP	£75	$135	€100
DS	£40	$75	€55
AP	£30	$55	€40

MCALLISTER, GARY

SP	£50	$90	€65
DS	£30	$55	€40
AP	£20	$35	€30

MARADONA, DIEGO

SP	£295	$525	€385
DS	£200	$355	€260
AP	£150	$270	€195

Diego Maradona

Considered by many to be the greatest footballer of all time, Diego Armando Maradona has certainly led a colourful life. Born in a shantytown outside Buenos Aires in 1960, Maradona would soon make his name at Argentinos Juniors, wowing spectators during half-time intervals with amazing ball tricks and skills as a 12 year old. He didn't have to wait too long for a chance in the first team, making his debut 10 days before his 16th birthday. 5 years and a glut of goals at Argentinos Juniors earned him a big money move to Boca Juniors where he won his first ever league title. A move to FC Barcelona followed, but injury and ill health would rob the Catalans of Maradona at his free-flowing best.

In 1984, Maradona found his spiritual home when he was transferred to Napoli. The Neapolitans idolised him, and not without reason. Maradona was the catalyst for the most successful time in the club's history. Napoli won two Series A titles, the only two in their history, and a host of other trophies. All this while, the giants from Milan and Turin were spending big money in an effort to build world beating dream teams.

Despite his success in club football, Maradona will be best remembered for leading Argentina to the World Cup in 1986. His passion, inimitable dribbling style and wonderful goals earned him the Golden Ball, the trophy given to the tournament's best player. A battle with cocaine addiction and weight gain in the late 1990's cannot sully the glittering career of such a mercurial talent, and one of football's true geniuses.

MCCALLIOG, JIM

SP	£35	$65	€50
DS	£25	$45	€35
AP	£15	$30	€20

MCCARTHY, MICK

SP	£50	$90	€65
DS	£30	$55	€40
AP	£20	$35	€30

MCCLAIR, BRIAN

SP	£50	$90	€65
DS	£30	$55	€40
AP	£20	$35	€30

MCCLINTOCK, FRANK

SP	£50	$90	€65
DS	£30	$55	€40
AP	£20	$35	€30

MCGARVEY, FRANK

SP	£50	$90	€65
DS	£30	$55	€40
AP	£20	$35	€30

MCGUINNESS, WILF

SP	£75	$135	€100
DS	£40	$75	€55
AP	£30	$55	€40

MCMAHON, STEVE

SP	£50	$90	€65
DS	£30	$55	€40
AP	£20	$35	€30

MCQUEEN, GORDON

SP	£50	$90	€65
DS	£30	$55	€40
AP	£20	$35	€30

MEGSON, GARY

SP	£50	$90	€65
DS	£30	$55	€40
AP	£20	$35	€30

MELCHIOT, MARIO

SP	£50	$90	€65
DS	£30	$55	€40
AP	£20	$35	€30

MERSON, PAUL

SP	£50	$90	€65
DS	£30	$55	€40
AP	£20	$35	€30

MICHAEL BALLACK

SP	£95	$170	€125
DS	£55	$100	€75
AP	£45	$80	€60

MICHAEL ESSIEN

SP	£75		$135		€100
DS	£40		$75		€55
AP	£30		$55		€40

MULLER, GERD

SP	£50		$90		€65
DS	£30		$55		€40
AP	£20		$35		€30

NORMAN, MAURICE

SP	£50		$90		€65
DS	£40		$75		€55
AP	£35		$65		€50

MOORE, BOBBY

SP	£750		$1,330		€975
DS	£595		$1,055		€775
AP	£300		$535		€390

NEWMAN, JOHNNY

SP	£50		$90		€65
DS	£30		$55		€40
AP	£20		$35		€30

O'LEARY, DAVID

SP	£50		$90		€65
DS	£30		$55		€40
AP	£20		$35		€30

MORIENTES, FERNANDO

SP	£75		$135		€100
DS	£60		$110		€80
AP	£40		$75		€55

NICHOLAS, CHARLIE

SP	£75		$135		€100
DS	£40		$75		€55
AP	£30		$55		€40

O'NEILL, MARTIN

SP	£50		$90		€65
DS	£30		$55		€40
AP	£20		$35		€30

MOURINHO, JOSE

SP	£75		$135		€100
DS	£40		$75		€55
AP	£30		$55		€40

NICHOLL, JIMMY

SP	£75		$135		€100
DS	£40		$75		€55
AP	£30		$55		€40

OVERMARS, MARK

SP	£50		$90		€65
DS	£30		$55		€40
AP	£20		$35		€30

OWEN, MICHAEL

SP	£125	$225	€165
DS	£90	$160	€120
AP	£60	$110	€80

PETIT, EMMANUEL

SP	£50	$90	€65
DS	£30	$55	€40
AP	£20	$35	€30

PIRES, ROBERT

SP	£75	$135	€100
DS	£70	$125	€95
AP	£30	$55	€40

PAINE, TERRY

SP	£50	$90	€65
DS	£30	$55	€40
AP	£20	$35	€30

PIPER, MATT

SP	£50	$90	€65
DS	£30	$55	€40
AP	£20	$35	€30

POYET, GUSTAVO

SP	£50	$90	€65
DS	£30	$55	€40
AP	£20	$35	€30

PEARCE, STUART

SP	£75	$135	€100
DS	£40	$75	€55
AP	£30	$55	€40

PELE

SP	£475	$845	€620
DS	£400	$710	€520
AP	£300	$535	€390

PETER CROUCH

SP	£95	$170	€125
DS	£55	$100	€75
AP	£45	$80	€60

Pele

Pele or Maradona. They are normally the answers given to the question *'Who is the greatest footballer of all time?'* FIFA could not decide. The football governing body awarded both men the *'Footballer of the Century'* award in 2000.

One thing is for sure, Pele is the greatest goal scorer of all time, having scored a staggering 1,281 goals in a 21 year career.

Born in 1940, few would have predicted his meteoric rise to football stardom until he was picked up by Brazilian giants Santos. Making his debut at 15, Pele was soon called up to the Brazilian national side at the age of 16. His precocious talent exploded on the world stage when he won the World Cup in 1958, scoring 6 goals in just 4 games in the process, all at the tender age of just 17. Pele would go on to win a further two World Cups with Brazil in 1962 and 1970. He retired from international football in 1971 with a scoring record of 77 goals in 92 games for his country. At the tail-end of his career Pele joined the New York Cosmos for two years, raising the profile of the game in America to a new level, before retiring from playing completely in 1977.

Since his retirement, Pele has become an Ambassador for football and has tried his hand at acting and other commercial ventures.

RAMSEY, ALF

SP	£100	$180	€130
DS	£80	$145	€105
AP	£60	$110	€80

RANIERI, CLAUDIO

SP	£50	$90	€65
DS	£30	$55	€40
AP	£20	$35	€30

REDKNAPP, JAMIE

SP	£75	$135	€100
DS	£45	$80	€60
AP	£35	$65	€50

REID, PETER

SP	£50	$90	€65
DS	£30	$55	€40
AP	£20	$35	€30

REVIE, DON

SP	£50	$90	€65
DS	£30	$55	€40
AP	£20	$35	€30

REYES, JOSE ANTONIA

SP	£75	$135	€100
DS	£60	$110	€80
AP	£50	$90	€65

RIVALDO

SP	£200	$355	€260
DS	£175	$310	€230
AP	£125	$225	€165

ROBINSON, MICHAEL

SP	£75	$135	€100
DS	£40	$75	€55
AP	£30	$55	€40

ROBSON, BRYAN

SP	£50	$90	€65
DS	£30	$55	€40
AP	£20	$35	€30

ROMARIO

SP	£150	$270	€195
DS	£100	$180	€130
AP	£60	$110	€80

RONALDINHO

SP	£225	$400	€295
DS	£175	$310	€230
AP	£125	$225	€165

RONALDO

SP	£225	$400	€295
DS	£180	$320	€235
AP	£125	$225	€165

RONALDO, CRISTIANO

SP	£150	$270	€195
DS	£90	$160	€120
AP	£75	$135	€100

SAMMELS, JON

SP	£50	$90	€65
DS	£30	$55	€40
AP	£20	$35	€30

SHAUN WRIGHT PHILLIPS

SP	£75	$135	€100
DS	£40	$75	€55
AP	£30	$55	€40

ROONEY, WAYNE

SP	£150	$270	€195
DS	£125	$225	€165
AP	£70	$125	€95

SAMMI HYYPIA

SP	£75	$135	€100
DS	£40	$75	€55
AP	£30	$55	€40

SHAW, GARY

SP	£75	$135	€100
DS	£40	$75	€55
AP	£30	$55	€40

ROSICKY, TOMAS

SP	£60	$110	€80
DS	£40	$75	€55
AP	£30	$55	€40

SCHMEICHEL, PETER

SP	£100	$180	€130
DS	£60	$110	€80
AP	£40	$75	€55

SHEARER, ALAN

SP	£85	$155	€115
DS	£60	$110	€80
AP	£50	$90	€65

ROYLE, JOE

SP	£50	$90	€65
DS	£30	$55	€40
AP	£20	$35	€30

SCHOLES, PAUL

SP	£100	$180	€130
DS	£75	$135	€100
AP	£40	$75	€55

SHERINGHAM, TEDDY

SP	£50	$90	€65
DS	£40	$75	€55
AP	£30	$55	€40

SHEVCHENKO, ANDRIY

SP	£75	$135	€100
DS	£50	$90	€65
AP	£40	$75	€55

SHILTON, PETER

SP	£100	$180	€130
DS	£60	$110	€80
AP	£50	$90	€65

SHUNSUKE NAKAMURA

SP	£75	$135	€100
DS	£40	$75	€55
AP	£30	$55	€40

SMITH, ALAN

SP	£75	$135	€100
DS	£65	$115	€85
AP	£40	$75	€55

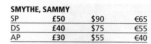

SMYTHE, SAMMY

SP	£50	$90	€65
DS	£40	$75	€55
AP	£30	$55	€40

SOLSKJAER, OLE GUNNAR

SP	£75	$135	€100
DS	£40	$75	€55
AP	£30	$55	€40

SOUTHGATE, GARETH

SP	£50	$90	€65
DS	£40	$75	€55
AP	£30	$55	€40

SPRAKE, GARETH

SP	£50	$90	€65
DS	£30	$55	€40
AP	£20	$35	€30

STANLEY, GARRY

SP	£50	$90	€65
DS	£30	$55	€40
AP	£20	$35	€30

STAPLETON, FRANK

SP	£75	$135	€100
DS	£40	$75	€55
AP	£30	$55	€40

STEPNEY, ALEX

SP	£75	$135	€100
DS	£40	$75	€55
AP	£30	$55	€40

STEVEN PRESSLEY

SP	£75	$135	€100
DS	£40	$75	€55
AP	£30	$55	€40

STILES, NOBBY

SP	£75	$135	€100
DS	£60	$110	€80
AP	£40	$75	€55

STRACHAN, GORDON

SP	£50	$90	€65
DS	£30	$55	€40
AP	£20	$35	€30

STRINGFELLOW, MIKE

SP	£50	$90	€65
DS	£40	$75	€55
AP	£30	$55	€40

STURROCK, PAUL

SP	£50	$90	€65
DS	£30	$55	€40
AP	£20	$35	€30

TAYLOR, PETER

SP	£50	$90	€65
DS	£30	$55	€40
AP	£20	$35	€30

TERRY, JOHN

SP	£100	$180	€130
DS	£75	$135	€100
AP	£50	$90	€65

THEO WALCOTT

SP	£75	$135	€100
DS	£40	$75	€55
AP	£30	$55	€40

THIRLWELL, PAUL

SP	£50	$90	€65
DS	£30	$55	€40
AP	£20	$35	€30

TODD, COLIN

SP	£50	$90	€65
DS	£30	$55	€40
AP	£20	$35	€30

TODD, RITCHIE

SP	£50	$90	€65
DS	£30	$55	€40
AP	£20	$35	€30

TOM HUDDLESTONE

SP	£75	$135	€100
DS	£40	$75	€55
AP	£30	$55	€40

VAN NISTELROOY, RUUD

SP	£125	$225	€165
DS	£75	$135	€100
AP	£50	$90	€65

VENABLES, TERRY

SP	£85	$155	€115
DS	£60	$110	€80
AP	£40	$75	€55

VIDUKA, MARK

SP	£50	$90	€65
DS	£30	$55	€40
AP	£20	$35	€30

VIEIRA, PATRICK

SP	£75	$135	€100
DS	£60	$110	€80
AP	£40	$75	€55

VILLA, RICKY

SP	£75	$135	€100
DS	£40	$75	€55
AP	£30	$55	€40

WALLACE, IAN

SP	£75	$135	€100
DS	£40	$75	€55
AP	£30	$55	€40

WARNOCK, NEIL

SP	£50	$90	€65
DS	£30	$55	€40
AP	£20	$35	€30

WAYNE BRIDGE

SP	£75	$135	€100
DS	£40	$75	€55
AP	£30	$55	€40

WEBER, WOLFGANG

SP	£75	$135	€100
DS	£40	$75	€55
AP	£30	$55	€40

WESTERVELD, SANDER

SP	£75	$135	€100
DS	£40	$75	€55
AP	£30	$55	€40

WHELAN, RONNIE

SP	£50	$90	€65
DS	£30	$55	€40
AP	£20	$35	€30

WILKINS, RAY

SP	£50	$90	€65
DS	£30	$55	€40
AP	£20	$35	€30

WILLIAMS, DARREN

SP	£50	$90	€65
DS	£30	$55	€40
AP	£20	$35	€30

WILLIAMS, STEVE

SP	£50	$90	€65
DS	£30	$55	€40
AP	£20	$35	€30

WILSON, RAY

SP	£50	$90	€65
DS	£30	$55	€40
AP	£20	$35	€30

XAVIER, ABEL

SP	£50	$90	€65
DS	£30	$55	€40
AP	£20	$35	€30

WISE, DENNIS

SP	£30	$55	€40
DS	£25	$45	€35
AP	£15	$30	€20

YORKE, DWIGHT

SP	£50	$90	€65
DS	£30	$55	€40
AP	£20	$35	€30

WORTHINGTON, NIGEL

SP	£50	$90	€65
DS	£30	$55	€40
AP	£20	$35	€30

YOSSI BENAYOUN

SP	£75	$135	€100
DS	£40	$75	€55
AP	£30	$55	€40

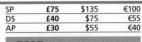

SP	£75	$135	€100
DS	£40	$75	€55
AP	£30	$55	€40

BRAID, JAMES

SP	£850	$1,510	€1,105
DS	£600	$1,065	€780
AP	£475	$845	€620

GILFORD, DAVID

SP	£30	$55	€40
DS	£25	$45	€35
AP	£15	$30	€20

HUGGETT, BRIAN

SP	£75	$135	€100
DS	£40	$75	€55
AP	£30	$55	€40

KEITH, ALISTAIR

SP	£75	$135	€100
DS	£40	$75	€55
AP	£30	$55	€40

LANGER, BERNHARD

SP	£60	$110	€80
DS	£50	$90	€65
AP	£45	$80	€60

LOCKE, BOBBY

SP	£750	$1,330	€975
DS	£450	$800	€585
AP	£250	$445	€325

WRIGHT, IAN

SP	£100	$180	€130
DS	£75	$135	€100
AP	£50	$90	€65

ZIDANE, ZINEDINE

SP	£190	$340	€250
DS	£125	$225	€165
AP	£70	$125	€95

ZOLA, GIANFRANO

Sport Motorsports

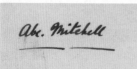

MITCHELL, ABE

SP	£350	$620	€455
DS	£175	$310	€230
AP	£150	$270	€195

114th
OPEN GOLF
CHAMPIONSHIP

The Royal St George's Golf Club
Sandwich

18th – 21st July 1985

STEWART, PAYNE

SP	£395	$700	€515
DS	£225	$400	€295
AP	£175	$315	€230

SWARZENBACK, ALFRED

SP	£75	$135	€100
DS	£50	$90	€65
AP	£35	$65	€50

THOMSON, PETER

SP	£75	$135	€100
DS	£50	$90	€65
AP	£35	$65	€50

TREVINO, LEE

SP	£50	$90	€65
DS	£30	$55	€40
AP	£20	$35	€30

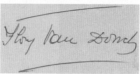

VAN DONCK, FLORY

SP	£75	$135	€100
DS	£50	$90	€65
AP	£35	$65	€50

VARDON, HARRY

SP	£1,500	$2,660	€1,950
DS	£1,000	$1,775	€1,300
AP	£775	$1,375	€1,010

WEETMAN, HARRY

SP	£35	$65	€50
DS	£25	$45	€35
AP	£15	$30	€20

WOODS, TIGER

SP	£1,500	$2,660	€1,950
DS	£1,250	$2,215	€1,625
AP	£850	$1,510	€1,105

IAN WOOSNAM

WOOSNAM, IAN

SP	£50	$90	€65
DS	£30	$55	€40
AP	£20	$35	€30

MOTOR SPORTS

ALESI, JEAN

SP	£75	$135	€100
DS	£40	$75	€55
AP	£30	$55	€40

ALONSO, FERNANDO

SP	£250	$445	€325
DS	£175	$310	€230
AP	£150	$270	€195

ANDRETTI, MARIO

SP	£160	$285	€210
DS	£125	$225	€165
AP	£70	$125	€95

BARRICHELLO, RUBENS

SP	£75	$135	€100
DS	£50	$90	€65
AP	£40	$75	€55

BERGER, GERHARD
SP	£50	$90	€65
DS	£30	$55	€40
AP	£20	$35	€30

BRABHAM, JACK
SP	£100	$180	€130
DS	£75	$135	€100
AP	£50	$90	€65

BRAWN, ROSS
SP	£75	$135	€100
DS	£40	$75	€55
AP	£30	$55	€40

BRIATORE, FLAVIO
SP	£195	$345	€255
DS	£125	$225	€165
AP	£70	$125	€95

BUTTON, JENSON
SP	£125	$225	€165
DS	£85	$155	€115
AP	£50	$90	€65

CAMPBELL, DONALD
SP	£250	$445	€325
DS	£225	$400	€295
AP	£195	$345	€255

CAMPBELL, MALCOLM
SP	£225	$400	€295
DS	£175	$310	€230
AP	£150	$270	€195

CLARK, JIM
SP	£4,500	$7,975	€5,850
DS	£3,500	$6,205	€4,550
AP	£1,500	$2,660	€1,950

COULTHARD, DAVID
SP	£75	$135	€100
DS	£40	$75	€55
AP	£30	$55	€40

DUKE, GEOFF
SP	£45	$80	€60
DS	£35	$65	€50
AP	£25	$45	€35

ECCLESTONE, BERNIE
SP	£50	$90	€65
DS	£30	$55	€40
AP	£20	$35	€30

FANGIO, JUAN MANUEL
SP	£375	$665	€490
DS	£300	$535	€390
AP	£225	$400	€295

FOGARTY, CARL

SP	£75	$135	€100
DS	£100	$180	€130
AP	£50	$90	€65

HAKKINEN, MIKA

SP	£75	$135	€100
DS	£40	$75	€55
AP	£30	$55	€40

HERBERT, JOHNNY

SP	£50	$90	€65
DS	£30	$55	€40
AP	£20	$35	€30

HILL, DAMON

SP	£75	$135	€100
DS	£40	$75	€55
AP	£30	$55	€40

HILL, GRAHAM

SP	£395	$700	€515
DS	£295	$525	€385
AP	£150	$270	€195

HUNT, JAMES

SP	£750	$1,330	€975
DS	£500	$890	€650
AP	£250	$445	€325

IRVINE, EDDIE

SP	£50	$90	€65
DS	£30	$55	€40
AP	£20	$35	€30

MANSELL, NIGEL

SP	£75	$135	€100
DS	£40	$75	€55
AP	£30	$55	€40

MOSS, STIRLING

SP	£300	$535	€390
DS	£150	$270	€195
AP	£100	$180	€130

PROST, ALAIN

SP	£50	$90	€65
DS	£40	$75	€55
AP	£30	$55	€40

SCHUMACHER, MICHAEL

SP	£275	$490	€360
DS	£225	$400	€295
AP	£150	$270	€195

Ayrton Senna

One of the greatest drivers in F1 history, Ayrton Senna won the driver's championship 3 times, despite, in the eyes of many, racing in an inferior car to his competitors.

Racing was in Senna's blood and his appetite was whetted at the age of 4 when he started kart racing in Brazil. He moved to Great Britain in 1981 to pursue his racing career, but it wasn't until 1984 that he joined an F1 team. He raced with Toleman for just one season, before joining Lotus in 1985. Senna built up a good reputation with Lotus and he was picked up as McClaren's number one driver in 1987. He enjoyed his best times with McClaren, winning the championship in 1988, 1990 and 1991.

Senna eventually joined Williams in 1994, but this would end in tragedy, when on 1 May 1994 he was fatally injured after he crashed into a wall during the early laps of the San Marino Grand Prix. He was just 34 years old.

VALENTINO ROSSI

SP	£100	$180	€130
DS	£50	$90	€65
AP	£40	$75	€55

VAN DAMM, SHEILA

SP	£50	$90	€65
DS	£30	$55	€40
AP	£20	$35	€30

VILLENEUVE, JACQUES

SP	£50	$90	€65
DS	£30	$55	€40
AP	£20	$35	€30

RUGBY

SEARS, JACK

SP	£75	$135	€100
DS	£50	$90	€65
AP	£40	$75	€55

SENNA, AYRTON

SP	£1,500	$2,660	€1,950
DS	£1,250	$2,215	€1,625
AP	£750	$1,330	€975

STEWART, JACKIE

SP	£50	$90	€65
DS	£35	$65	€50
AP	£25	$45	€35

TODT, JEAN

SP	£75	$135	€100
DS	£40	$75	€55
AP	£30	$55	€40

JARNO TRULLI
1999 FORMULA 1 WORLD CHAMPIONSHIP
GAUROISES PROST PEUGEOT

TRULLI, JARNO

SP	£50	$90	€65
DS	£30	$55	€40
AP	£20	$35	€30

CARLING, WILL

SP	£50	$90	€65
DS	£30	$55	€40
AP	£15	$30	€20

John Surtees
Arai

SURTEES, JOHN

SP	£75	$135	€100
DS	£40	$75	€55
AP	£30	$55	€40

DALLAGLIO, LAURENCE

SP	**£150**	$270	€195
DS	**£100**	$180	€130
AP	**£75**	$135	€100

FRANCIS, ROY

SP	**£40**	$75	€55
DS	**£25**	$45	€35
AP	**£15**	$30	€20

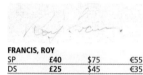

UNDERWOOD, RORY

SP	**£75**	$135	€100
DS	**£40**	$75	€55
AP	**£30**	$55	€40

WALLABIES CENTENARY TEST

SP	**£475**	$845	€620
DS	**£400**	$710	€520
AP	**£325**	$580	€425

WILKINSON, JONNY

SP	**£175**	$310	€230
DS	**£125**	$225	€165
AP	**£80**	$145	€105

TENNIS

AUSTIN, H W "BUNNY"

SP	**£50**	$90	€65
DS	**£35**	$65	€50
AP	**£25**	$45	€35

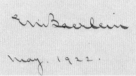

BAERLEIN, EDGAR

SP	**£50**	$90	€65
DS	**£35**	$65	€50
AP	**£25**	$45	€35

BATES, JEREMY

SP	**£75**	$135	€100
DS	**£40**	$75	€55
AP	**£30**	$55	€40

BERGELIN, LENNART

SP	**£40**	$75	€55
DS	**£25**	$45	€35
AP	**£15**	$30	€20

BORG, BJORN

SP	**£250**	$445	€325
DS	**£150**	$270	€195
AP	**£100**	$180	€130

CAPRIATI, JENNIFER

SP	**£75**	$135	€100
DS	**£40**	$75	€55
AP	**£30**	$55	€40

CASH, PAT

SP	**£125**	$225	€165
DS	**£85**	$155	€115
AP	**£60**	$110	€80

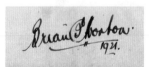

CHORTON, BRIAN

SP	**£40**	$75	€55
DS	**£25**	$45	€35
AP	**£15**	$30	€20

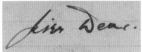

DEAR, JIM

SP	£40	$75	€55
DS	£25	$45	€35
AP	£15	$30	€20

FEDERER, ROGER

SP	£75	$135	€100
DS	£40	$75	€55
AP	£30	$55	€40

GILBERT, J. BRIAN

SP	£40	$75	€55
DS	£25	$45	€35
AP	£15	$30	€20

HENIN, JUSTINE

SP	£75	$135	€100
DS	£40	$75	€55
AP	£30	$55	€40

HINGIS, MARTINA

SP	£75	$135	€100
DS	£40	$75	€55
AP	£30	$55	€40

Anke Huber

TALKLINE

HUBER, ANKE

SP	£75	$135	€100
DS	£40	$75	€55
AP	£30	$55	€40

IVANISEVIC, GORAN

SP	£75	$135	€100
DS	£40	$75	€55
AP	£30	$55	€40

FACES IN THE CROWD ... Billie Jean King (top) of the United States, and Britain's Virginia Wade sit in the stand to watch the Chris Evert-Rosie Casals quarter-final.

KING, BILLIE JEAN

SP	£75	$135	€100
DS	£40	$75	€55
AP	£30	$55	€40

KOURNIKOVA, ANNA

SP	£75	$135	€100
DS	£50	$90	€65
AP	£40	$75	€55

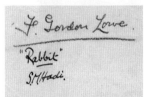

LOWE, F. GORDON

SP	£60	$110	€80
DS	£40	$75	€55
AP	£25	$45	€35

MARIA SHARAPOVA

SP	£100	$180	€130
DS	£50	$90	€65
AP	£40	$75	€55

NAVRATILOVA, MARTINA

SP	£100	$180	€130
DS	£75	$135	€100
AP	£50	$90	€65

PERRY, FRED

SP	£90	$160	€120
DS	£75	$135	€100
AP	£50	$90	€65

Sport Tennis / Various

RAFAEL NADAL

SP	£75	$135	€100
DS	£40	$75	€55
AP	£30	$55	€40

RAFTER, PATRICK

SP	£50	$90	€65
DS	£30	$55	€40
AP	£20	$35	€30

RIGGS, BOBBY

SP	£50	$90	€65
DS	£30	$55	€40
AP	£20	$35	€30

RUSEDSKI, GREG

SP	£150	$270	€195
DS	£100	$180	€130
AP	£50	$90	€65

SANCHEZ-VICARIO, ARANTXA

SP	£50	$90	€65
DS	£30	$55	€40
AP	£20	$35	€30

SERENA WILLIAMS

SP	£75	$135	€100
DS	£40	$75	€55
AP	£30	$55	€40

TILDEN, BILL

SP	£395	$700	€515
DS	£295	$525	€385
AP	£225	$400	€295

TIM HENMAN

SP	£75	$135	€100
DS	£40	$75	€55
AP	£30	$55	€40

WILLIAMS, VENUS

SP	£550	$975	€715
DS	£350	$620	€455
AP	£200	$355	€260

VARIOUS

ARMSTRONG, LANCE

SP	£1,500	$2,660	€1,950
DS	£1,950	$3,455	€2,535
AP	£1,250	$2,215	€1,625

Lance Armstrong

To categorise Lance Armstrong as *'just a cyclist'* would be massively incorrect. An inspiration to millions, Armstrong battled back from his death bed to win one of the most physically gruelling sporting events, the *Tour de France*, a record 7 consecutive times between 1999 and 2005. All this after being diagnosed with testicular cancer that spread to his lungs, abdomen and brain. Many credit Armstrong's battle with cancer as key to his ability to dig deeper and push himself further than any other cyclist on the tour, propelling him to unparalleled greatness in cycling.

Profoundly affected by his cancer experience and the people that he shared that experience with, Armstrong set up *The Lance Armstrong Foundation* in 1997 to *'inspire and empower'* cancer survivors and their families. The Foundation has been an enormous success and the *'Livestrong'* message promoted by the Foundation has been recognised on a global scale, most notably in the form of the yellow wristbands. Ever the competitor, Armstrong announced his intention to compete in the 2009 Tour de France in September 2008. Despite his four year break from cycling, few would bet against him recording an eighth victory.

ATLAS, CHARLES

SP	£550	$975	€715
DS	£495	$880	€645
AP	£395	$700	€515

BANNISTER, ROGER

SP	£250	$445	€325
DS	£200	$355	€260
AP	£150	$270	€195

BASEBALL: 500 HOME RUN CLUB

SP	£1,250	$2,215	€1,625
DS	£950	$1,685	€1,235
AP	£750	$1,330	€975

BOUGH, FRANK

SP	£45	$80	€60
DS	£25	$45	€35
AP	£15	$30	€20

FISCHER, ROBERT

SP	£4,500	$7,975	€5,850
DS	£3,500	$6,200	€4,550
AP	£2,750	$4,875	€3,575

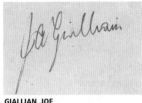

GIALLIAN, JOE

SP	£45	$80	€60
DS	£25	$45	€35
AP	£15	$30	€20

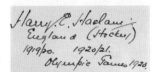

HASLAUE, HARRY E

SP	£50	$90	€65
DS	£30	$55	€40
AP	£20	$35	€30

JOHNSON, MAGIC

SP	£75	$135	€100
DS	£60	$110	€80
AP	£40	$75	€55

JORDAN, MICHAEL

SP	£175	$310	€230
DS	£125	$225	€165
AP	£90	$160	€120

KIDD, EDDIE

SP	£75	$135	€100
DS	£40	$75	€55
AP	£30	$55	€40

KOLTSCHAK, ERIC

SP	£60	$110	€80
DS	£40	$75	€55
AP	£30	$55	€40

KOSTAS, JONNY

SP	£60	$110	€80
DS	£40	$75	€55
AP	£30	$55	€40

KUTI, MIHALYI

SP	£60	$110	€80
DS	£40	$75	€55
AP	£30	$55	€40

LAGEAT, JACQUES

SP	£60	$110	€80
DS	£40	$75	€55
AP	£30	$55	€40

LEES, JOHN

SP	£60	$110	€80
DS	£40	$75	€55
AP	£30	$55	€40

MACARTHUR, ELLEN

SP	£100	$180	€130
DS	£60	$110	€80
AP	£40	$75	€55

MANN, TOMMY

SP	£60	$110	€80
DS	£40	$75	€55
AP	£30	$55	€40

MANNEYEAU, MARCEL

SP	£60	$110	€80
DS	£40	$75	€55
AP	£30	$55	€40

MARINO, MIKE

SP	£60	$110	€80
DS	£40	$75	€55
AP	£30	$55	€40

MCLAUGHLIN, ANDRA

SP	£60	$110	€80
DS	£40	$75	€55
AP	£30	$55	€40

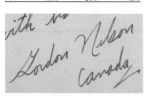

MURPHY, JOE

SP	£50	$90	€65
DS	£30	$55	€40
AP	£20	$35	€30

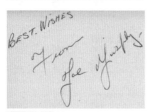

NELSON, GORDON

SP	£60	$110	€80
DS	£40	$75	€55
AP	£30	$55	€40

O'NEILL, SUSIE

SP	£80	$145	€105
DS	£60	$110	€80
AP	£40	$75	€55

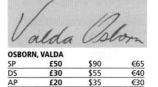

OSBORN, VALDA

SP	£50	$90	€65
DS	£30	$55	€40
AP	£20	$35	€30

PHILLIPS, GLENDA

SP	£60	$110	€80
DS	£35	$65	€50
AP	£25	$45	€35

PIGGOT, LESTER

SP	£65	$120	€85
DS	£35	$65	€50
AP	£20	$35	€30

PIRIE, GORDON

SP	£85	$155	€115
DS	£60	$110	€80
AP	£50	$90	€65

REDGRAVE, STEVE

SP	£85	$155	€115
DS	£60	$110	€80
AP	£40	$75	€55

REISS, HERMAN

SP	£60	$110	€80
DS	£40	$75	€55
AP	£30	$55	€40

REMIRO, ANGELO

SP	£60	$110	€80
DS	£40	$75	€55
AP	£30	$55	€40

RIANDI, TOMAS

SP	£60	$110	€80
DS	£40	$75	€55
AP	£50	$90	€65

RISS, MELWYN

SP	£60	$110	€80
DS	£40	$75	€55
AP	£30	$55	€40

ROYAL, BERT

SP	£60	$110	€80
DS	£40	$75	€55
AP	£30	$55	€40

SCOTT, BARBARA ANN

SP	£60	$110	€80
DS	£40	$75	€55
AP	£30	$55	€40

SELENKOVITCH, NICOLA

SP	£50	$90	€65
DS	£40	$75	€55
AP	£30	$55	€40

SHEPHERD, ALAN

SP	£50	$90	€65
DS	£40	$75	€55
AP	£30	$55	€40

SIMUNOVICH, LUCKY

SP	£50	$90	€65
DS	£40	$75	€55
AP	£30	$55	€40

ST CLAIR, ROY

SP	£50	$90	€65
DS	£40	$75	€55
AP	£30	$55	€40

THOMSON, CLAYTON

SP	£45	$80	€60
DS	£30	$55	€40
AP	£20	$35	€30

TOWNSEND, FRANK

SP	£45	$80	€60
DS	£30	$55	€40
AP	£20	$35	€30

VON HECZY, BARON

SP	£45	$80	€60
DS	£30	$55	€40
AP	£20	$35	€30

WADE, TOMMY

SP	£45	$80	€60
DS	£30	$55	€40
AP	£20	$35	€30

WALDO, RICKY

SP	£45	$80	€60
DS	£30	$55	€40
AP	£20	$35	€30

WARD, ANGELA

SP	£45	$80	€60
DS	£30	$55	€40
AP	£20	$35	€30

WHITEHEAD, SUE

SP	£45	$80	€60
DS	£30	$55	€40
AP	£20	$35	€30

WILLCOX, SHEILA

SP	£45	$80	€60
DS	£30	$55	€40
AP	£20	$35	€30

WILLIAMSON, W 'BILL'

SP	£45	$80	€60
DS	£30	$55	€40
AP	£20	$35	€30

WINKLER, HANS GUNTER

SP	£45	$80	€60
DS	£30	$55	€40
AP	£20	$35	€30

WOODHOUSE, LORD

SP	£40	$75	€55
DS	£25	$45	€35
AP	£15	$30	€20

Various

CRIME RELATED

Thank you for your kindness to me From Ruth Ellis

ELLIS, RUTH
SP	£1,750	$3,080	€2,275
DS	£1,500	$2,640	€1,950
AP	£800	$1,410	€1,040

GACY, JOHN WAYNE
SP	£350	$620	€455
DS	£195	$345	€255
AP	£100	$180	€130

GAMBINO, CARLO
SP	£750	$1,320	€975
DS	£595	$1,050	€775
AP	£450	$795	€585

JAMES, FRANK
SP		*	
DS	£12,500	$21,990	€16,250
AP	£7,500	$13,195	€9,750

KRAY, REG
SP	£300	$530	€390
DS	£175	$310	€230
AP	£100	$180	€130

G.G.BLESS GEOFF From Ron Kray

KRAY, RONNIE
SP	£300	$530	€390
DS	£175	$310	€230
AP	£200	$355	€260

Officer M. Nick McDonald - Captor of Oswald. 11-22-63

MCDONALD, M 'NICK'
SP	£75	$135	€100
DS	£50	$90	€65
AP	£30	$55	€40

ENTERTAINMENT

BARNUM, PHINEAS TAYLOR
SP	£1,750	$3,080	€2,275
DS	£950	$1,675	€1,235
AP	£450	$795	€585

CODY, WILLIAM FREDERICK - BUFFALO BILL
SP	£2,950	$5,190	€3,835
DS	£2,750	$4,840	€3,575
AP	£1,750	$3,080	€2,275

COPPERFIELD, DAVID
SP	£150	$265	€195
DS	£120	$215	€160
AP	£75	$135	€100

GELLER, URI
SP	£50	$90	€65
DS	£40	$75	€55
AP	£30	$55	€40

HOUDINI, HARRY
SP	£3,000	$5,280	€3,900
DS	£2,500	$4,400	€3,250
AP	£1,200	$2,115	€1,560

EXPLORATION

Various

BONNINGTON, CHRIS

SP	£60	$110	€80
DS	£40	$75	€55
AP	£25	$45	€35

Ranulph Fiennes uses Olympus Cameras   **OLYMPUS**

FIENNES, RANULPH

SP	£50	$90	€65
DS	£40	$75	€55
AP	£30	$55	€40

FUCHS, VIVIAN

SP	£50	$90	€65
DS	£40	$75	€55
AP	£30	$55	€40

HILLARY, EDMUND

SP	£350	$620	€455
DS	£175	$310	€230
AP	£75	$135	€100

Harry Houdini

Erik Weisz was born in Budapest in 1874 and was the son of a Rabbi. His family moved to the USA in 1878. Initially his magic career was not a success. He travelled around various shows doing card tricks and even being a wild man at a circus. It was when he and his brother started experimenting with escape acts his career really took off.

By 1900 he travelled to Europe where he was an instant hit. He regularly challenged people to try ever more elaborate contraptions for him to escape from, including a Siberian Prison transport van. He joked afterwards *"If I couldn't get out of that one I'd have had to go to Siberia, where the only key was!"*

Houdini continued his career back in the States and even featured in several movies, although his attempt at owning his own studio failed in 1923. Possibly the least known fact about Houdini is that he is accredited with the first powered flight across Australia, when he flew his own aircraft whilst on tour there.

Houdini died in 1926 from a ruptured appendix he sustained from being punched in the stomach by a student. However his legacy lives on and he is generally considered the best escapologist of all time.

HUNT, JOHN

SP	£150	$265	€195
DS	*		
AP	£70	$125	€95

LIVINGSTONE, DAVID

SP	*		
DS	£2,000	$3,520	€2,600
AP	£1,500	$2,640	€1,950

NORGAY, TENZING

SP	£475	$840	€620
DS	£450	$795	€585
AP	£350	$620	€455

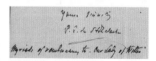

SHACKLETON, ERNEST

SP	£2,950	$5,190	€3,835
DS	£1,450	$2,555	€1,885
AP	£1,750	$3,080	€2,275

STRZELECKI, PAUL EDMUND

SP	*		
DS	£295	$520	€385
AP	£175	$310	€230

Various

MISCELLANEOUS

BADEN-POWELL, OLAVE

SP	£80	$145	€105
DS	£60	$110	€80
AP	£40	$75	€55

BADEN-POWELL, ROBERT

SP	£750	$1,320	€975
DS	£500	$880	€650
AP	£450	$795	€585

BAILEY, TEMPLE

SP	£50	$90	€65
DS	£40	$75	€55
AP	£30	$55	€40

BEATON, CECIL

SP	£75	$135	€100
DS	£50	$90	€65
AP	£30	$55	€40

BEECHING, RICHARD

SP	£50	$90	€65
DS	£40	$75	€55
AP	£30	$55	€40

BROWN, JOHN

SP		*	
DS	£4,500	$7,920	€5,850
AP	£1,950	$3,435	€2,535

BRUNEL, ISAMBARD KINGDOM

SP	£1,500	$2,640	€1,950
DS	£850	$1,500	€1,105
AP	£495	$875	€645

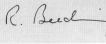

DALAI LAMA

SP	£995	$1,755	€1,295
DS	£750	$1,320	€975
AP	£450	$795	€585

DEAN, MILLVINA - TITANIC SURVIVOR

SP	£75	$135	€100
DS	£65	$115	€85
AP	£40	$75	€55

DUNELM, W

SP	£50	$90	€65
DS	£40	$75	€55
AP	£30	$55	€40

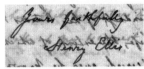

ELLIS, GEORGE AGAN

SP	£50	$90	€65
DS	£40	$75	€55
AP	£30	$55	€40

ELLIS, HENRY

SP	£45	$80	€60
DS	£30	$55	€40
AP	£25	$45	€35

FARGO, WILLIAM G.

SP	£1,250	$2,200	€1,625
DS	£975	$1,720	€1,270
AP	£450	$795	€585

FORD, HENRY

SP	£2,500	$4,400	€3,250
DS	£2,000	$3,520	€2,600
AP	£1,200	$2,115	€1,560

FOY, FREDDIE

SP	**£50**	$90	€65
DS	**£40**	$75	€55
AP	**£30**	$55	€40

GATLING, RICHARD

SP	**£2,500**	$4,400	€3,250
DS	**£2,200**	$3,870	€2,860
AP	**£950**	$1,675	€1,235

GAULTIER, JEAN-PAUL

SP	**£275**	$485	€360
DS	**£250**	$440	€325
AP	**£100**	$180	€130

GETTY, J.P.

SP	**£250**	$440	€325
DS	**£195**	$345	€255
AP	**£100**	$180	€130

GUILLOTIN, JOSEPH IGNACE

SP		*	
DS	**£950**	$1,675	€1,235
AP	**£750**	$1,320	€975

HAMILTON, EMMA

SP		*	
DS	**£1,950**	$3,435	€2,535
AP	**£1,500**	$2,640	€1,950

HARI, MATA

SP		*	
DS	**£2,500**	$4,400	€3,250
AP	**£1,750**	$3,080	€2,275

HEARST, WILLIAM RANDOLPH

SP		*	
DS	**£475**	$840	€620
AP	**£395**	$695	€515

HEFNER, HUGH

SP	**£75**	$135	€100
DS	**£60**	$110	€80
AP	**£40**	$75	€55

HOFFMANN, DEZO

SP	**£500**	$880	€650
DS	**£400**	$705	€520
AP	**£250**	$440	€325

HURTS HALL

SP	**£60**	$110	€80
DS	**£45**	$80	€60
AP	**£30**	$55	€40

KEYNES, J.M.

SP	**£700**	$1,235	€910
DS	**£650**	$1,145	€845
AP	**£300**	$530	€390

LEWINSKY, MONICA

SP	**£175**	$310	€230
DS	**£175**	$310	€230
AP	**£75**	$135	€100

LITCHFIELD, PATRICK

SP	**£50**	$90	€65
DS	**£40**	$75	€55
AP	**£30**	$55	€40

MARTIN, GEORGE

SP	**£40**	$75	€55
DS	**£30**	$55	€40
AP	**£20**	$40	€30

MAURICE, FREDERICK

SP	**£60**	$110	€80
DS	**£45**	$80	€60
AP	**£30**	$55	€40

MCDONALD, RICHARD

SP	£1,000	$1,760	€1,300
DS	£850	$1,500	€1,105
AP	£595	$1,050	€775

MOTHER TERESA

SP	£995	$1,755	€1,295
DS	£875	$1,540	€1,140
AP	£800	$1,410	€1,040

NIGHTINGALE, FLORENCE

SP	£1,500	$2,640	€1,950
DS	£1,200	$2,115	€1,560
AP	£750	$1,320	€975

PAINE, WILLIAM A.

SP	£400	$705	€520
DS	£325	$575	€425
AP	£200	$355	€260

PARKS, ROSA

SP	£600	$1,060	€780
DS	£500	$880	€650
AP	£300	$530	€390

POPE JOHN PAUL II

SP	£1,950	$3,435	€2,535
DS	£1,800	$3,170	€2,340
AP	£800	$1,410	€1,040

RALEGH, WALTER (RALEIGH)

SP	*		
DS	£26,000	$45,740	€33,800
AP	£13,500	$23,750	€17,550

SNOWDON, ANTONY ARMSTRONG-JONES

SP	£60	$110	€80
DS	£45	$80	€60
AP	£30	$55	€40

POPE BENEDICT XVI

SP	£475	$840	€620
DS	£395	$695	€515
AP	£295	$520	€385

Sir Walter Raleigh

Raleigh is one of the more colourful characters to emerge from the Tudor era. He is accredited with bringing the potato and tobacco to England albeit both were known already via the Spanish.

He was to become one of Elizabeth I's favourites when he quelled an uprising in Munster and soon carried the high rank of Captain of the Queens Guard. However, he was thrown in the tower when the jealous Queen discovered his secret marriage to one of her maids of honour, Elizabeth Throckmorton. Upon release he promised to appease the Queen by discovering the mythical land of El Dorado. He failed.

After the Queen's death her successor James I, accused Raleigh of a plot against him and sentenced him to death. Raleigh's sentence was reduced to life but in the end he only spent 12 years there.

Upon release he travelled in search of El Dorado again but ignored the King's direct orders and attacked the Spanish. He returned to England, was sentenced and finally was put to death on 29 October 1618.

SOUTHCOTT, JOANNA

SP	*		
DS	£295	$520	€385
AP	£195	$345	€255

STOPES, MARIE

SP	£295	$520	€385
DS	£150	$265	€195
AP	£125	$220	€165

WADLOW, ROBERT

SP	£595	$1,050	€775
DS	£500	$880	€650
AP	£250	$440	€325

WREN, SIR CHRISTOPHER

SP	*		
DS	£13,500	$23,750	€17,550
AP	£7,500	$13,195	€9,750

WRIGHT, FRANK LLOYD

SP	£3,950	$6,950	€5,135
DS	£1,500	$2,640	€1,950
AP	£950	$1,675	€1,235

PHILOSOPHY

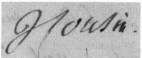

COUSIN, DR VICTOR

SP	£45	$80	€60
DS	£30	$55	€40
AP	£25	$45	€35

HEGEL, GEORGE WILHELM

SP	*		
DS	£5,500	$9,675	€7,150
AP	£2,950	$5,190	€3,835

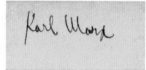

MARX, KARL

SP	£10,000	$17,595	€13,000
DS	£8,000	$14,075	€10,400
AP	£4,500	$7,920	€5,850

SARTRE, JEAN-PAUL

SP	£900	$1,585	€1,170
DS	£800	$1,410	€1,040
AP	£425	$750	€555

SCHWEITZER, ALBERT

SP	£995	$1,755	€1,295
DS	£900	$1,585	€1,170
AP	£695	$1,225	€905

TROTSKY, LEON

SP	£1,750	$3,080	€2,275
DS	£1,500	$2,640	€1,950
AP	£800	$1,410	€1,040

SCIENCE

BAILLIE, MATTHEW

SP	£50	$90	€65
DS	£40	$75	€55
AP	£30	$55	€40

Albert Einstein

Born in south west Germany in March 1879, Einstein took physics at the Institute of Technology in Zurich. He gained his diploma in 1903 but was unable to find any teaching work so took a job as a humble patent clerk in Zurich. It was during this time that he came to realise the inability of physics to explain fully what the math's was predicting. So it was in 1905, the year he gained his doctorate, that he published four of the most ground breaking science papers of all time, literally turning scientific thought on its head.

Einstein received the 1921 Nobel Prize in Physics for his discovery of the law of the photoelectric effect and he continued to lecture throughout the world until in 1933 he was forced to escape Nazi Germany.

After moving to the United States, Albert remained a staunch pacifist and spoke regularly for the peace movement. Until his death in 1955, Einstein's outspokenness continued to enhance his reputation as one of the foremost thinkers of all time. *"In my opinion,"* he once said *"there are only two things that are infinite. The universe and human stupidity, and I am not too sure of the first."*

BAIRD, JOHN LOGIE
SP	£750	$1,320	€975
DS	£600	$1,060	€780
AP	£395	$695	€515

BOWMAN, WILLIAM
SP	£60	$110	€80
DS	£40	$75	€55
AP	£30	$55	€40

DE FOREST, LEE
SP	£50	$90	€65
DS	£40	$75	€55
AP	£30	$55	€40

EDISON, THOMAS
SP	£4,500	$7,920	€5,850
DS	£2,000	$3,520	€2,600
AP	£750	$1,320	€975

BARNARDO, THOMAS
SP	£750	$1,320	€975
DS	£600	$1,060	€780
AP	£395	$695	€515

BRODIE, BENJAMIN
SP	£80	$145	€105
DS	£60	$110	€80
AP	£40	$75	€55

EINSTEIN, ALBERT
SP	£5,500	$9,675	€7,150
DS	£4,250	$7,480	€5,525
AP	£2,500	$4,400	€3,250

BRUNELL, MARC ISAMBART
SP	*		
DS	£450	$795	€585
AP	£250	$440	€325

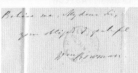

DARWIN, CHARLES
SP	£5,000	$8,800	€6,500
DS	£3,500	$6,160	€4,550
AP	£2,500	$4,400	€3,250

BELL, ALEXANDER GRAHAM
SP	*		
DS	£3,500	$6,160	€4,550
AP	£2,500	$4,400	€3,250

FARADAY, MICHAEL
SP	£1,500	$2,640	€1,950
DS	£1,400	$2,465	€1,820
AP	£750	$1,320	€975

BELL, ARTHUR V
SP	£100	$180	€130
DS	£75	$135	€100
AP	£50	$90	€65

DARWIN, GEORGE
SP	£60	$110	€80
DS	£45	$80	€60
AP	£30	$55	€40

FLEMING, ALEXANDER

SP	£4,250	$7,480	€5,525
DS	£3,750	$6,600	€4,875
AP	£1,750	$3,080	€2,275

GARDNER, CHARLES

SP	£50	$90	€65
DS	£40	$75	€55
AP	£30	$55	€40

GREENOUGH, GEORGE BELLAS

SP	£45	$80	€60
DS	£30	$55	€40
AP	£25	$45	€35

GURNEY, ANNA

SP	£60	$110	€80
DS	£45	$80	€60
AP	£30	$55	€40

LISTER, JOSEPH

SP	*		
DS	£850	$1,500	€1,105
AP	£375	$660	€490

MORSE, SAMUEL F.B.

SP	£2,500	$4,400	€3,250
DS	£995	$1,755	€1,295
AP	£795	$1,400	€1,035

Le Savant PASTEUR
Académicien.

PASTEUR, LOUIS

SP	*		
DS	£1,500	$2,640	€1,950
AP	£995	$1,755	€1,295

The
BIRTH *and* **BABYHOOD**
OF THE
TELEPHONE

THOMAS A. WATSON

WATSON, THOMAS A.

SP	*		
DS	£1,950	$3,435	€2,535
AP	£1,250	$2,200	€1,625

CHAPMAN, MARK DAVID

SP	£595	$1,050	€775
DS	£400	$705	€520
AP	£295	$520	€385

COUSTEAU, JACQUES

SP	£775	$1,365	€1,010
DS	£550	$970	€715
AP	£450	$795	€585

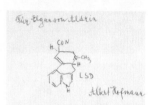

HOFMANN, ALBERT

SP	*		
DS	£995	$1,755	€1,295
AP	£695	$1,225	€905

KELLER, HELEN

SP	£750	$1,320	€975
DS	£495	$875	€645
AP	£350	$620	€455

RUBY, JACK

SP	*		
DS	£475	$840	€620
AP	£295	$520	€385

Index

Index

Index

Index

Index

The **Stanley Gibbons**
Investment Department

Offering life changing and unique investment ideas

Just take a look at some of the fantastic items below and the returns that they have achieved over the past few years.

Andy Warhol
1997 £175
2008 £1,950
24.5% per annum

Pele
1997 £100
2008 £950
22.7% per annum

Neil Armstrong..
1997 £475..
2008 £5,500..
24.9% per annum

Walt Disney
1997 £395
2008 £3,950
23.3% per annum

Fidel Castro..
1997 £300..
2008 £3,500..
25% per annum

Elvis Presley..
1997 £600..
2008 £3,750.
18.1% per annum

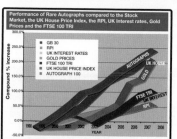

- The index has recorded a 12.32% average compound increase over the past 10 years

- The best performer in the index increased by 1185.7% and the worst performer still went up by 30%

Guaranteed Minimum Return Rare Stamp and Autograph Investment Contract
5 year 5% p.a. Guaranteed Minimum Return
Contracts contact us today

Find out more about rare stamp and autograph investment.

For your free, full colour, 16 page investment guide, please;

Call us on 01481 708 270

Visit us at:
www.stanleygibbons.com/investment

Email us at:
investment@stanleygibbons.co.uk

* Subject to terms and conditions

 **Stanley Gibbons (Guernsey) Limited**
18-20 Le Bordage, St Peter Port,
Guernsey, Channel Islands,
British Isles, GY1 1DE

How it can work for you:

Take out a Guranteed Minimum Return Contract for guaranteed returns and unlimited upside potential. Here is just one example of how an item can far exceed the guaranteed return on offer.

The Beatles (signed photograph)

Sold in 1997 for £4,950
Sold in 2007 for £22,500
355% increase in 5 years

If you had purchased this item in 1997 under a 10 year Stanley Gibbons contract at 6% guaranteed return per annum you have the following options at the end of the contract

GUARANTEED OPTIONS

1 Take the guaranteed minimum return of 60% giving you a return of £2,970 over the contract period on your original investment of £4,950.
   or
2 Roll over your investment for another contract at available terms

OTHER OPTIONS

3 Sell through Stanley Gibbons Auctions, commission free
   or
4 Retain the item for your collection
   or
5 Sell the item privately.

> "Stanley Gibbons' Guaranteed Minimum Return Contracts must be the investment equivalent of relaxing in front of an open fire, sipping a fine cognac, contemplating your collection - while all around you are losing their heads, as the markets crash and burn!"
>
> **Andrew Merricks** *Head of Investments Skerritt Consultants Ltd*

Find out more about rare stamp and autograph investment.

Call us on 01481 708 270

Visit us at:
www.stanleygibbons.com/investment

Email us at:
investment@stanleygibbons.co.uk

Stanley Gibbons (Guernsey) Limited
18-20 Le Bordage, St Peter Port,
Guernsey, Channel Islands,
British Isles, GY1 1DE

investment

In one year's time this market will take off

Investment Director Adrian Roose explores the investment potential of moon landing memorabilia.

A little over 39 years ago Neil Armstrong became the first man to walk on the Moon.

You'll see an awful lot of media coverage on this in a year's time on the 40th anniversary. Armstrong was joined by colleague Edwin "Buzz" Aldrin at 0315 GMT on 21 July 1969 and the two collected data before planting the Stars and Stripes flag at 0341 GMT.

They also unveiled a plaque bearing President Nixon's signature and an inscription reading: "Here men from the planet Earth first set foot upon the Moon July 1969 AD. We came in peace for all mankind."

After filming their experience with a portable television camera the astronauts received a message from the US President. President Nixon, in the White House, spoke of the pride of the American people and said: "This certainly has to be the most historic telephone call ever made."

Armstrong lives the life of a virtual recluse. He doesn't sign autographs anymore.

Already, Neil Armstrong is the most elusive living signature.

In less than one year's time we believe the market will take off. The Moon Landings will once again be in the news.

The 40th anniversary of the Moon Landing is less than one year away.

And we love anniversaries. Why? They generate publicity and publicity increases prices. Position yourself now. In one year's time the world's media will latch on to this news anniversary.

All the emotive memories will come flooding back.

The children who watched the Moon Landings in 1969 now have money in the bank.

Many will already be collectors, investing in the history of their country.

They will buy autographs and memorabilia relating to the Moon Landings.

And consider this:

Three of the twelve men who have walked on the moon have since passed away. Moon Landing memorabilia can only get rarer.

We have a limited amount of Moon Landing material available.

In one year's time we believe these prices will be looking very cheap.

They are already doing very nicely.

Armstrong alone is +847.4% in the last 10 years.

The Apollo 11 threesome are +442.9% in the same period.

And we believe the 40 year anniversary will provide a further boost.

Remember, Armstrong doesn't sign anymore...these items can only get rarer.

Call me on +44 (0) 1481 708 277
email aroose@stanleygibbons.co.uk
Regards
Adrian Roose

Example autograph portfolio

The portfolio below was selected by our experts based on scarcity and investment potential.
Each item is of the highest quality and sold with the Stanley Gibbons Guarantee of Authenticity.
This portfolio has seen incredible growth of 336% in just 10 years, far eclipsing the guaranteed 6%
per annum we offer on our 10 year Guaranteed Minimum Return Contracts, thus highlighting the
substantial potential upside that investors in rare autographs can enjoy.

Purchase Price (1997): £14,875   Current Value (2007): £64,900

The Beatles (signed photograph)
1997: £4,950   2007: £22,500
Growth **355%**

Nelson (signed document)
1997: £1,500   2007: £8,950
Growth **497%**

Elvis Presley (signed photograph)
1997: £600   2007: £3,500
Growth **483%**

Winston Churchill (signed
photograph)
1997: £2,500   2007: £6,950
Growth **178%**

James Dean (signed photograph)
1997: £1,500   2007: £7,500
Growth 400%

Marlon Brando (signed
photograph)
1997: £875   2007: £2,500
Growth **186%**

Apollo 11 (signed photograph)
1997: £1,750   2007: £9,500
Growth **443%**

England 1966 (signed photograph)
1997: £1,200   2007: £3,500
Growth **192%**

www.stanleygibbons.com/investment

investment